YOGA *for* YOUR TYPE

An Ayurvedic Approach to Your Asana Practice

Yoga For Your Type presents Yoga asanas to an ayurvedic constitutional and energetic model, with a particular regard for ayurvedic mind-body types of Vata *(air)*, Pitta *(fire)* and Kapha *(water)*. It delineates the practice and effects of asanas, both singly and in sequence, showing how to apply them and link them together in a therapeutic manner in harmony with ayurvedic principles.

YOGA *for* YOUR TYPE

An Ayurvedic Approach to Your Asana Practice

DAVID FRAWLEY
(Vamadeva Shastri), OMD

SANDRA SUMMERFIELD KOZAK
(Mahasarasvati), M.S.

New Age Books

YOGA FOR YOUR TYPE

ISBN: 978-81-7822-111-3

Reprint: Delhi, 2006, 2011
First Indian Edition: Delhi, 2003

First Published in 2001, USA

Disclaimer
This book is not intended to treat, diagnose, or prescribe. The information contained herein is in no way to be considered as a substitute for your own inner guidance or consultation with a duly licensed health care professional.

Published by
NEW AGE BOOKS
A-44 Naraina Industrial Area, Phase-I
New Delhi (India)-110 028
Email: nab@vsnl.in
Website: www.newagebooksindia.com

For Sale in South Asia Only

Printed in India
at Shri Jainendra Press
A-45 Naraina Indl. Area, Phase-I, New Delhi-110 028

ACKNOWLEDGMENTS

We would like to acknowledge the dedication to design of Sue Tinkle, the generosity and keen eyes of Jerry Harrison and Myra Lewin, the vision and commitment of Santosh Krinsky, our editor Cathy Hoselton, the generosity of the asana models, our so-nice-to-work-with photographers Jason Grubb and John Balinkie, our yoga friends who contributed their images to this work, Tammy Wong for her valuable support, and Dr. Peter Robert Ciriscioli who makes most things possible. Thank you all.

This book is dedicated to the great teachers of Yoga and Ayurveda who, for thousands of years, have carried the tradition, making our experience of these two ancient sciences possible today. We especially honor our own teachers for carrying this light to us by their generous sharing of the knowledge and of themselves. To each we offer this work with our humble gratitude.

Namaste!

☙ CONTENTS ❧

FOREWORD

Beginning in the late 19th century with Swami Vivekananda's speech at the Congress of World Religions in New York City, Yoga has gradually found more and more of a home in the West. Now one can hardly pick up a magazine without reading about Yoga, or drive across any medium-sized town without seeing a Yoga studio.

Even though Yoga is now a household word, it does not follow that the philosophical background of Yoga is equally as well known and understood. In fact, quite the opposite is true. Yoga originated in a culture quite different from the modern West. It was a culture in which health, poetry, dance, music, religion, philosophy and other aspects of life were interwoven. Worship was a part of daily activities and food was considered the first and best medicine available to create and restore health. The physical practices of Yoga were part of this world-view. It follows that the Yoga asanas given to a student should consider the particular student's individual constitution, lifestyle and health. This tailor-made approach to teaching asana existed for centuries in India.

When Yoga practice began to be adopted in modern times this ancient approach was not widespread. Sandra Summerfield Kozak and David Frawley's book will rectify that oversight. In *Yoga for Your Type* they present not only the basic tenets of Ayurveda, the Indian science of health, but also how the knowledge of that science can be integrated into our Yoga practice today.

The reader will be able to understand and determine which constitutional type he or she may be, and then, importantly, how to apply that knowledge to the personal selection of Yoga poses. While this process may seem like something new to many readers, it is actually a reflection of a very old teaching.

When I first met Sandra Summerfield Kozak, she was a student in my class in a teacher training program in 1974. I was struck by her dedication and interest in the subject of Yoga. I am not surprised, therefore, to read her new book, done along with recognized ayurvedic expert David Frawley, which so seamlessly blends the ancient science of Ayurveda into the modern practice of Yoga in the West.

I hope you will read this book slowly and integrate its wisdom not only into your Yoga practice, but also into your life. I further hope that you will take the chance to slow down, to relax and to learn to know yourself, and then live your life from that knowledge. That is what the practice of Yoga is all about.

Judith Hanson Lasater, Ph.D.
Physical Therapist
Author of *Living Your Yoga: Finding the Spiritual in Everyday Life*, and *Relax and Renew: Restful Yoga for Stressful Times*

January 2001, San Francisco, CA

PREFACE

Yoga is an extraordinary spiritual science of self-development and self-realization that shows us how to develop our full potential in our many-sided lives. It was first devised by the rishis and sages of ancient India and has been maintained by a stream of living teachers ever since, who have continually adapted this science to every generation. Yoga's integrative approach brings deep harmony and unshakeable balance to body and mind in order to awaken our latent capacity for a higher consciousness that is the true purpose of human evolution. The many methods of Yoga span a vast range from physical postures to breathing practices, mantra and meditation, all based upon a philosophy of consciousness and natural way of life.

Ayurveda is the traditional medicine of India, its powerful natural healing system for body, mind and spirit, with an antiquity and depth parallel to the Yoga tradition. Like Yoga, ayurvedic methods cover a wide array of health practices including diet, herbs, exercise, bodywork, detoxification programs and life-style management regimens relative to our unique individual constitution and environmental impacts.

Yoga and Ayurveda have long been linked together as two complementary systems of human development. They grew up organically intertwined through their common ancient Vedic roots—the legacy of the legendary Himalayan rishis who understood the laws of the universe and the inner process of cosmogenesis that holds the keys to all transformations. The two systems have maintained a long and intimate history, interacting upon and enhancing one another up to the present day.

Today there are many books that explain Yoga postures from different angles, often in great detail. However, so far there is no single book that explains Yoga postures in a simple and comprehensive manner according to its related healing system of ayurvedic medicine. Many books are similarly available on

Ayurveda, particularly explaining its dietary and herbal concerns. While some ayurvedic books deal with Yoga postures briefly, no single book is yet dedicated to this important topic. To meet this lack of information on the asana-Ayurveda connection we decided to produce the present volume. For those seeking to understand either Yoga or Ayurveda, a book showing the ayurvedic application of Yoga postures is essential. It is particularly important for those practicing Yoga therapy, who use asana to treat disease, and would like to do so in harmony with older yogic healing traditions.

There are also many typology books available today, describing how to eat or live right according to your body type as defined one way or another. Some of these typologies are insightful; others probably won't stand the test of time. So too, in the application of Yoga, an individual typology is necessary to make Yoga relevant to our particular needs. To merely prescribe asanas en masse does not do justice to the Yoga tradition that has always emphasized different paths for different people. The present book presents a yogic typology based on proven traditional models to fulfill this need as well.

Yoga For Your Type presents Yoga asanas according to an ayurvedic constitutional and energetic model, with a particular regard for ayurvedic mind-body types of Vata (air), Pitta (fire) and Kapha (water). It delineates the practice and effects of asanas, both singly and in sequence, showing how to apply them and link them together in a therapeutic manner in harmony with ayurvedic principles.

Two types of doshic reducing programs are prescribed to balance each ayurvedic doshic type. First are the 'Instant Change Programs' to immediately relieve pain and discomfort. Second are 'Long Term Programs' that provide six to nine month of dosha reducing classes. These also contain suggestions for more advanced students to help them develop their own long term practice. Programs and suggestions are given at four levels of difficulty, beginning through advanced, in order to address all levels of students and teachers.

We have aimed at both simplicity and flexibility in our approach, providing clear practices but not reducing them to a rigid formula. We cannot reduce the ayurvedic application of Yoga practices to a mere cookbook approach, noting what asana is good or bad for what type in a black and white manner. Adaptation on an individual basis relative to time and circumstances is the essence of both Yoga and Ayurveda.

The book follows from the recent title *Yoga and Ayurveda: Self-Healing and Self-Realization* by Dr. Frawley. This previous title addressed the broader interface of integral Yoga and integral Ayurveda relative to all aspects of our nature from the body to pure awareness, considering different practices and life-style factors from diet and asana to mantra and meditation. The scope of the present volume is focused on asana, which requires a more detailed examination.

Sandra Summerfield Kozak brings thirty years of experience and teaching all aspects of Yoga technique, Yoga psychology and Yoga philosophy. She is well known and respected for her teaching methods and style, training Yoga teachers and students in a variety of contexts and settings throughout the world. Dr. Frawley brings a specific understanding of Ayurveda, both on physical and psychological levels, having taught for over twenty years. He has written over a dozen books on Ayurveda and related Vedic sciences, including textbook material for ayurvedic schools. Sandra and David have worked together over the last seven years and have developed programs for courses and classes.

Relative to the material in the book, Sandra provided the practical instruction and details about the different asanas and asana sequences presented. David provided the background material on Yoga and Ayurveda, and most of the theory of ayurvedic asana practice. But this division is only general. Both authors looked over all aspects of the book.

May the healing power of Ayurveda and the spiritual power of Yoga awaken in the readers of this book!

David Frawley
Sandra Summerfield Kozak

ꟹ HOW TO USE THIS BOOK ꟹ

- Part I explains the background of Yoga and Ayurveda, particularly ayurvedic methods for determining mind and body types. Those who do not have a significant background in either subject should make sure to read this section first.
- Part II outlines the principles and guidelines of asana practice, with specific ayurvedic concerns. It provides the background for starting a Yoga practice.
- Part III explains how to perform individual asanas according to their ayurvedic effects. For those interested in the ayurvedic application of particular asanas, they can proceed directly to these descriptions. See sample Asana page, pg viii, for guidance to the instructions.
- Part IV describes ayurvedic routines for asana practice on different levels. Those wishing to create an ayurvedic asana practice should focus on this section.
- The Appendix offers a glossary and bibliography.

Sanskrit Name of Pose

ENGLISH NAME OF POSE

VATA ↓	PITTA ↑	KAPHA

↓ means the pose naturally reduces the dosha
↓↓ strongly reduces dosha
↓↓↓ very strongly reduces dosha
↑ or ↓ means the pose can affect the dosha either way

↑ means the pose naturally increases the dosha
↑↑ strongly increases the dosha
↑↑↑ very strongly increases dosha
a blank indicates a neutral effect on the dosha

TIME			
BREATH			
FOCUS			
MOVE			

The information in this box is given to guide you toward the best way to practice the pose to balance each doshic type.

MOVING INTO THE POSE

Where to begin, how to move each body part, and instruction for the correct positioning of the body for safety and maximum benefit. Also breathing information to help you coordinate your breath with each movement.

HOLDING THE POSE

Instructions for holding the pose; how to work your body and breath together, the most effective techniques for alignment and extension.

COMPLETING THE POSE

How to move away from the pose and return to your beginning or resting position.

LEARNING AT HOME: MODIFICATIONS

This section offers ways to modify the posture to help when you are first learning. Also alternate ways to practice the pose.

DOSHIC NOTES

How the pose affects the doshas.

IMPORTANT POINTS

- These points are vital to the success of the pose. Refer to them while moving into and holding the pose.

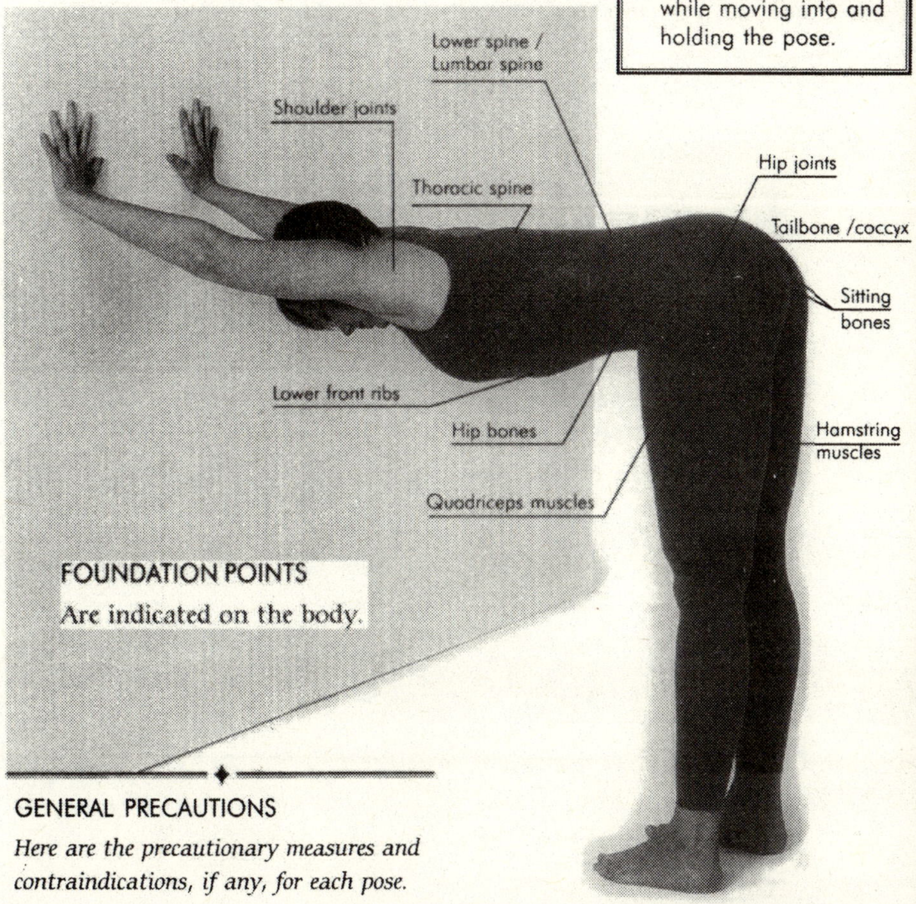

FOUNDATION POINTS

Are indicated on the body.

GENERAL PRECAUTIONS

Here are the precautionary measures and contraindications, if any, for each pose.

PART I

Background of Yoga & Ayurveda

DAVID FRAWLEY IN PADMASANA

I. 1 YOGA FOR YOUR TYPE

Most of us have some idea about Yoga today. Yoga has become a visible part of our diversifying culture that we all have encountered in one form or another. Yoga as a popular exercise trend, Yoga as an alternative medical therapy, and Yoga as a profound spiritual path all color our vision of Yoga. To put Yoga into the proper perspective, let us look at it anew, particularly with regard to the need to apply it on an individual basis, on whatever level we may choose to use it.

Yoga is a Sanskrit term meaning to "unite, coordinate, or energize." It refers to the proper integration of body, mind and spirit to unfold our higher potential in life. Yoga takes our ordinary capacities and extends them exponentially to help us develop an awareness that goes beyond our ordinary personal and human limitations. Yoga uses the foundation of the body—its secret energies and natural intelligence—to reach the summits of the spirit. It is part of the millennial human quest for health, happiness and enlightenment that addresses the entire human being and all of life. Therefore, it is no wonder that Yoga is gaining recognition worldwide as we gradually enter into a planetary age of consciousness and unity.

Yoga classes are available today—often in great abundance—in every town, gym, spa or health center in the United States. Yoga is no longer something novel or foreign as it was but a few years ago. Trendy images of people performing difficult Yoga postures or sitting cross-legged in meditation occur throughout the media. Yogic terms like mantra, guru and shakti are used in newspapers and in magazines. We have a cultural emulation of the yogi, whether as the asana expert, the great guru, swami or magical healer.

Yet Yoga is much more than a great exercise system. Yoga has an extraordinary healing potential for both body and mind. Yoga addresses not only structural imbalances in the body, like bone and joint problems, but also organic dysfunctions, including hormonal and immune system disorders. In addition—particularly through its meditation methods—Yoga treats nervous system disorders, emotional tension and psychological difficulties of all types from stress to psychosis.

For its healing purpose, Yoga is closely aligned with Ayurveda, 'the science of life,' which can also be called 'yogic medicine.' Ayurveda uses diet, herbs, bodywork, pranayama and meditation as part of a holistic system of healing that parallels the practices of Yoga relative to body, mind and spirit. Yoga and Ayurveda are sister sciences that grew up from the same root in ancient India. They both reflect a dharmic approach to life, a seeking to keep all beings in harmony with the benefic laws of the universe. As yogic healing becomes emphasized we must naturally turn our gaze to Ayurveda as well.

In Yoga, the nature of the individual student is of prime importance. Practices are not given mechanically en masse but adjusted on an individual basis. The same thing is true of Yoga when applied for healing purposes. An understanding of our individual constitution, both physically and psychologically, is essential for healing ourselves. This brings Yoga back to Ayurveda, which provides the traditional mind-body typology for Yoga practice.

YOGA FOR YOUR TYPE: THE AYURVEDIC ENERGETICS OF HEALTH

Whether it is diet, exercise or even meditation, the question is—What is the right practice for us individually? How can we address our real needs on a daily basis? We are now recognizing more and more that each individual is unique. The food that is good for one person, even if wholesome, may not be good for another. Herbs and exercise also require an individualized orientation and cannot work the same for all body types. Even meditation, to be really effective, requires some individual adjustment. We have different physical, mental and spiritual capacities and potentials that require the appropriate personal orientation to develop. We need to know what will work for us. What is our type and what kind of Yoga should we follow for it? Particularly, which asanas or Yoga postures are best for us?

Naturally, this depends upon the typology that we use to describe ourselves. Various mind and body type classifications have been proposed that we might consider for this purpose, some new, some very old. In this regard, we should remember that Yoga and Ayurveda contain their own profound system of typology that has been proven through thousands of years of experience. Yoga and Ayurveda show our mind-body types according to the energies and elements that predominate within us—the three doshas of Vata, Pitta and Kapha and the three gunas (mental qualities) of sattva, rajas and tamas. Later in the book we will provide you with a detailed examination of these types and specific tests to determine which you belong to.

For optimal health we require an individual diagnosis and treatment plan that addresses our specific needs, not merely a general or standardized prescription. This is the importance of Ayurveda, which rests on a precise constitutional model of wellbeing. It prescribes individualized treatment plans and life-style regimens that encompass all aspects of our behavior. Through Ayurveda we gain a proper understanding of our unique nature so that our Yoga practice is relevant to who we really are and to our particular condition at the time of practice.

I. 2 CLASSICAL YOGA AND ASANA PRACTICE

To understand Yoga and Ayurveda, we first need an overview of Yoga, both in its modern application and in its classical roots. Yoga is a broad system with detailed teachings for all aspects of human development, everything from music and dance to psychology and sociology. It is like a great mountain that contains wonderful animals, plants, minerals and vast vistas, which requires a long examination from many points of view.

The main Yoga practice that we observe in the world today is asana, or Yoga postures. Asana extends to all manner of yogic exercises done with the body, which are usually aligned with the breath and the mind as well. Asana is the outer face of Yoga and, for most people, their first step on the yogic path. For most of us the image of the Yogi is a person performing a difficult Yoga posture, almost like a great gymnast.

Asana-based Yoga is rooted in the *Hatha Yoga* tradition in which asana (postures), pranayama (breathing exercises) and meditation form a tripod of spiritual practices aimed at developing our internal energies. Asana-based Yoga is sometimes called Hatha Yoga because Hatha Yoga texts contain the most elaborate description of asanas, but we should remember that it only covers one aspect of Hatha Yoga, not the complete system.

The Hatha Yoga tradition is rooted in classical Yoga centered in the *Yoga Sutras* of the great sage Patanjali (c. 200 BCE), which is called the *Yoga Darshana* or Yoga philosophy, in which the greater system of Yoga can be found. Patanjali, however, was not the inventor of Yoga, which goes back many centuries before him. Patanjali organized and codified the long Yoga tradition into a series of concise aphorisms that remain today the best summary of the system, which has been adopted by various Yoga paths in different ways.

Patanjali's Yoga is called *Raja Yoga* or the royal Yoga because of its high level of teaching. It is called *Ashtanga Yoga* or 'eight-limbed Yoga' because of its eight levels of practice, of which asana is but one. Hatha Yoga relates to the initial stages of Raja Yoga, particularly the preparation of the body and the prana, and is said to be a stepping stone to its full development.

Patanjali's Raja Yoga system in turn is rooted in older Hindu Yoga teachings in the *Upanishads*, *Bhagavad Gita*, *Mahabharata* and *Puranas* and the Samkhya system of philosophy that is found in them. These Sanskrit texts explain different yogic practices of meditation, mantra, devotion and the development of Prana. After Patanjali, the *Gita* itself is usually regarded as the prime text of Yoga, outlining an integral approach similar to the *Yoga Sutras*. Similarly, Krishna, the great teacher of the *Bhagavad Gita*, is often regarded as the greatest of all yogis.

Older yogic teachings in India go all the way back to the *Vedas*, the teachings of the ancient Himalayan rishis over five thousand years ago. The *Vedas* represent the vast and diverse spiritual heritage of the ancient world, most of which has been lost or forgotten, that once extended to many lands and peoples.

Indeed, Yoga is as old as humanity and represents the higher spiritual heritage that we all hold deep within our hearts, whatever name or form we may choose to give it. Yoga is part of our perennial quest for Self-realization that we must all address in one life or another. Its methods and ideas are relevant to everyone, regardless of their background, applicable whenever the person is ready to look within and develop an interior life of consciousness and joy.

THE EIGHT LIMBS OF YOGA

Patanjali outlines a complete eightfold Yoga path that deals with all aspects of our life, inwardly and outwardly. Its eight parts or limbs (ashtanga) are:

1. *Yamas*	Behavior
2. *Niyamas*	Life-Style Development
3. *Asana*	Yoga Postures
4. *Pranayama*	Control of Prana
5. *Pratyahara*	Control of the Senses
6. *Dharana*	Concentration
7. *Dhyana*	Meditation
8. *Samadhi*	Realization

1. THE FIVE YAMAS: THE FIVE PRACTICES OF SOCIAL AND PERSONAL BEHAVIOR

The Yamas are practices to eliminate wrong, harmful or disturbing behavior. They create a foundation of right living, peace and harmony both socially and personally. With these five, Yoga provides a simple model of self-discipline that eliminates the problems that arise through materialistic ways of living. It provides a good ethical code for Yoga teachers and for ayurvedic doctors.

The Five Yamas

1. *Ahimsa*	Non-harming
2. *Satya*	Truthfulness or not-lying
3. *Brahmacharya*	Right use of sexual energy
4. *Asteya*	Non-stealing
5. *Aparigraha*	Non-possessiveness

Ahimsa or non-harming comes first. The basis of any truly wise or healing life-style is to wish no harm to any living creature, not only humans, but all creation, including the rocks! Remember that harming others—whether through thought, action, or emotion—always harms us as well. Non-harming implies avoiding any actions that cause harm and promoting those that reduce harm or protect from injury.

Truthfulness is the second principle. Truthfulness in thought and conduct is necessary for clarity and peace of mind and for creating social interactions that establish trust and eliminate conflict. Truthfulness begins with ourselves. We can deceive others but we ourselves know the truth of what we are doing.

Non-stealing means not taking what does not belong to us. This naturally refers to material things but also extends to psychological factors, like taking someone's reputation away from them by speaking ill of them. Material things hold a psychic force. If we take things that are not legitimately ours, their negative psychic force will weigh us down.

Brahmacharya means avoiding sexual misconduct, which is a great cause of both deception and harm to ourselves and to others. Wrong use of sexual energy is the main factor of social and psychological suffering. Sexual energy used rightly is the basis for both healing and spiritual energies.

Non-possessiveness means that we shouldn't think that we really own things. We should look upon our possessions as part of the common good and ourselves as their stewards for the benefit of all. Non-possessiveness encompasses non-coveting and non-greed and does not merely refer to having few possessions. It shows a material simplicity behind Yoga practice.

2. THE FIVE NIYAMAS: THE FIVE PRACTICES OF PERSONAL DEVELOPMENT, THE PRINCIPLES OF A YOGIC LIFE-STYLE

The Niyamas are principles of personal practice both for self-healing and self-development. Who we are is the result of how we live and act on a daily basis. Our daily actions reflect our prime values and motivations.

The Five Niyamas

1. *Shaucha*	Cleanliness and purity
2. *Santosha*	Contentment
3. *Tapas*	Self discipline
4. *Svadhyaya*	Self-study
5. *Ishvara Pranidhana*	Surrender to the Divine Will

Purity refers to outer cleanliness, including following a pure or vegetarian diet. A vegetarian diet is considered to be one of the most powerful aids for meditation and should be followed by all serious Yoga students. Purity and cleanliness also refer to purity of heart and mind. We must be free of mental and physical toxins in order to function with full vitality and capacity. A clean mind, free of neediness, avarice, fear, and other emotional impediments creates clarity and wisdom.

Contentment means to maintain a balanced attitude whatever we do. It does not mean to be complacent. To remain unperturbed through all of life's ups and downs is true contentment, santosha. To be even minded, able to remain centered and clear, in all our actions and throughout all of life's experiences is the key to our success.

Tapas means discipline, referring to a steady application of the will to achieve a meaningful goal, which implies being able to sacrifice lesser pursuits along the way. In any field in life, whether it is running a race or a business, we need the right motivation and discipline, the will to continue under any circumstances. So, to continue to work toward and achieve a higher consciousness we must remain steady in our exercise of tapas.

Self-study means that we must understand who we are and what our real capacities and affinities may be. Each one of us has a unique nature and potential that we must uncover. What is good for one person may not be good for another.

Therefore, following this principle, Yoga is always adapted on an individual basis. All yogic practices are a means of self-development, not an external system imposed upon us.

Surrender to the Divine or cosmic will is not a matter of mere religious belief. It means to sublimate the ego and its needs to the higher consciousness working through life and governing this vast universe. With the ego integrated it is possible to experience the 'whole' rather than remain trapped in the small "I".

3. ASANA

Asana consists of physical postures and movements to release tension, remove toxins and prepare the mind for meditation. It consists not only of familiar Yoga postures like the shoulderstand, but also less familiar movement sequences. It is the first stage of personal practice aimed at the physical body—the foundation of all that we do in life.

Asana taken to other levels offers even more. Focusing on the process of the asana practice rather than execution of a particular posture, the practitioner can learn about the workings of their minds and the obstacles created from past experiences. Asana can then become a kind of meditation in form.

4. PRANAYAMA

Extra prana or energy is necessary to achieve our goals or to accomplish anything significant in life. Most pranayama practices consist of breathing exercises that develop the life-force in order to promote energy, awaken the mind and cleanse the body. They consist of specific types and ratios of breathing practices. Asana puts the body in a state of balance so that we can work on our Prana through pranayama.

However, pranayama extends to all means of developing and controlling Prana in the body and mind, and accessing new sources of Prana both inwardly (as through meditation) and outwardly (for example, drawing in the Prana of the sun). Some pranayama techniques are spiritual practices specifically devised for developing a deeper connection with the cosmic life and its powerful transformative forces.

5. PRATYAHARA

Pratyahara refers to various methods of managing impressions and controlling the senses that are our main source of contact with the external world. Whatever we take in through the senses affects the mind, just as the food that we eat affects the body. Many great masters have said, "you become what you are around." Your senses take in your environment. Through right use of the senses we are able to interact with choice, harmonious with the world around us.

Most pratyahara methods consist of withdrawing from external sensory overload and accessing the peace and silence within ourselves. Deep relaxation is also part of pratyahara, which involves putting the motor organs to rest. Most asana practice should end with some form of pratyahara, like the use of Savasana (corpse pose).

6. DHARANA

Dharana consists of concentration practices that focus and stabilize our attention. Attention is the main power of the mind. We must learn to exercise it like a muscle if we wish to unfold our higher mental capacities. Otherwise we fall under the control of external forces and fail to realize our higher purpose in life. By cultivating the power of attention all the powers of the mind are gradually opened up to us.

Typical dharana methods consist of concentration on various chakras (internal energy sources) or holding our gaze on particular objects (like a candle flame), until our mind becomes steady. Concentration is the foundation for meditation. By concentrating the body in a steady pose, asana aids in concentrating the mind.

7. DHYANA

Dhyana refers to meditation, which is a sustained concentration or deep reflection on a particular object of thought. Through holding a 'one-pointed' attention, we can arrive at a deep understanding of the reality of whatever we meditate on. Whatever we fully give our attention to in a consistent manner unfolds its inner meaning for us. All of life speaks to us if we can enter the meditative mind. The greatest instrument of knowledge is not any machine or any book but our own awareness once it is steady.

Meditation is the main method of classical Yoga that aims at controlling the mind. Various yogic meditation methods include Self-inquiry, surrender to the Divine (with or without form), devotional practices, energy practices and the use of mantra (primordial sound). Asana stills the body in order to help still the mind for meditation.

8. SAMADHI

Samadhi consists of merging the mind with the object of its attention, which occurs naturally through prolonged meditation. Once the mind becomes one with its object we experience profound peace and blissful happiness. We understand all that we see as a facet of our own greater and universal nature. We can probably understand Samadhi better as total concentration in which we are so completely dedicated to what we are doing that we forget ourselves completely. We return to our deeper spiritual heart and forget all the worries of the external world.

Samadhi is the ultimate goal of Yoga practice that arises through long-term meditation. Yoga shows us how to approach this internal state of bliss in a step-by-step manner working with body, Prana, senses, mind and heart. It shows us how to organize our life and behavior on all levels to arrive at this sublime goal that is usually reserved for only a few rare mystics.

THE IMPORTANCE OF ASANA PRACTICE

Asana is related to all the limbs of Yoga, which are intertwined in various ways. Asana is part of the life-style practices of the yamas and niyamas because it is a means of self-study and self-discipline. Asana is a form of pranayama because through right posture we can control our Prana. Asana is a form of pratyahara because it gives control of both our sense and motor organs. Asana is a form of dharana because through it we can concentrate our energies. Lastly, asana is a form of meditation because its proper practice requires that we keep our minds in a clear and reflective state.

Apart from the other aspects of Yoga, asanas are also useful in themselves for promoting health and vitality and for treating many diseases, even if we don't use them for spiritual development. Asanas relieve stress and tension and calm the nerves, which are common problems in our hectic lives. They are an important part of a healthy life-style and have therapeutic effects both physically and psychologically. For this reason people who aren't interested in the spiritual dimension of Yoga can still find benefit from asana practice.

RELEVANCE OF THE EIGHT LIMBS OF YOGA

The eight limbs of Yoga are something quite extraordinary. Yet they also reflect how our life is naturally structured. They are not an artificial construct but part of the natural movement of body and mind.

- We all have various values and beliefs that motivate us in life (yamas and niyamas), that become the basis of our vocations, our hobbies and our deeper pursuits.
- From these values we develop a primary physical activity or posture (asana), whether

it is sitting at a desk in an office or jogging. This is like the signature asana of our individual lives and affects our mind as well.

- Our primary physical activity causes a particular projection of vitality (pranayama)—how we hold our breath or exert our energies in the main physical postures we assume. For some of us, this may be how we suppress our breath, sitting before a computer screen. For others, it is the energy that we are able to put in our work.
- Our projection of energy brings about a specific orientation of the senses (pratyahara), like a person focusing on a computer screen or an artist focusing on the painting they are drawing in which they lose awareness of the other things going on around them.
- This orientation of the senses leads us to concentration on a particular project (dharana), whether it is a business project, a creative pursuit or some spiritual practice.
- Sustained concentration leads to a state of reflection (dhyana) in which we continually think about a particular project and become absorbed in it. Many of us are absorbed in worries, ambitions or conflicts and don't know how to use our minds to reflect upon something transcendent.
- This reflection over time causes us to be engrossed in the object of our attention (samadhi) to the extent that we become one with it, like an athlete one with his exertion, the artist one with his work or the devotee one with divinity. Samadhi also refers to the peak experiences in which we attain the objects of our seeking, our successes, accomplishments and fulfillments that bring us great happiness.

Most of the time we follow this process, outlined above, in a mechanical or unconscious manner, driven by our desires rather than guided by a higher spiritual aspiration. Yoga shows us how to follow this process in a conscious way in order to develop a higher awareness and creativity. We are always practicing Yoga or seeking to achieve some goal in life that makes us feel more happy, whole or wise. The eightfold Yoga process provides a guideline how to do this in an optimal way and opens us up to a higher spiritual aspiration. So it is not a question of beginning Yoga practice but of making our natural Yoga practice (life activity) awake, aware and inspired to go beyond ourselves.

I. 3 AYURVEDA AND YOGA

Ayurveda is a more recent arrival on the Western scene than Yoga, following closely in its footsteps. Up to fifteen years ago knowledge of Ayurveda was confined to a small number of people who knew the greater tradition behind Yoga. In the past few years, along with the explosion of interest in alternative and complementary medicines, Ayurveda has gained a growing recognition. It has now emerged as one of the most important systems of mind-body medicine in the world today.

Ayurveda offers a unique system of treatment based upon life-style adjustments, individualized dietary programs, powerful herbal formulas, and a spiritual focus of Yoga and meditation. Its profound classification of mind-body types provides a clear assessment of individual constitution and how to treat it holistically. This makes Ayurveda an ideal practice for disease prevention, promotion of longevity, and increasing our creative powers. It is not simply limited to countering disease, though Ayurveda can do this quite well with special treatment plans for all health complaints from the common cold to cancer.

Ayurveda has become a major part in what we could call the 'second phase' of interest in Yoga, which is as a therapy and a tool for healing. This builds upon the first phase interest in Yoga as an exercise system. People looking into the therapeutic aspect of Yoga are inherently drawn to Ayurveda because of the historical affinity between the two systems.

As the healing aspect of Yoga continues to develop, its ayurvedic connections must continue to unfold. This is resulting in a new encounter between the two disciplines, in which each is revitalizing the other. Yoga has developed modern approaches through various forms of bodywork, physical therapy and psychology, which have arisen primarily from an encounter with modern medicine. Now it must also reclaim its traditional medical roots in Ayurveda and consider how these fit together in the greater picture of its healing potential.

Ayurveda has also encountered modern medicine and the new health problems of our current information age. It is similarly adjusting itself with new forms of treatment and life-style adjustments. It is coming into contact with new forms of Yoga, particularly in the West, that is broadening its perspectives as well. This new interface of Yoga and Ayurveda, self-healing and self-realization, is one of the most important trends in Yoga and is bound to become more significant for the future.

THE AYURVEDIC VIEW OF LIFE

Ayurveda means the 'wisdom of life'—life in its deepest sense as a creative and spiritual adventure—an adventure in consciousness. Such a life aims not merely at health but at the harmony of the individual with the physical, mental and spiritual aspects of the universe. In this regard, the concept of life (ayu) in Ayurveda goes far beyond any personal or materialistic definition and embraces the entirety of what we can become. Ayurveda defines true health or wellbeing (svastha) as the proper alignment of body, senses, mind and soul (Atman or Purusha). It is a complete connection of the outer aspects of our being with its inner core as pure awareness. The alignment of the spine in asana practice is a part of this greater alignment of the outer and inner aspects of our nature that allows our energies to flow upwards towards transformation.

The body is the foundation of all that we do. It should be strong, healthy and pure, free of toxins, with a good immune function, healthy appetite and good capacity for exercise. The senses are the instruments through which we contact the external world. They should be sharp and clear, sensitive and free of unnatural urges and addictions. The mind is the basis of our consciousness. It should be calm, at peace and receptive, free of emotional turbulence and harmful opinions. Behind both body and mind we have a soul or inner consciousness, a feeling of unity with all, that is not bound by time or space and connects us with the entire universe. That must be part of all that we do, the source of our motivation, for anything to have real or lasting meaning.

For treating the body we need the right food, herbs and exercise, not simply medical drugs or the last medical equipment but an entire balanced life-style. For treating the mind we need the right impressions, expressions and associations, a full regimen for psychological happiness, not merely analysis or counseling. And for the soul, we need the appropriate spiritual practice to connect us with the eternal and the infinite beyond our outer cares and concerns. All these considerations are integral to the vast scope of Ayurveda.

Ayurvedic treatment has two main components, which are interrelated. The first consists of specific recommendations to treat particular diseases, which is more the scope of medicine as we know it, like Ayurveda's powerful herbal formulas and Pancha Karma treatments. The second—and more fundamental—consists of ayurvedic recommendations to promote general health and wellbeing. This includes life-style factors of exercise and meditation, individualized health plans, an entire system of social health practices and a loving care of our natural environment.

Ayurveda makes us aware of our place in the world of nature through the movement of time. It teaches how to harmonize ourselves with sunrise and sunset, the seasons of the year, and the stages of life from birth through death. It shows us how to adapt to environmental forces of heat and cold, dampness and dryness, and clear or cloudy days. Ayurveda rises with the sun, shines beautifully with the moon, and moves unpredictably with the wind. Along with its natural rhythm, Ayurveda includes an awareness of our internal nature through our thoughts and emotions that also follow an organic model. It makes us aware of our own internal landscape, the climate and seasons of our minds and hearts. In its multileveled approach, Ayurveda shows the right diet for the physical body, the right breathing for the pranic body, the right impressions for the mind, harmonious emotions for the heart, and the right thoughts for our higher intelligence.

Ayurveda is based upon a recognition of the life-force called *Prana* in Sanskrit. It sees the body as a form, a mere shell, created and energized by Prana as a vehicle for consciousness. Ayurveda teaches us about the pranic forces that rule our lives and shows us how to master them for our greater unfoldment. It has its own language of these vital forces, which become the doshas (biological humors) that mark our individual mind-body types. We will explore these in detail throughout the book.

According to Ayurveda, we develop disease because of two factors that usually go together: externally, a wrong relationship with environmental forces like food or climate and, internally, a wrong movement of internal energies brought about by disharmonious thoughts and emotions. Resolving these two factors is the movement of ayurvedic healing that occurs both on the outside and on the inside.

YOGA AND AYURVEDA

Ayurveda, like Yoga, arose as part of various Himalayan spiritual teachings. Its traditional deity is Dhanvantari, the Hindu God of medicine, who is a form of Lord Vishnu, the aspect of cosmic consciousness that preserves and protects the universe. Its traditional founders are Charaka and Sushruta (c. 1500 BCE), who produced the two main classic texts on Ayurveda, *Charaka Samhita* and *Sushruta Samhita*. The great Yoga teacher Patanjali himself wrote a commentary on Charaka's work, which indicates how closely Yoga and Ayurveda have always been.

Yoga traditionally has been taught using the terminology of Ayurveda, particularly for explaining the physical impact and health benefits of various asanas. Similarly, Ayurveda uses the language of Yoga and its understanding of the mind and the subtle body for the psychological and spiritual dimensions of its healing practices.

Classical Yoga has as its main purpose Self-realization, which is unification with our higher Self or pure awareness that transcends the outer world and its limitations. Ayurveda has as its main purpose optimal living, manifesting our full potential of health and energy on all levels. Both go together. Without a complete flowering of our vital energy, we cannot realize our true capacity for higher awareness. Without self-understanding, we cannot use our vitality properly or fully, but will dissipate it in unconscious pursuits. Yoga rests upon ayurvedic medicine for its health implications. Ayurveda rests upon Yoga for its mental and spiritual dimension.

Both Yoga and Ayurveda reflect the Vedic idea that we must live according to our unique nature and its particular capacities. According to Ayurveda we all possess different individual constitutional types in mind and body. The requirements of one type in terms of food, exercise and life-style will be different from that of other types.

Yoga similarly should be done in harmony with one's individual constitution both physically and psychologically. The type of asana and meditation good for one person may prove harmful to another. Just as we should eat right for our type, we should also exercise right for our type. Asana regimens do better if designed according to individual needs and ayurvedic constitutional considerations. In this regard, asana practice can be employed on three different levels:

- Asana as Exercise—as part of healthy living
- Asana as Therapy—to treat specific diseases or dysfunctions of body and mind
- Asana as Spiritual Practice—for Self-knowledge and Self-development

Most commonly, people perform asanas for the easy to observe exercise and health benefits. Some people perform asanas to treat particular diseases as part of Yoga therapy, using Yoga for back pain, heart disease, nervous system disorders, AIDS or other conditions. Classical Yoga as in the *Yoga Sutras* places asana as part of a sadhana or spiritual practice but says little about the health or exercise value of particular poses, which are alluded to only in passing.

Ayurvedic treatment includes exercise prescriptions for maintaining good health and for treating specific diseases. It emphasizes asana practice as the ideal and complete exercise system to keep the body functioning at its best. According to Ayurveda, we should follow a type of exercise that agrees with our individual constitution as defined according to the doshas of Vata, Pitta and Kapha. For this reason, Ayurveda prescribes asanas based upon doshic or body-type implications. Those who want to practice Yoga as either exercise or as therapy should look to Ayurveda in order to learn how to integrate yogic practices into constitutional measures and individualized disease treatment plans.

Ayurveda is the Vedic discipline for health of body and mind, while classical Yoga is the corresponding system of spiritual practice. This means that as life-style regimens, asanas fall in the field of ayurvedic life-style treatments and should consider the ayurvedic constitution of the person. As therapies to treat specific disorders of body or mind, asanas also fall within the field of Ayurveda and should consider the doshic imbalances behind particular diseases.

Yoga therapy (Yoga chikitsa) was traditionally in the field of Ayurveda that has as its scope both life-style recommendations and prescriptions to treat specific diseases. This is not only true of the Hindu Yoga tradition but also Tibetan Buddhism, which relies heavily on Ayurveda for the therapy part of its tradition.

However, few modern Yoga teachers, even in India, are aware of the ayurvedic implications of Yoga practice. If they prescribe asanas, they may not look beyond the physical condition of the person as defined by modern medical standards. They tend to look at asanas in a non-yogic language in which their energetic connections with Prana and the higher Self are not clear. On the other hand, traditional Yoga describes asanas in terms of ayurvedic terms and energetics, which sheds much light upon their application. Yoga students should learn this ayurvedic language so that they can adapt their asana practice for the best possible results. The Ayurvedic view of asana practice complements what Yoga has already taught them, providing a medical language that is user friendly to the entire field of yogic concepts and techniques.

For those using asana practice on any level, an ayurvedic understanding of asana is very helpful, if not transformative. Similarly, those looking into the spiritual benefits of ayurvedic medicine should look to Yoga in the broader sense as a path of Self-knowledge. In the following chapters we will explain how to use asanas both for health maintenance and to treat energy imbalances as defined according to Ayurveda. But first let us examine the main concepts of Ayurveda.

THE THREE DOSHAS: THE AYURVEDIC ENERGIES OF HEALTH

Ayurveda recognizes three forms of pranic or life energy as the basis for health and disease for all people. These are the three doshas or biological humors of Vata (air), Pitta (fire) and Kapha (water). Dosha means 'what causes things to spoil' and relates to the disease-creating potential of the humors. Vata means 'wind'; Pitta means 'bile'; and Kapha refers to 'mucus or phlegm.' Wind, bile and mucus are the three main forms of toxins that cause pain and disease as they accumulate in the body. Wind causes dryness, stiffness, nervousness and debility. Bile, which is a form of fire, causes infection, inflammation, bleeding and fever. Mucus causes congestion, edema, and obesity.

THE THREE DOSHAS AND WHAT THEY DO

Vata Dosha
Vata is the propulsive or energetic force responsible for movement, expression and the discharge of all impulses.
Vata acts primarily through the nervous system through which it flows like an electric current.
The colon is its main site in the disease process, in which waste gases or toxic Vata accumulates and spreads to the blood, bones and other parts of the body.
Pitta Dosha
Pitta is the fiery or transformative force responsible for digestion, warmth and perception of all types.
Pitta acts primarily through the digestive system and the blood as the body's basic thermogenic power.
The small intestine is its main site in the disease process, in which excess acids or toxic Pitta accumulates and spreads through the blood to different parts of the body.
Kapha Dosha
Kapha is the sustaining or conserving force responsible for tissue formation, substance, cohesiveness and support.
Kapha acts primarily through the plasma or lymphatic system as the underlying nutrient solution making up the bulk of the body and providing nourishment to all the tissues.
The stomach is its main site in the disease process, in which excess mucus (waste Kapha) accumulates and spreads through the blood and lymph to different parts of the body.

The purpose of asana practice is to keep the doshas in their proper flow, to sustain them as forces of health and vitality. It aims at preventing the doshas from accumulating at their primary sites (Vata-large intestine, Pitta-small intestine, Kapha-stomach) and starting the disease process.

Asana, with its soothing, stretching and relaxing action, is the main physical exercise for balancing the doshas. It calms Vata, cools Pitta and releases Kapha. Asanas keep our physical structure and energy in harmony so that the doshas are not disturbed, assuring proper circulation of blood and Prana to the entire body. The three doshas are always intertwined in what they do:

- Vata is the carrier
- Pitta pushes or provokes
- Kapha strengthens or resists

Vata, which relates to Prana or life-energy as a whole, is the moving force that keeps everything in the body circulating and working. Pitta is the transformational force that causes things to change from one condition to another, like food becoming tissue through the digestive fire. Kapha is the sustaining force that upholds previous conditions, whether of health or disease.

Vata moves forward in a propulsive motion, making us active and on the go. We must deal with Vata first and make sure that our lives are moving in the right direction. Pitta brings about a change of level or manifestation. It causes things to move up or down and brings in the new. We deal with Pitta second to make sure that we are digesting our life-experience properly. Kapha holds back and preserves both inhibiting the horizontal movement of Vata and the vertical movement of Pitta. It also provides the fuel that the other two doshas rely upon to produce their energy, which serves to stabilize them. We deal with Kapha third in order to guard our base.

The doshas have psychological implications as temperamental forces, factors of emotion that in excess have their imbalances as well. Vata or wind creates fear and anxiety, which results from feelings of ungroundedness and instability. Pitta or fire creates anger, the consequence of too much heat or passion in our system. Kapha as water creates greed and attachment, states of clinging and holding.

I. 4 CONSTITUTIONAL TYPES

To practice Yoga for your type, you must first be able to determine what your type really is. In the following chapter, we will examine the constitutional types of Yoga and Ayurveda to allow you to do this.

There are two levels of yogic typology. The first, and more important from the spiritual side, is defined by the three gunas of sattva, rajas and tamas. The second, and more important in terms of health issues, is according to the three doshas of Vata, Pitta and Kapha. The gunas present a mental-spiritual model to help us understand our capacity for higher yogic practices. The doshas reflect a psychophysical model to help us balance the conditions of our body-mind complex. Both models are essential for a proper estimation of our nature and its capacities. Both provide the foundation for a Yoga practice that reflects both the dynamics our particular mind-body type and the particular level of our spiritual development.

1. MENTAL TYPE ACCORDING TO THE GUNAS

Yoga and Ayurveda define human psychology according to the three great qualities of Primal Nature (Prakriti)—the gunas of *sattva* (balance), *rajas* (aggression) and *tamas* (inertia). The mind's original nature is sattva, which is clarity, peace and harmony. However, coming under external influences through the senses, the mind gets disturbed (rajas) and loses its internal focus, which leads to an external seeking for happiness. This disturbance over time results in a long term inertia or resistance (tamas), which is an attachment to the external world of the senses and blindness to the internal world of consciousness.

Our ordinary mental condition is a combination of our states of clarity (sattva), agitation (rajas) and dullness (tamas). Yoga is about returning the mind to its original clear or sattvic quality so that it can perceive the truth and function as a vehicle for pure awareness. That is why traditional Yoga so much emphasizes the development of sattva. To develop a yogic consciousness we must always strive to increase our sattva.

In terms of the disease process, we can view the state of tamas as the negative disease condition that we wish to correct—the state of inertia or wrong action that has created and sustains our health problems. Rajas is the activity needed to correct the disease—the various therapies and changes we need to employ to break up the disease pattern. Sattva is the new state of harmony that we seek to create that is free of disease—the state of balance or freedom from disease.

MENTAL TYPES OF YOGA AND AYURVEDA

Sattvic Types
Sattvic individuals are peaceful, calm and concentrated in mind. They have good thoughts and intentions and spontaneously do good actions. They are considerate, compassionate and selfless, placing the needs of others above their own. Emotionally, they have much love, faith, devotion and contentment.
Rajasic Types
Rajasic types are ever active and agitated in mind, running from one thing to another in the pursuit of their desires. They have much drive, ambitious and assertion but little peace or calm. They promote their own interest, protect those who serve them and are hostile to those who oppose them. Emotionally, they have a fair amount of anger and don't like to be obstructed in what they do.
Tamasic Types
Tamasic types suffer from mental dullness, inertia and lethargy. They have little motivation to achieve either spiritual or material goals. Emotionally, they have severe blockages and are unable to express themselves harmoniously, easily falling into violence and delusion. Their lives generally remain in a stagnant state, with little ability to change or improve themselves.

However, we should note that the quality of rajas has a dual potential. It can move either upward to sattva or downward to tamas. Activity can help us reach a higher state of harmony and wellbeing or it can cause us to create a negative condition of inertia and dissipation. The management of rajas, or our type of activity, is thus the key to the gunas.

ASANA AND THE GUNAS

According to the classic text *Hatha Yoga Pradipika* the main purpose of asana practice is 'to reduce the quality of rajas.' This means to reduce heat, agitation and aggression and to create calm and peace in the body and mind. It requires moving from disturbed physical activity to a state of relaxation and rest, in which we are content to sit and meditate.

However, using asana to move from rajas to sattva, implies that the person performing asanas has already reduced the quality of tamas—that they have eliminated inertia and dullness from the body and mind. This is not the case for most of us today. Most of us are suffering from tamas owing to a sedentary life-style, a heavy diet and other factors. Such an energy of tamas is behind most of the obesity, depression and low energy that so many people suffer from today.

If tamas does exist in a person, one must first do active practices to reduce it. This requires increasing rajas through strong physical exercise, including walking or running, some sort of service work, or through a more active asana practice. Without first practicing asana to get their energies moving, if they attempt to meditate they are likely to fall asleep or to get contracted into their own inertia and dullness.

Those who have sattvic or clear minds usually don't need as much asana practice. They easily take to sitting postures. Their bodies are usually flexible and free of toxins. Their minds are at peace. Their mental and pranic energies are moving and their body is light. However, such people are rare, particularly in this age of rajas in which we are overly busy and overly stimulated.

However, people who are too much in their heads and neglect their bodies may develop sattva in the mind but can still allow tamas to continue in the body. They can exhibit much stiffness and lack of flexibility, particularly in the neck and shoulders. They need a strong, regular asana practice to break up the physical tamas that may accompany their mental sattva.

Those who have rajasic minds, particularly high achievement-oriented types, need asanas to release their built up energy and aggression. They need to control their turbulent Prana and develop sitting poses for meditation. However, rajasic types can become overly involved in physical practice and use asana as another form of stress-producing (rajasic) movement. We must remember asana is not about personal achievement but of letting go of the ego.

PHASES OF PRACTICE

As each one of us has all three gunas, *the first stage of practice aims at breaking up tamas*. It consists of active or stimulating postures to remove tiredness and dullness and dispel toxins. One has to bring more attention into the physical body to remove the inertia accumulated there. For example, the quality of tamas predominates in the early morning after sleep (which is a tamasic state). More active asanas and more stimulating pranayama may be necessary to counter it.

The second phase of practice requires calming rajas or reducing agitation. This means calming and relaxing asanas and pranayama are required. One should remove one's attention from the physical body to the mind and heart. Internal practices of mantra, affirmations and visualizations become important for this purpose.

The third phase of practice is increasing sattva, which occurs through calm and focused meditation in which the body is largely forgotten and the Prana is at rest. This is the higher level of Yoga practice that proceeds through pure sattva in which we come to contact our higher Self.

MENTAL CONSTITUTION ACCORDING TO THE THREE GUNAS

Ayurveda and Yoga use the three gunas for determining individual mental or spiritual nature. Generally, one guna predominates within us. We are either primarily tamasic, rajasic or sattvic types. However, while we can define individuals as primarily one type or another, we must remember that we all possess aspects of each of the gunas. We all have our peaceful (sattvic) periods, our disturbed (rajasic) fluctuations, and our inertia or blindness (tamas). The key is to increase our sattvic qualities and reduce those of rajas and tamas. We must evolve from tamas (latent potential) to rajas (active development) to sattva (full mastery).

TABLE OF THE GUNAS

Physical Management	
Sattvic Body	Cleanliness, flexibility, detachment, gentle exercise
Rajasic Body	Self-adornment, ostentation, self-indulgence, harsh exercise
Tamasic Body	Uncleanliness, sloppy appearance, laziness, lack of exercise
Emotional State	
Sattvic Emotions	Love, faith, devotion, compassion, loyalty
Rajasic Emotions	Ambition, assertion, anger, passion, pride
Tamasic Emotions	Hatred, paranoia, violence, megalomania
Mental State	
Sattvic Mind	Peaceful, truthful, receptive, clear, perceptive
Rajasic Mind	Restless, agitated, assertive, argumentative
Tamasic Mind	Ignorant, dull, untruthful, obstinate
Spiritual Level	
Sattvic Soul	Spiritual, compassionate, loving, enlightened
Rajasic Soul	Egoistic, passionate, ambitious, manipulative
Tamasic Soul	Unaware, harmful, deceptive, criminal, perverted

2. AYURVEDIC DOSHIC CONSTITUTION

The three doshas are not only general factors responsible for physiological responses; they are specific factors that create the different energetic types of human beings. These doshic types can be easily understood according to their elemental equivalents. Vata types are dominated by air but have a secondary component of ether as the space, mainly in the bones and joints, which contains Vata in the body. Pitta types are dominated by fire but have a secondary component of water as the hot liquids like the blood and digestive juices, which hold Pitta. Kapha types are dominated by water and but have a secondary component of earth as the lining of the skin and mucus membranes, which contains it.

AYURVEDIC DOSHIC TYPES

Vata Types
On a physical level, Vata types are taller or shorter than average, thin in build, with a tendency to low body weight. They have poor circulation, dry skin, prominent veins and low body fat. Their digestion is nervous and variable and they easily get constipated. They suffer most from exposure to wind, dryness and cold.
On a psychological level, Vatas are nervous types, restless, active, expressive and creative. They are emotionally sensitive and prone to fear and anxiety, with quickly fluctuating moods and opinions.
Relative to Yoga practice, Vatas are attracted to all types of energy practices including asana, pranayama, and mantra. They like to be active doing things to change their lives.

Pitta Types
On a physical level, Pitta types are average in height and build. They have a good circulation, bright complexion, warm extremities, and a warm and oily skin. Their appetite and thirst is high and their elimination is good but usually on the loose side. They suffer most from exposure to heat, sunlight and fire.
On a psychological level, Pittas are aggressive types, dynamic, willful, focused and determined. They are emotionally pointed and assertive, with strong opinions and a tendency towards anger.
Relative to Yoga practice, Pittas are most attracted to meditation and to working on the mind. They naturally seek enlightenment as the goal of life. They will take up asana practice as a means of developing energy, however.

Kapha Types
On a physical level, Kapha types are generally shorter than average in height but can be tall. However, they always have a big or bulky build with a tendency to hold weight and water. They have a poor circulation and a thick skin that tends to be damp. Their appetite is constant, but their metabolism is low, and their elimination tends to be sluggish. They suffer most from dampness and cold.
On a psychological level, Kaphas are emotional types with strong and steady feelings. They are calm, content, loyal and consistent. They can develop deep-seated attachments and find it difficult to let go.
Relative to Yoga practice, Kaphas prefer devotional approaches, including chanting, prayer and worship of Deities. They will take up asanas if convinced it is necessary for health purposes.

THE DOSHAS AS CONSTITUTIONAL FACTORS

The three doshas create three different primary types of individual constitutions or mind-body types as Vata, Pitta or Kapha, which are emphasized throughout Ayurveda. We should note that no single type is necessarily better or worse than the others. Each type has its benefits as well as its weaknesses. Each requires a specific adjustment or adaptation to keep it in balance. Learn to become aware of both the strengths and the weaknesses of your type.

- With their watery and earthy nature, Kapha types possess the strongest bodily build and reserve of vital energy, but can lack in the motivation and adaptation to use it properly.
- With their fluctuating airy nature, Vata types have the weakest build and stamina, but also have the greatest capacity for change and adaptation in order to protect it.
- With their fiery nature, Pitta types possess a moderate physical strength and stamina, but have a mental and emotional force and determination that can make them strongly pursue the factors of health or disease, depending upon their values.

EXAMINATION OF CONSTITUTION

The following is a detailed examination of constitution taken from the book *Ayurvedic Healing*. As you go through the exam, remember that you are a combination of all three doshas in varying amounts. Note which dosha you check the most. This will usually be your predominant dosha. Some people may be dual types with two doshas in relatively equal proportion. Others may have all three in about the same amounts. When it is particularly difficult to make a decision, give more weight to factors that are most prominent. Generally speaking, we know ourselves well enough to determine our own constitution. Determining that of others is more difficult.

Our natural or birth constitution is best revealed by the fixed attributes of the physical body, particularly our bodily frame and long term weight tendencies. Our general metabolism and digestion over time is another good indicator. Lifelong habits and proclivities, and lifelong disease tendencies are other important indicators.

Though constitution tends to remain the same throughout life, exceptional factors like a long-term illness can change it, particularly if a person is originally a dual type. Sometimes the constitution changes with the stages of life, like Vata coming out in old age, which is its stage of life. Or we can experience another dosha in a transient way relative to daily or seasonal changes. For example, we are all more fiery (Pitta) during the summer, the Pitta season, more watery (Kapha) during the spring, the Kapha season, and more airy (Vata) during the fall, the Vata season. For this reason, we should remain aware of all three doshas and their possible health impacts, even if we are strongly one type or another.

AYURVEDIC CONSTITUTIONAL TEST

BODILY STRUCTURE AND APPEARANCE

	VATA	PITTA	KAPHA
FRAME	Tall or short, thin; poorly developed physique	Medium; moderately developed physique	Stout, stocky, short, big; well developed physique
WEIGHT	Low, hard to hold weight, prominent veins and bones	Moderate, good muscles	Heavy, tends towards obesity
COMPLEXION	Dull, brown, darkish	Red, ruddy, flushed, glowing	White, pale
SKIN TEXTURE and TEMPERATURE	Thin, dry, cold, rough, cracked, prominent veins	Warm, moist, pink, with moles, freckles, acne	Thick, white, moist, cold, soft, smooth
HAIR	Scanty, coarse, dry, brown, slightly wavy	Moderate, fine, soft, early gray or bald	Abundant, oily, thick, very wavy, lustrous
HEAD	Small, thin, long, unsteady	Moderate	Large, stocky, steady
FOREHEAD	Small, wrinkled	Moderate, with folds	Large, broad
FACE	Thin, small, long, wrinkled, dusky, dull	Moderate, ruddy, sharp contours	Large, round, fat, white or pale, soft contours
NECK	Thin, long	Medium	Large, thick
EYEBROWS	Small, thin, unsteady	Moderate, fine	Thick, bushy, many hairs
EYELASHES	Small, dry, firm	Small, thin, fine	Large, thick, oily, firm
EYES	Small, dry, thin, brown, dull, unsteady	Medium, thin, red (inflamed easily), green, piercing	Wide, prominent, thick, oily, white, attractive
NOSE	Thin, small, long, dry, crooked	Medium	Thick, big, firm, oily
LIPS	Thin, small, darkish, dry, unsteady	Medium, soft, red	Thick, large, oily, smooth, firm

	VATA	PITTA	KAPHA
TEETH & GUMS	Thin, dry, small, rough, crooked, receding gums	Medium, soft, pink, gums bleed easily	Large, thick, soft, pink, oily
SHOULDERS	Thin, small, flat, hunched	Medium	Broad, thick, firm, oily
CHEST	Thin, small, narrow, poorly developed	Medium	Broad, large, well or overly developed
ARMS	Thin, overly small or long, poorly developed	Medium	Large, thick, round, well developed
HANDS	Small, thin, dry, cold, rough, fissured, unsteady	Medium, warm, pink	Large, thick, oily, cool, firm
THIGHS	Thin, narrow	Medium	Well-developed, round, fat
LEGS	Thin, excessively long or short, prominent knees	Medium	Large, stocky
CALVES	Small, hard, tight	Loose, soft	Shapely, firm
FEET	Small, thin, long, dry, rough, fissured, unsteady	Medium, soft, pink	Large, thick, hard, firm
JOINTS	Small, thin, dry, unsteady, cracking	Medium, soft, loose	Large, thick, well built
NAILS	Small, thin, dry, rough, fissured, cracked, darkish	Medium, soft, pink	Large, thick, smooth, white, firm, oily

WASTE MATERIALS/METABOLISM

	VATA	PITTA	KAPHA
URINE	Scanty, difficult, colorless	Profuse, yellow, red, burning	Moderate, whitish, milky
FECES	Scanty, dry, hard, difficult or painful, gas, tends towards constipation	Abundant, loose, yellowish, tends to diarrhea, with burning sensation	Moderate, solid, sometimes pale in color, mucus in stool

	VATA	PITTA	KAPHA
SWEAT/BODY ODOR	Scanty, no smell	Profuse, hot, strong smell	Moderate, cold, pleasant smell
APPETITE	Variable, erratic	Strong, sharp	Constant, low
TASTE PREFERENCES	Prefers sweet, sour, or salty food, cooked with oil and spiced	Prefers sweet, bitter or astringent food, raw, lightly cooked without spices or extra salt	Prefers pungent, bitter or astringent food, cooked with spices but not oil
CIRCULATION	Poor, variable, erratic	Good, warm	Slow, steady

GENERAL CHARACTERISTICS

	VATA	PITTA	KAPHA
ACTIVITY	Quick, fast, unsteady, erratic, hyperactive	Medium, motivated, purposeful, goal seeking	Slow, steady, stately
STRENGTH/ ENDURANCE	Low, poor endurance, starts and stops quickly	Medium, intolerant of heat	Strong, good endurance, but slow in starting
SEXUAL NATURE	Variable, erratic, deviant, strong desire but low energy, few children	Moderate, passionate, quarrelsome, dominating	Low but constant sexual desire, good sexual energy, devoted, many children
SENSITIVITY	Fear of cold, wind, sensitive to dryness	Fear of heat, dislike of sun, fire	Fear of cold, damp, likes wind and sun
RESISTANCE TO DISEASE	Poor, variable, weak immune system	Medium, prone to infection	Good, prone to congestive disorders
DISEASE TENDENCY	Nervous system diseases, pain, arthritis, mental disorders	Fevers, infections, inflammatory diseases	Respiratory system diseases, mucus, edema
REACTION TO MEDICATIONS	Quick, low dosage needed, unexpected side effects or nervous reactions	Medium, average dosage	Slow, high dosage required, effects slow to manifest
PULSE	Thready, rapid, superficial, irregular, weak; like a snake	Wiry, bounding, moderate; like a frog	Deep, slow, steady, rolling, slippery; like a swan

MENTAL FACTORS AND EXPRESSION

	VATA	PITTA	KAPHA
VOICE	Low, weak, hoarse	High pitch, sharp	Pleasant, deep, good tone
SPEECH	Quick, inconsistent, erratic, talkative	Moderate, argumentative, convincing	Slow, definite, not talkative
MENTAL NATURE	Quick, adaptable, indecisive	Intelligent, penetrating, critical	Slow, steady, dull
MEMORY	Poor, notices things easily but easily forgets	Sharp, clear	Slow to take notice but will not forget
FINANCES	Earns and spends quickly, erratically	Spends on specific goals, causes or projects	Holds on to what one earns, particularly property
EMOTIONAL TENDENCIES	Fearful, anxious, nervous	Angry, irritable, contentious	Calm, content, attached, sentimental
NEUROTIC TENDENCIES	Hysteria, trembling, anxiety attacks	Extreme temper, rage, tantrums	Depression, unresponsiveness, sorrow
FAITH	Erratic, changeable, rebel	Determined, fanatic, leader	Constant, loyal, conservative
SLEEP	Light, tends towards insomnia	Moderate, may wake up but will fall asleep again	Heavy, difficulty in waking up
DREAMS	Flying, moving, restless, nightmares	Colorful, passionate, conflict	Romantic, sentimental, watery, few dreams
HABITS	Likes speed, traveling, parks, plays, jokes, stories, trivia, artistic activities, dancing	Likes competitive sports, debates, politics, hunting, research	Likes water, sailing, flowers, cosmetics, business ventures, cooking

TOTAL (50) V________ P________ K________

NOTES

PART II

Principles of Asana Practice

VICTOR VAN KOOTEN AND ANGELA FARMER IN ARDHA CHANDRASANA

II. 5 WHAT ASANA DOES

Asana (Yoga poses), which consciously use the mind and body together, bring about profound changes in the body and in our overall energy flow. Asana has many aspects and must be looked at from many sides. On a purely physical level, asanas are organically derived positions that keep the body's systems running smoothly, comfortably, and in the best possible health. A regular asana practice helps you feel relaxed, at ease, and happy in your body.

Yoga asanas balance the body by bringing the appropriate tone and suppleness to the musculature. They strengthen muscles that are weak and stretch muscles that are tight. They adjust the muscles, ligaments, and tendons ensuring their proper functioning. Asanas also manage the internal energetic systems of the body. With consistent practice they tone the body's governing systems like the glandular system, nervous system, and cardiovascular system. A consistent asana practice can bring awareness of unknown problems in the body, uncovering hidden areas of stress or pain. Through continued practice these problems are improved and often permanently resolved.

Yoga philosophy teaches us that negative experiences, like trauma, and negative emotions, like fear and anger, lodge in the nerve tissue and the subconscious mind. These emotional toxins do not simply lie dormant but are a cause of underlying depression or agitation in our behavior. They can also be carried, as karmic propensities, into our future lives even after the body dies. Through asana practice we can release this built up tension from past experience that lodges in our bones and nervous systems. Eliminating the past from our bodies and our minds creates new flexibility and increases energy. We become reconnected to our natural unlimited source of vitality.

The practice of Yoga can address many chronic physical ailments. Structural body problems and specific diseases can be greatly improved by regular practice. Scientific research has proven that Yoga has a dramatic effect on many ailments. Conditions that Yoga has been shown to help improve, reverse, or eliminate include:

- Heart disease
- Asthma
- Hypertension
- Back pain
- Neck pain
- Stress
- Scoliosis
- Arthritis
- Diabetes
- Constipation
- Digestive problems
- Insomnia
- Emotional instability
- Fatigue
- Thyroid problems
- Weakened immune system

Asanas derive from life and nature. Some mirror the attitudes of great warriors like the force and direction of Virabhadra as in the warrior poses. Other asanas reflect the world of plants as in the tree pose (Vrksasana) or the lotus pose (Padmasana). Others reflect the movements of various animals like the dog pose (Adho Muka Svansana), or lion pose (Simhasana). The practice of these poses brings us the attributes and energies of their namesakes.

For example, the cobra pose (Bhujangasana) creates the attributes of the snake in our bodies. Just as the snake has a very supple spine but enough strength to hold its body weight when it needs to strike, the cobra pose creates the same kind of suppleness and strength in our human bodies. It stimulates the 'fight or flight', sympathetic, nervous system of our bodies making us ready for action like the snake. Similarly, we gain strength and courage from the warrior positions, and a slowing, sense of withdrawal from the tortoise pose.

Yoga asana is a sophisticated system of energy management. The energy of each position is learned through the repeated experience of the pose. The body is changed in a way specific to each pose and to the conditions that it reflects. When the practitioner has mastered these changes, he or she can use their practice for balancing emotional, mental, and physical conditions, applying the necessary asanas to counter any disturbances.

Asana is the first formal practice of Patanjali's eight-limbed (Ashtanga) Yoga system. It begins the internalizing process that is Yoga, through making us conscious of how we are using our bodies. In our hectic lives we spend our time thinking of the future, remembering experiences or facts about the past, or a list of things that need to be managed right now. And we do all of this while we run from errands to appointments and meetings in busy traffic and changing relationships. With so much going on at once, we seldom experience the present moment in its fullness. Some of us live our lives as if we were in a constant state of emergency.

The practice of asana opens us up to the rich experience of the present. By bringing the body, mind, spirit, and breath together in one place, a concentrated experience of wholeness and wellbeing is available in the Now. The external flow of energy is balanced with the internal flow and we experience contact with our higher Self. Not only does this experience feel wonderful; it also feeds and nourishes us at very deep levels physically, mentally and emotionally.

Just as plants require nourishment from the soil, water, and sun in order to grow and flower, we human beings need a balance between the outward and inward flows of energy in our daily lives. When our lives are focused primarily outward, we can become like a withering plant; our contact with the Self and the balance that nourishes us is lost. A regular Yoga practice is an excellent vehicle for managing the flow of our energy, sustaining our health and feeling of well-being. It takes our energy back within so that we can renew and rejuvenate ourselves.

Yet asanas are much more than healing tools and means of energy management, they are also paths to self-discovery. Asanas can be used as a mirror to reveal behavior and conditioning of which we are not normally aware. The mirror of asana practice provides us a way to see ourselves, a way into the consciousness that drives our reactions in life, a perspective on our thoughts, attitudes and personality. Living life out of reaction rather than choice leaves a discomfort in our lives in which we get trapped. Using asana practice as a mirror we can see the changes that we want to make within ourselves in order to feel better and freer. We can learn what we are doing to create the circumstances that perpetuate unhappiness and permanently change them.

Asana means pose or posture. When you look in the dictionary you will find a definition of the word pose or posture as 'attitude.' When we regularly practice asana, we have the opportunity to see not only the postures that we adopt in our physical body but also the attitudes that we follow in our minds. These mental attitudes determine how we behave in our relationships, in business and in our own homes. Being able to see this behavior frees us from unconscious reactions, taking us into a conscious awareness in which we can guide our own experience.

With freedom from behavioral compulsions, we can move into the higher purpose of Yoga, which is to control our thoughts. Our bodies react to each one of our thoughts. Our minds give instruction to the millions of cells in our body. Every thought that we think is an instruction from the head of our system to the millions of subjects, the individual cells. And the cells respond. With Yoga practice we can control our thoughts and gain peace of mind, which in turn gives harmony to the body, good health, balanced weight and increased energy. Through control of our thoughts, we gain control of the body, our emotions, our breathing and our lives. We are no longer driven by our emotions and the dualities of this world can no longer afflict us. We are free to experience the bliss of residing in our own true nature.

On a deeper level, the practice of asana prepares us for the unfoldment of the subtle body and its powerful pranic forces. The channels of the subtle body, called *Nadis*, are cleansed by asana and pranayama for the greater energy transmission necessary for higher levels of Yoga in which the energy centers (chakras) of the subtle body are opened.

ASANA PROMOTES PHYSICAL HEALTH AND LONGEVITY BY

- Balancing the muscles in relationship to each other and relative to their appropriate function
- Maintaining the health and integrity of the joints and spine
- Managing the energetic system of the body
- Relaxing, strengthening, stretching and energizing the body
- Toning and nourishing every bodily system: glandular, nervous, cardiovascular and digestive
- Cleansing and nourishing the body on every level
- Bringing body problems to light and often correcting them
- Providing a system of energy patterns that, when fit onto the body, can prescriptively change the body's existing energy flow
- Providing a mirror in which we can see our behavior and attitudes and choose to change them
- Preparing the body for the subtler energies to flow, as a vehicle for a higher consciousness

II. 6 AYURVEDIC EFFECTS OF ASANA PRACTICE

According to the philosophy of Yoga, the physical body is a manifestation of consciousness. It is a crystallization of karmic (behavioral) patterns created by the mind. The key to working with the body, therefore, is to understand the consciousness behind it, much of which lies outside our ordinary awareness. This requires that we practice asanas aware not only of the technicalities of the postures but also of the mental and emotional states that they create within us.

Ayurveda shares this Yoga theory. It views the body as a manifestation of the doshas, which are not merely physical but also pranic and psychological energies—factors of consciousness. We cannot look into the doshic impact of asanas purely on a physical level but must consider their psychological effects as well.

Yoga views asanas not merely as static poses but as conditions of energy, which in turn are manifestations of consciousness. The energy and attention that we put into the pose is as important as the pose itself. We can see this in ordinary life in which how we feel on a psychological level determines how we move on a physical level. Long term patterns of feeling and energy determine the form and rhythm of the body.

ASANA AS PHYSICAL STRUCTURE

At the most basic level, an asana is a physical pose, a kind of bodily gesture. In asana practice we place the body into a position that has a specific result and message depending upon the shape that it creates with the body. Each asana has its own structural effect. Sitting poses provide stability in the spine. Some of them create flexibility in the backs of the legs. Since most sitting postures create parasympathetic stimulation, they create a pleasant calming influence. Standing poses increase general strength and energy levels. Backbends tend to excite us (sympathetic stimulation), increase spinal extension, and create strength in the trunk elevator muscles. Relaxation poses even out and calm the energies created by our asana practice. All asanas, whether in groups or individually, have their own energetics depending upon what they do to the body. Like a house they have their own architecture.

However, since all our bodies do not have the same structure, the experience of an asana will vary depending upon the build, flexibility and organic condition of the individual. The effect of the asana is a combination of the structure of the asana, which is the same for everyone, and the person's own bodily structure, which will vary not only by individual but also changes through the course of time.

ASANA AS PRANIC ENERGY

The physical body is a vehicle for our internal energies, which are defined through Prana. Asanas are vehicles through which Prana is directed. An asana is not merely a physical structure but a condition of energy. Asanas express a quality of energy and even quieting poses can contain behind them a dynamic condition of mind and Prana. This fact gives all asanas a certain neutrality in their energetic effects, just as a vehicle in itself is neutral, with the goal of its travel depending on the driver. The asana is like a car with Prana as the driving force. It is not just a question of having the right vehicle but also of moving it in the right way. The pranic impulse behind the asana is as important as the asana itself.

This means that depending upon how we direct our Prana, the same asana can take us to different places. For example, a sitting posture done with strong pranayama can have a very energizing effect, while with ordinary breathing it will quiet us or even put us to sleep. The pranic energetics of an asana depend upon various factors including on how quickly we do the posture, the degree of force we use and, above all, on how we breathe during the asana. In fact, the goal of asana practice is to calm the body so that we can work on our Prana. Prana manifests when the body is still. This is the importance of sitting poses for internal healing.

ASANA AS THOUGHT AND INTENTION

Asana is not only structure and energy but also reflects thought and intention. We could call asana a 'thoughtful' or 'mindful' form of exercise. The effects of the same asana will vary depending upon whether our mind is clear or cloudy and our emotions are calm or turbulent. We may perform an asana with technical precision but our state of mind will determine how liberating the asana actually is for our consciousness.

Our mental state is reflected in our breath. When the mind is calm, the breath is calm. When the mind is disturbed, the breath is disturbed. So, mental and pranic energetics go together. While we can change the pranic effect of an asana through the breath, we can also change the mental effects of an asana through concentration and meditation. An asana should be a kind of meditation in form or movement. Therefore, we should always put our minds into a sacred space of silence, observation, and detachment while performing Yoga.

If our consciousness is not engaged during the asana, then our practice remains at a superficial level. Prana follows the energy of attention. The bodily posture is an outcome of that. The kind of posture that a person has reflects how they place their attention in life, what they most commonly do. That is why so many of us are hunched over today. Our main posture is sitting at a desk, in a car, or on a couch! This places our energy outside ourselves and so our internal energy sinks or collapses.

In summary, therefore, the structural effect of the asana is the first factor. The way we energize the asana through Prana is the second. This includes how we move through the asana and breathe within it. Our state of mind is a third factor. The main rule in asana practice is to keep the mind calm, collected and attentive so that we don't lose focus in the practice. We must consider all three factors relative to an ayurvedic examination of asanas. All these factors are interrelated. The dosha often contains the key to a person's structural, pranic and emotional state.

AYURVEDIC EFFECTS OF ASANAS

Each asana has a particular effect defined relative to the three doshas. This is the same as how Ayurveda classifies foods according to their doshic effects as good or bad for Vata, Pitta and Kapha, depending upon the tastes and the elements that compose each food article. We can look upon different asanas according to their structural ability to increase or decrease the doshas.

However, this doshic equation of asanas should not be taken rigidly because the pranic effect of an asana can outweigh its structural affect as we just noted. The form of the asana is not its main factor. Through the use of the breath we can modify or even change the doshic effects of the asana. We must remember the importance of thought and intention in asana practice as well. Considering the asana, Prana and the mind, we can alter a particular asana or adjust the entire practice toward a particular doshic result. Through combining specific asanas, pranayama and meditation a complete internal balance can be created and sustained.

Doshic application of asanas is twofold:

- According to the constitution of the individual defined by their doshic type as Vata, Pitta and Kapha and their intermixtures.
- Relative to the impact of asana on the doshas as general physiological functions. Each dosha has its sites and actions in the body that asanas will effect depending upon their orientation.

Constitutional Application

Vata types have a different bodily structure and move in a different way than do Pitta or Kapha types. Similarly, Pittas and Kaphas have their own particular movements and postures that they assume as part of the doshic signature on their bodies and minds. This difference between the doshas is reflected in the pulse of each type.

- Vata types have a pulse with a snake-like motion. They move in a snake-like way—like a discharge of electricity, with quick, abrupt, unpredictable and irregular movements. Their internal energy and thoughts have the same quickness, brilliance, unpredictability and discontinuity.
- Pitta types have a frog-like pulse that is wiry, tight or bounding in nature. They move like a frog—jumping up in continuous motion until they achieve their particular goal. Their movement is like how a fire leaps up when fed with new fuel. They act with focus and determination, going from step to step. Their internal energy and thoughts have the same determined and bounding movement and flow.
- Kapha types have a pulse like a swan that is broad and flowing. They move like a swan—slow, stately and elegant, taking their time in an undulating manner. Their energy flows like a slow meandering river, taking its time along the way, assured of its ultimate goal. Yet when Kapha accumulates, their movement resembles water flowing through a marshland, with resistance and leading to stagnation. Their internal energy and thoughts have the same watery movement and possible inertia.

Impact of the Asana on the Doshas

Each doshic type has its own particular structure and energetic of life that extends to asana practice. Asana practice must consider the dosha of the person to be really effective.

- Vata energy is impulsive and erratic, like the wind that blows hard but not for long. Yet if we oppose it, it will flee or break. Vata must be gently restrained and supported, grounded and stabilized. It should be harmonized and given continuity in a consistent and determined manner.
- Pitta energy is focused and penetrating and can cut and harm. It must be gently relaxed and diffused. It is like a high beam that hurts the eyes and is narrow in its field of illumination but, when expanded, can be a truly enlightening force.
- Kapha energy is resistant and complacent. It must be moved and stimulated by degrees, like ice that must be slowly melted until it can flow smoothly. We must consistently energize and stimulate the Kapha type to further action.

However, that an asana may not be good for a particular doshic type doesn't mean that they should never do it. It means they should practice the asana in a way which guards against any potential imbalances. Take, for example, backbends. Forceful or quickly done full backbends can cause major Vata aggravation, with severe strain to the nervous system perhaps more so than any other asana. However, gentle partial backbends are great for reducing Vata that accumulates in the upper back and shoulders.

Each asana family like standing poses, forward bends, or inverted postures has general benefits for the body as a whole and its overall movement potential. Each asana family exercises certain muscles and organs that, as part of our entire bodily structure, should not be neglected. To counter any tendencies toward imbalance, you should select poses within each asana family that are better for your body type than others within the same group. In general, you should make sure that all the main muscle groups in the body are represented in your practice at least several days each week.

Similarly, that an asana is good for a particular dosha doesn't mean all persons of that doshic type should do it. It means that the asana can be good for them if done in the right way and if they are physically capable of it. Each asana also has its degree of difficulty that may require certain warm up or preparatory postures to approach it safely. For example, the right preparation for a headstand creates the arm and shoulder musculature needed to sustain a good and safe head balance. Because a headstand is good for your doshic type doesn't mean that you should simply jump into the posture or can it without possible side-effects.

In addition, the effects of different asanas vary according to the sequence in which they are done. This means that asana practice should always be viewed as a whole—not merely in terms of the single asanas that compose it but in terms of the flow and the relationship between all the particular asanas done. Asana practice—meaning the sequence and manner of doing asana as well as the specific asanas—should be designed to keep the doshas in balance relative to the individual's constitution and condition.

It is helpful to view asana sequence like an herbal formula. An ayurvedic herbal formula contains a number of herbs used for various purposes that contribute to the overall effect of the formula, fulfilling specific roles. The overall doshic effect of the formula is determined by the formula as a whole, not by any single herb within it viewed in isolation. Combining these ayurvedic considerations with the general factors listed above, to effectively prescribe asanas teachers must learn to:

- Assess the ayurvedic type and imbalances of the person.
- Assess the structural condition of the person, including their posture, age and physical condition.
- Assess their pranic condition, their control of the breath and senses, along with their vitality and enthusiasm.
- Assess the mental state of the person, their attention, will and motivation, as well as their emotional condition.

The same asana should be done differently relative to whether the person is Vata, Pitta or Kapha. The same asana should be done differently depending upon the age, sex and physical condition of the person. It should vary depending upon the whether the person has a strong or weak vitality. Additional variations will occur if a person is suffering from anger, grief, stress or depression. This reflects four primary goals for an ayurvedic asana practice:

1. To balance the doshas
2. To improve the structural condition of the body
3. To facilitate the movement and development of prana
4. To calm and energize the mind

AYURVEDIC BODY TYPES AND ASANA PRACTICE

To understand the asana potentials of different people we will want to look at them according to their doshic body types.

VATA BODY TYPE

Vata types have thin and long bones that are often weak or brittle. They have low body weight and poor development of the muscles, but a good deal of speed and flexibility. Their bone structure makes them good at bending and stretching, particularly of the arms and legs, when they are young. As they get older, however, the dry quality of Vata increases and causes them to lose mobility if they don't exercise regularly.

A gentle, slow asana practice evenly balanced on both sides of the body is the ideal exercise for Vata types. Vatas are most in need of asana practice because asana alleviates accumulated Vata from the back and the bones, where it easily gets lodged. Vata diseases begin with an accumulation of the downward moving air (Apana Vayu) in the colon, which gets transferred to the bones, where it causes bone and joint problems. Vata benefits from the massaging action of asana on the muscles and joints, which releases nervous tension and balances out the system.

Negative Potential of Vata
Vata types more commonly suffer from stiffness owing to dryness and deficiency in the tissues. Their lack of body weight does not allow for adequate cushioning of the joints and nerves or proper hydration of the tissues. They are more prone to injury because they like to initiate sudden and abrupt movements, as well as going to extremes in their practice.
Positive Potential of Vata
Vata types like exercise and enjoy movement. They prefer to be active and expressive both physically and mentally and like to do new things. Asana is something that they easily take to and grow accustomed to as part of their active nature. It is a soothing way for them to exercise.

Blocked and Deficient Vata

There are two basic conditions of Vata, called *blocked Vata* or *deficient Vata*. Blocked Vata exhibits a stuck energy somewhere in the body along with pain or discomfort, but otherwise normal body weight. Deficient Vata exhibits low energy, low body weight and hypersensitivity, often without any acute pain. Blocked Vata requires movement oriented or pranic asanas to release it. Deficient Vata requires a gentle and building approach, avoiding strong exertion. Blocked Vata is more common in young people who have adequate energy but get it blocked, while deficient Vata is more common in the elderly whose tissue quality is in decline.

PITTA BODY TYPE

Pitta types have an average build with a generally good development of the muscles and a looseness of the joints, which gives them a fair amount of flexibility. They are good at asana practice but cannot do some of the more exotic poses that Vatas can do because of their shorter bones. Pittas benefit from asana practice to cool down the head and the blood, calm the heart and relieve tension. For example, Pittas tend to hypertension because of their fiery temperament that drives them to succeed or to win.

Negative Potential of Pitta

Pitta types tend to be overheated and irritable owing to excess internal heat. They may lack the patience to get started in practice or to stick with it over time. On the other hand, once involved they can overdo postures and be aggressive and militant in their practice. Pittas who have pushed too hard in their practice will feel more irritable or even angry after they finish. Pittas will also tend to stick with poses that they can do well and ignore those that may help them develop further.

Positive Potential of Pitta

Pittas have the best focus and determination of the doshic types. They easily get into a consistent discipline and determined practice once they have gotten it started and oriented correctly. They are the most orderly and consistent of the types. They just have to discover the right path to place their energies.

KAPHA BODY TYPE

Kaphas are typically short and stocky, gaining weight easily. With their short and thick bones they lack flexibility and cannot do poses that require flexibility like the lotus pose. Yet they are sturdy and strong and have the best endurance of the different types. Kaphas need movement and stimulation to counter their tendency to complacency and inertia. They are good at keeping a practice going for longer periods of time, once they get it going in the first place.

Negative Potential of Kapha

Kaphas tend to be overweight, which limits their movement and makes them sedentary. They often have congestion in the lungs that makes deep breathing difficult. They lack in positive effort and find it hard to change without some sort of external stimulation. They need to be constantly prodded to do more or they will stop short in their efforts.

Positive Potential of Kapha

Kaphas are steady and consistent in what they do. Once they take something up they do it faithfully over time. They remain emotionally calm and even in their practice regardless of the results. They view life with love and work as a service.

THE AYURVEDIC WAY OF PERFORMING ASANAS

Ayurveda does not look upon asanas as fixed forms that by themselves either decrease or increase the doshas. It views them as vehicles for energy that can be used to help balance the doshas, if used correctly. The same is true of the ayurvedic view of food. While individual food items have their specific effects to increase or decrease the doshas, how we prepare the food, how we antidote it with spices, how we combine it, or how we cook it to blend food qualities into an harmonious whole, is as significant as the particular foods themselves.

While Ayurveda says that foods of certain tastes are more likely to increase or decrease specific doshas, it also says that we need some degree of all the tastes. So too, we need to do all the major types of asanas to some degree. It is the degree and exertion that varies with the doshic type. Each person requires a full range of exercise that deals with the full range of motion in the body.

Your overall asana practice should be like a meal. Each meal should contain some degree of all six tastes (sweet, sour, salty, pungent, bitter and astringent) and some amount of all nutrient types required for the body (starches, sugars, proteins, oils, vitamins and minerals) but as adjusted to the needs of individual constitution. So too, asana practice should contain all the main types of asanas necessary for exercising and relaxing the entire body adjusted to individual constitutional factors. It should include sitting, standing and prone postures, expansive, contractive, ascending and descending movements, but in a manner and sequence that keeps us in balance and considers our individual structural, energetic and mental conditions.

KEYS TO PRACTICING ASANA FOR YOUR TYPE

VATA

General	Keep your energy firm, even and consistent; moderate and sustain your enthusiasm
Body	Keep the body calm, centered and relaxed; do the asana slowly, gently and without undue or sudden use of force, avoid abrupt movements, use strong muscles
Prana	Keep the breath deep, calm and strong, emphasizing inhalation
Mind	Keep the mind calm and concentrated, grounded in the present moment

PITTA

General	Keep your energy cool, open and receptive, like the newly waxing Moon
Body	Keep the body cool and relaxed; do the asanas in a surrendering manner to remove heat and tension
Prana	Keep the breath cool, relaxed and diffused; exhale through the mouth to relieve heat as needed
Mind	Keep the mind receptive, detached and aware but not sharp or critical

KAPHA

General	Make sure to warm up properly and then do the asana with effort, speed and determination
Body	Keep the body light and moving, warm and dry
Prana	Keep the Prana upward moving and circulating; take deep, rapid breaths if necessary to maintain energy
Mind	Keep the mind enthusiastic, wakeful and focused like a flame

II. 7 ADVANCING YOUR PRACTICE

YOGIC KEYS FOR ADVANCING YOUR PRACTICE

THE POINT OF STRETCH

Remember that you are responsible for your own experience. Your focus determines your behavior which, in turn, determines the results. If you want to deepen your practice, try the following: Instead of overpowering the body, go only to the point of the stretch that you can hold without great effort. This should be a point where you can stay for a long time without having to stop or release the stretch. After about twenty to thirty seconds the muscles will release a little so that there is less 'stretching sensation.' The pose then becomes easier.

After this first release, take up the slack by establishing a new point of stretch. Again, you are at the place where the stretch is strong enough to hold your whole attention but not overpowering. In these increments the body gradually continues to release, extending the pose and its benefits for you.

THE BREATH

Another good method is to make a conscious awareness of the breath your primary focus. Try beginning your practice from the time you enter into the room. Focus on your breath as you walk in, warm up, and start to practice the asanas. Make keeping your attention constantly on the movement of the breath your Yoga practice. An easy and effective way to focus and use the breath is to apply a light Ujjayi sound, taking in the breath consciously through the nostrils with a noticeable sound. In this way, you can use the breath to monitor the degree of stress in the poses, to maintain focus, and to link postures and movements together. You will be able to hear any disturbances in the pose in the sound of the breath. You can then refocus on the smooth sound of the breath and release the stress in the pose. And you can link the postures together with the breath, holding a focus on the breath as you move from pose to pose.

Practicing asanas with conscious breathing is very effective. We suggest that you practice in the following way. With each inhalation be aware of your grounding and alignment. Be aware of the back body, the side body and the front. Each exhalation is the time to increase the extension of the pose. This style of practice can be done by anyone beginner through advanced. Practicing in this way brings you into a more dynamic awareness and balance. As Vanda Scaravelli says: "If is it not 'with the breath,' it is not Yoga."

Through conscious inhalation you focus on the experience of what is happening around you. You are open to receive the life-force with every breath and so you do. Through the exhalation you are reminded that you are a part of the whole, the entire universe. This teaches you to respect the gift of life, to work in rhythm with life, and be responsible for your environment. This organic and ego-sublimating form of practice has a strong internalizing effect and brings us quickly to the deeper levels of Yoga. After a month or two of this practice, you will see extraordinary change.

ENJOY YOUR PRACTICE

Remember to enjoy your practice and make time your friend. There is no hurry. Nothing has to be achieved. Leave all the pressures that push you outside the door of the practice area. You can practice easily, without striving as you remember Patanjali's *Yoga Sutras* on asana that say 'be steady and comfortable, relaxing into the infinite.' Vata and Pitta types especially should not strain body or mind in their practice.

Remember that it takes time to learn the poses and additional time for the body to change in harmony with them, particularly at a structural level. Expect to learn and practice the poses repeatedly over time. As an example, B.K.S. Iyengar once said that it can take ten years to learn the Triangle Pose, Trikonasana, correctly. There is plenty of time. Yoga is of the ages, not a temporary fad.

GUIDELINES FOR EFFECTIVE, SAFE, PRACTICE

•	Eliminate striving. Remove the pressure that pushes you.
•	DO less—BE more.
•	Time goes into the preparation of the pose. There is no hurry!
•	Do not overpower the body.
•	Mistakes, repeated, are paid for — often repeatedly.
•	Stay fresh and observe yourself without judgment.
•	Let go of roles, categories, and labels. Let go into the moment. Use the mirror of Yoga to see yourself and work in the unknown.
•	Your focus determines your behavior, which produces your results. To change the results you are getting, change your focus.

AYURVEDIC KEYS TO ADVANCING YOUR PRACTICE

The ayurvedic rule in treatment is to treat Vata like a *flower*, Pitta like a *friend* and Kapha like an *enemy*.

Vata types are sensitive like a flower that easily wilts. While they have much initial enthusiasm they easily get frustrated and give up. They need special attention, care and encouragement. They require a gentle, warm and soothing practice, mindful of their sensitivity and volatility.

Pittas need the companionship and guidance of friends. They like to work as part of a team. They do best with a practice that is engaging and challenging, but ultimately relaxing, diffusing and releasing—letting go after making a significant effort.

Kaphas need strong motivation, if not criticism, to put forth their best efforts. They do best with a practice that pushes them beyond what they think are their limits. Yet while Kaphas require more discipline and force to get their bodies moving, it should be increased in a consistent manner day by day.

AYURVEDIC MASSAGE OILS

Massage oils protect the skin, muscles, joints and bones. Oil massage improves flexibility and guards against injury. Particularly if you are a Vata type, it is best to apply oil to your skin and joints on a regular basis. This will give you more flexibility and counter any dryness and stiffness from developing. Before showers or before sleep are good times for oil application, but in small amounts it can be helpful before asana practice as well. Sesame oil is the best oil for this purpose because it has special moisturizing, nutritive and analgesic properties. It counters Vata, relieves dryness and stiffness, stops pain and improves flexibility. It is also useful for Kapha types who have dry skin owing to poor circulation.

Pitta types benefit from applying coconut, a cooling oil, to the skin, particularly applied to their heads where they get overheated. Kaphas do best with a light stimulating oil like mustard oil. They should not apply oil before their practice because it may make them drowsy.

In addition, make sure to have good oils in your diet, just as people today make sure to drink good water. Ghee (clarified butter) is the best cooking oil. Sesame oil is also good. Sunflower is good oil for Pitta and Kapha. Many other natural oils are good as well, such as olive, almond, safflower and avocado. Besides oil massage, Vata types benefit from mineral salt baths. This is another helpful aid in asana practice.

AYURVEDIC HERBS

Many ayurvedic herbs can function as internal catalysts for advancing your practice, either as aids in detoxification or for the purpose of rejuvenation. Ayurvedic herbal teas are great to take either before or after a practice. Before a practice, herbal teas aid in warming up, improve circulation and promote sweating to cleanse the body. After practice, they aid in rehydration and removal of toxins that have been dislodged by the practice.

Vata people should take a moisturizing liquid before practice, such as warm milk or a warm cinnamon tea (with a little milk and sugar). Kaphas should take a stimulating spicy beverage like ginger tea with honey. Pittas should take a cooling beverage like fruit juice (apple, grape pineapple or pomegranate) or a mild green tea. Chai (Indian spice) tea is great before morning Yoga practice. The spices in it open the circulation and perception. The tea itself clears the mind and promotes urination, aiding in the cleansing of the blood. After practice, particularly when there is sweating, fruit juices are best for rehydration but spice teas are also good to keep our Prana moving.

Ginger is great as a stimulating tea to take before practice or off and on during the day for Vata and Kapha types. It keeps our Agni (digestive fire) going strong, helping to burn up toxins and improve digestion. It warms the heart, stimulates circulation and clears the head and sinuses. Cinnamon has similar properties, as do many other common spices like basil, cardamom, cloves and sage. Holy basil (tulsi) tea is used commonly in India to aid in Yoga and meditation because of its ability to open the mind and heart.

Turmeric, a common cooking spice, is excellent for promoting peripheral circulation, cleansing the blood and healing soft tissue injuries. It helps women with premenstrual pain and tension. Saffron is excellent in a similar manner and works well taken in warm milk. Guggul, a relative of myrrh, is great for improving flexibility, stopping pain in the bones, and strengthening the connective tissue. It is generally taken in a pill form, particularly in its special compound Yogaraj Guggul.

Aloe gel is an excellent mild internal cleansing agent for the liver, blood and urinogenital tract. Taken with spices like ginger and turmeric it stimulates digestion. A little aloe gel or juice before practice is great for Pittas and Kaphas who want to detoxify.

Ashwagandha is a great tonic for the bones and muscles, strengthening the lungs, kidneys and brain. It guards against injuries to the bones and joints, while improving stamina and performance. It is great for grounding Vatas and increases their capacity for exertion. Siberian ginseng is also excellent for promoting circulation, strengthening the bones and stopping pain.

Shatavari is a great hydrant and moisturizing agent. It guards against dehydration and improves stamina and endurance. It is particularly good for Pitta but helpful for Vata as well. Licorice is another important moisturizing agent like shatavari that helps moisten the head, throat and sinuses.

Amla is an excellent ayurvedic herb for nourishing the body and creating a sattvic type of body tissue on all levels from the skin to the brain. It counters acidity, builds the blood and nourishes the heart. Take it in the pleasant tasting ayurvedic herbal jelly, Chyavan Prash.

AROMATHERAPY

Another important and pleasant way to advance your practice is through the use of incense and aromatherapy. A few drops of one of various aromatic oils can be placed on the head or near the nostrils before Yoga practice.

Vatas do best with calming and strengthening oils like basil, frangipani, heena or cinnamon. Pittas do best with cooling and calming fragrances like sandalwood, rose, jasmine, champak, lotus or gardenia. Kaphas do best with warming, stimulating and spicy aromatic oils like camphor, eucalyptus, sage, frankincense or mint. Sweet fragrances are one of the best ways to lower high Pitta and to cool down after practice. A little sandalwood oil after practice reduces fatigue and settles the mind and heart.

NASYA AND NETI

Ayurvedic nasya (nasal) oils are excellent for pranayama. They are generally prepared in a sesame oil base. Strong spicy herbs like calamus, ginger, eucalyptus or camphor are added for cleansing purposes. They are best for Kapha and Vata, who suffer from cold and congestion in the head. For soothing or toning purposes, mild demulcent herbs like licorice are used. They are best for Pitta and Vata suffering from heat or dryness in the head. The *neti pot* is used for pouring a little salt water through the nostrils and often recommended by Yoga teachers. It is also helpful for pranayama, but not always as effective as the nasya oils.

PANCHA KARMA

For those who want to go deeply into yogic and ayurvedic cleansing techniques, Pancha Karma is an important practice to consider. Pancha Karma combines daily oil massage and steam therapy (snehana and svedana) for a period of a week or more, followed by cleansing practices of enemas, purgatives and emetics, depending upon the condition, to eliminate the disease-causing doshas from the body. It is an excellent way to cleanse the muscles, bones, joints and connective tissues.

Pancha Karma is a proven treatment for countering arthritic and rheumatic complaints and improves flexibility. It can take your Yoga practice to a new level, not only in terms of asana but also in terms of meditation. Generally, it is best done in the spring and summer as part of a detoxification program. Yet it can be employed to treat specific diseases as well.

We can easily monitor the success of our practice by key indicators of Ayurveda both on physical and mental levels.

USING ASANAS TO ELIMINATE THE DOSHAS

Asana practice, like ayurvedic therapies, can be designed to eliminate the disease-causing doshas from the body. At a physical level, Prana is the pure energy that arises through the proper digestion of food. This is the positive condition of Vata. Vata dosha or Vata as a toxin is the waste material or waste gas that is the by-product of the digestive process. It increases the more faulty the digestion is or the more toxic the food ingested happens to be. This waste gas or Vata dosha is produced in the large intestine, enters the blood stream and gets deposited in the bones, the seat of Vata, where it promotes Vata-type diseases like arthritis.

Pitta, as a positive force, is the pure vitality that arises through the proper development and circulation of the blood. It sustains the subtle energy of fire as courage, will power and daring, called *Tejas*. Pitta dosha, Pitta as a negative force, is the waste material of the blood that increases when the blood is toxic. Pitta dosha is produced as acid in the small intestine from which it enters the blood stream and damages the blood itself.

Kapha, as a positive force, is the nourishing power that arises through the proper development and circulation of the plasma. It sustains the subtle energy of water called *Ojas* that upholds our creativity, sexuality and immune function. Kapha dosha or mucus is a waste material of the plasma that increases when the plasma is not properly formed. Kapha dosha is produced as mucus in the stomach from which it enters into the circulatory and lymphatic system, damaging the plasma itself.

Dosha	Basis	Subtle Form	Waste Product	Site
Vata	Food	Prana	Gas	Large Intestine
Pitta	Blood	Tejas	Acid	Small Intestine
Kapha	Plasma	Ojas	Mucus	Stomach

The general rule of reducing the doshas through asana practice is to prevent the doshas from accumulating at their sites.

- Asanas aimed at reducing Vata release tension from the large intestine and lower abdomen, including dispelling gas and relieving distention.
- Asanas aimed at reducing Pitta release heat and stress from the small intestine and central abdomen, cooling the blood and liver.
- Asanas targeting Kapha release congestion and stagnation in the region of the stomach and chest, helping to dispel mucus.

There are also general effects of asanas on the different doshas:

- Most asanas reduce Vata because they use the muscles and create a pressure and a massaging action that soothes Vata.
- Asanas that open the circulation and the liver and reduce bile reduce Pitta.
- Asanas that increase and deepen the rate of breathing and heart rate reduce Kapha.

Vata and Pitta Are Released Downward

↓ Asanas that reduce Vata aim at drawing the energy downward from the large intestine and grounding it in the earth.

↓ Asanas that reduce Pitta draw the energy downward from the small intestine and release it into the earth.

Kapha Is Eliminated Upward

↑ Asanas that reduce Kapha bring the energy up from the stomach and chest, removing it as mucus from the mouth and nose.

Movement of Vata

Vata tends to either excess movement or deficient movement, just as the wind blows abruptly or not at all.

- Excessive movement of Vata (excess air)—erratic, excessive movement, tremors, shaking, agitation of the mind and disorientation of the senses.
- Deficient movement of Vata (excess ether)—paralysis, stiffness, muscle spasms, spacing out of the mind.

Movement of Pitta

Pitta tends to move either upward or downward, though it generally moves upward. Upward moving Pitta causes hypertension, headache, insomnia, inflamed eyes or nosebleeds. Moving downward it causes urinary tract infections, blood in the urine or reproductive system problems.

- Heat rising to the head and eyes—upward-moving Pitta.
- Heat descending through the lower orifices—downward-moving Pitta.

Accumulation of Kapha

Kapha tends to accumulate either in the upper half or the lower half of the body, though its main area of accumulation is usually above.

- Accumulation of Kapha above—mucus in chest, throat and head, congestion around the heart.
- Accumulation of Kapha below—fat deposits in lower abdomen and thighs or edema in the lower abdomen and legs.

AYURVEDIC SIGNS OF SUCCESSFUL YOGA PRACTICE

Overall	Good digestion, no tongue coating, pleasant fragrance to the body, good complexion, good elimination, lightness, flexibility, clarity and calm.
Vata	Removal of stiffness from the joints, steadiness of the muscles (reduction of tremors), feeling of groundedness, calm and support
Pitta	Feeling of coolness, calm, openness, patience, tolerance; reduction of inflammation, acidity or bleeding
Kapha	Normalization of body weight, reduction of congestion, removal of excess fat, mucus and water from the body, greater sense of detachment

SIGNS OF IMPROPER PRACTICE

Overall	Pain, tension, injury, agitation, indigestion
Vata	Pain, stiffness, anxiety, insomnia, constipation
Pitta	Tension, anger, irritability, fever
Kapha	Lethargy, drowsiness, dullness, congestion

ADVANCED YOGA PRACTICE

A good workout, however useful in itself, is not the real goal of Yoga practice. As Yoga practice advances it is meant to take us deeper into our own minds and hearts. An advanced Yogi should be an enlightened person, not simply someone who is very flexible or able to hold very difficult asanas for long periods of time. As you advance your practice remember the deeper aspects of Yoga as pranayama, mantra and meditation. After you have mastered the body, aim at mastering the mind as well. Use asana as a foundation for developing a deeper Yoga practice; do not make advancing your asana practice an end in itself. A good rule to follow is to spend at least as much time on the deeper aspects of Yoga as on asana practice.

Don't end your Yoga session after the completion of your Savasana. Spend at least a few minutes in a sitting position, practicing pranayama, chanting OM or some other mantra, and diving deep into meditation to discover your true Self. Remember that your Yoga can be unlimited without end. Yoga is union with universal consciousness itself.

II. 8 GETTING STARTED

PREPARING YOURSELF

Before you begin your asana practice, make sure to consult your physician if you have any questions about your health. It is important to find out what guidelines your health places on your practice. With any health issues, remember to go slowly, practice organically, and remain aware of your body's needs.

WHAT YOU WILL NEED

Asanas are best practiced on even ground or flooring with a wool blanket or rug, and a non-stick mat. If possible, use the same equipment each time you practice. Have what you need around you: pen and paper, candle and matches, mats, blankets, props, eye cover, and towels. The body-mind is soothed by familiarity and routine, so it is most effective to practice with the same special items in the same place and at the same time daily.

WHERE TO PRACTICE

Practice in a well-ventilated room. If you practice outdoors, it is best to avoid direct sun, excess heat, cold and drafts. Not only do these put a hardship on the body, they also distract from the inward focus essential to yoga. Pick a quiet, undisturbed place that is out of the mainstream of traffic, dry, free from dust with enough room for all your movements.

WHEN TO PRACTICE

The body loves regularity and easily falls into a rhythm. As much as you can, practice at the same time and place daily. Consistency creates a stronger sense of security. And following your word strengthens your self-esteem, underscores your commitment, and increases your ability to hold a strong focus. The most important thing is that you are consistent and attentive so choose a realistic time of day to begin your practice.

The following points are helpful in picking the best practice time for your type. The body is stiff in the early morning but the mind and prana are fresh. And morning asanas aid in detoxification. In the afternoon the body will respond more easily but the mind may be less disciplined and unable to begin the practice.

Vata types, with their changeable natures, are most in need of a regularly timed practice. Morning between sunrise and 10 am is best for them since their energy is often down in the late afternoon. Kaphas do best in the morning as well but as early as they can get going, which may take an alarm clock and some tea to manage. They also benefit from an evening asana practice. Pittas do well with a morning or afternoon practice but should avoid workouts in the 10 am - 2 pm time frame and any time that they are hungry. In general, a morning practice enriches everyone for their day, while daytime and the evening practices refresh and lessen the strain of the day.

Set aside a specific minimum amount of time that you will practice daily, whether it is ten minutes or two hours and be consistent with it. Be realistic in setting your amount of practice time so that you can avoid disappointment with yourself.

Stay fresh and alert. A few minutes of focused awareness is more valuable for your practice and life than hours of just going through the motions.

ASANA GUIDELINES

- Use non-restrictive clothing (no belts, jewelry or other encumbrances) and as little clothing as is comfortable.
- Practice only with empty bladder, stomach and bowels. Clean, eliminate and freshen your body before every practice.
- Practice at least two hours after your last meal. However if needed, a little lemon water or tea may be taken one half hour before asana practice.
- Keep your eyes open until you begin Savasana practice.
- Unless otherwise instructed, breathe through your nose.
- When you practice the body is active, but the mind should remain watchful, alert and still.
- Some people like to do the same well-balanced sequence daily while others like to vary their daily practice. Adjust your practice to how you feel each day. Remember to enjoy your practice making it a positive experience.
- If mistakes in technique are repeated over an extended period of time then imbalances and injuries may result. Use the alignment notes in this book to keep your body safe from injury.
- A good generic sequence to use for your asana practice is—Warm-ups, standing poses, inverted poses, backbends, forward bends and twists, ending with Savasana. This sequence is neutral and balances the energies created from the postures. Use this all purpose sequencing order even if you are not practicing all the categories listed. Or you may prefer to practice the basic 'body type' routines outlined in Part IV that are specifically designed to reduce each dosha.
- Twists are neutral and can be used in a variety of places as long as you breathe fully while performing them. Twists are wonderful for the diaphragm and intercostal muscles, and to rebalance the spine at the end of your asana practice just before doing savasana. Please remember that there can be less lung capacity in these postures so breathe fully. To make sure you get plenty of air you may want to breathe through your mouth.

- Practice the poses evenly on each side. If you practice a posture on the right side, then duplicate it on the left for the same amount of time. When you practice to correct a specific functional imbalance (musculature), you may practice more on one side than the other. An experienced teacher can assist you with that.
- Keep your throat, eyes and jaws relaxed as you practice. Remind yourself to relax all the places in which you habitually hold tension. Feel free to adjust the poses according to what relieves this tension. Yoga positions are not static; they are organic. Regardless of your body type, we recommend that you inhale as you ground and establish the alignment of the pose. With each exhalation lengthen, grow and extend in the position.
- Yoga poses are not gymnastic exercises. They are positions that create energy patterns, which can change your energy field and your life. Be slow and moderate in your movement. Remain aware and observe yourself both internally and externally.
- Yoga is a discipline. It is a personal experience and not in any way competitive either with others or with yourself. Practice suspending judgment altogether remaining in the present moment.
- If you are physically tired or ill practice only what heals you. Rest when you need to, work when you can. Yoga should strengthen your energy, not deplete it. In fact your Yoga practice can be a great energy management tool through which you can create health and longevity.
- Always complete your asana practice with savasana as the last pose, a deep relaxation for ten to twenty five minutes, depending on your type. Savasana is the most important position for both Vata and Pitta. One of the main purposes of asana practice is to be able to do Savasana well. It is the time when the body replenishes itself and balances the energy created in your practice. Many great teachers have said that savasana is the most important position and the reason we practice all of the other asanas. It is also a form of pratyahara or sensory withdrawal in which we can rest our motor organs and contact the peace within that is the real goal of Yoga.

NOTES FOR SPECIFIC PHYSICAL NEEDS

If your practice exhausts you, then you may be practicing too strongly or incorrectly (especially backbends), becoming dehydrated, or just practicing the wrong kind of asanas for your body type. If you are physically exhausted for any reason, do not push your body further. Practice only in a restorative way for as long as it takes until you are revitalized.

If you have the flu, practicing forward bends helps move the virus out of your body. Easy chest openers and exercising the lungs unseats the virus making it easier to remove with your strong forward bending practice.

With infections, keep them localized. Do not practice asana or any movement that spreads the infection to other bodily tissues.

If you are suffering from high or low blood pressure, asthma, hernias, or sciatica, a physician and an experienced, well-trained yoga teacher should be consulted before you begin. Yoga can be good for asthma if learned and practiced easily and slowly. For those experiencing hernias or sciatica, forward bends may make your situation worse. Go easily and, with all sciatica, only practice forward bends with a straight spine. Never round your spine forward and never "work through the pain."

PART III

Ayurvedic Asana Guide: Description of Asanas for Your Type

SANDRA SUMMERFIELD KOZAK IN VRKSASANA VARIATION

III. 9 DESCRIPTION OF ASANAS: HOW TO PERFORM THEM & THEIR AYURVEDIC EFFECTS

WARM UP MOVEMENTS

THEIR DESCRIPTIONS
& RELATIONSHIPS TO THE DOSHAS

RICHARD FREEMAN IN TRINI

Ujjayi Breath Sound

Tri-Doshic

Ujjayi breath is a slow and steady inhalation and exhalation breathing through both nostrils. When you partially close your glottis (your throat muscle), the flow of breath in and out of your lungs is controlled. You will be able to feel the breath in the roof of your mouth as you inhale and exhale. Slightly closing your glottis makes a soft *sa* sound on inhalation and a soft *ha* sound on exhalation.

TECHNIQUE

1 Begin sitting in Sukhasana or Siddhasana. With the mouth slightly open, inhale and exhale slowly making an 'ah' or 'ha' sound. It is not a sound from your vocal cords. Instead this sound is made by the passage of air through the throat.

2 Continue making this same breath sound as you slowly close your lips. Feel that the back of your throat is slightly closed. Closing of the throat feels the same as your throat closing naturally as it does when you begin to yawn.

3 With the mouth closed your inhalations make a soft *sa* sound and your exhalations make a soft *ha* sound. Take your time and explore the throat closing and these two sounds. Work with this until you can consistently control the breath and maintain steady, even breath sounds.

4 When this breath sound becomes second nature to you, use the Ujjayi sound with the practice of your asanas whenever you need to concentrate, slow the breathing down, or whenever it is suggested in this asana section.

Neck Stretch

Tri-Doshic

Use to Prepare Your Neck for Shoulderstand and Plow

TECHNIQUE

1 Lie on your back with your legs together. Tighten the muscles in your legs and push through the heels of your feet bringing your toes toward your face. Interlock your fingers, placing your hands at the base of your skull, elbows out to the sides on the floor.

2 Inhale and hold your legs and feet strongly grounded into the floor. Exhale and pull your head up, bringing your elbows together. Gently pull your chin to your chest until you feel stretch in your back muscles. Inhale. Exhale and replace your head, neck and shoulders on the floor. Repeat 3-4 times.

Hands interlocked behind the base of head

Toes pulled back toward your face

Elbows wide

GENERAL PRECAUTIONS

For back or neck problems, go gently and only as far as the neck is free of stress or discomfort. Consult your health professional with questions.

Neutral Spine

THE SPINE IN NEUTRAL

Tri-Doshic

Strengthens and tones the muscles of the lower spine and abdomen.
Grounding, Toning, Stretching

Since it is the basis of all backbending movements and spinal extensions, learning how to work with a neutr low spine is a must. Holding neutral spine protects you from injury in both backbending and forward bend movements. It is essential for anyone who experiences back discomfort.

ABOUT THE POSITION

Neutral spine is achieved without arching or rounding the spine. Use neutral spine in all your yoga practices confident that the low back and pelvic stabilizer muscles are held strong keeping you stable in each pose.

TECHNIQUE

1 Lie on your back. Bend your knees placing your feet close to your buttocks, hip distance apart. Turn the toes in slightly. The feet are firmly on the floor. Knees always remain directly over your feet.

2 Lengthen the back of your neck and tuck your shoulders under you with the shoulder blades flat on the floor. Your arms are outstretched beside you.

3 Inhale, relax your back completely. Exhale as you move your waist toward the floor. Feel the internal orga gravity relax ward.

4 Inhale, relax your back completely, letting it come off of the floor.

5 Exhale and again move your waist down to lightly 'kiss' the floor and hold it there for 1-3 minutes.

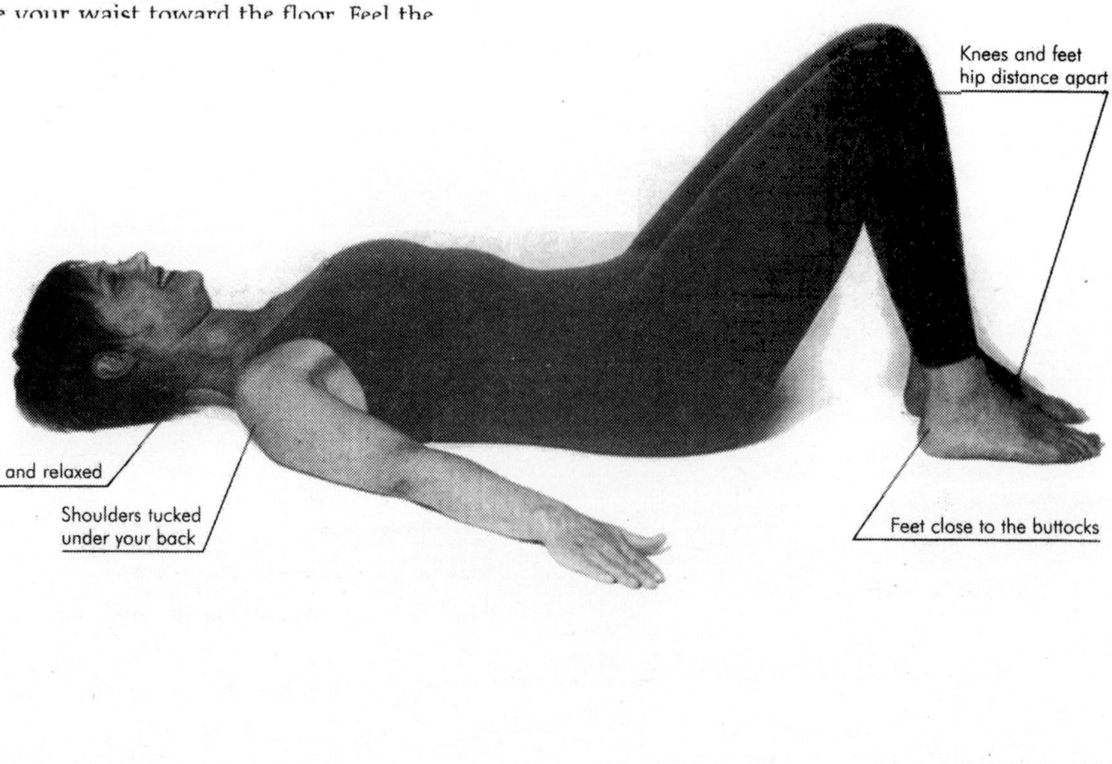

Pelvic Tilt

WITH NEUTRAL SPINE

Pelvic tilts are good for creating core strength in the lower abdominal and spinal muscles.

TECHNIQUE

1 Center your head on the floor. Inhale, relax your back completely. Exhale and soften your waist, bringing it to the floor. Feel your internal organs become heavy with the weight of gravity and let your whole back lengthen down to touch the floor (lifting your tailbone slightly.)

2 Inhale, relax your back completely. Do nothing on every inhalation.

3 Repeat, touching your back to the floor with every exhalation and continue relaxing on the inhalations. Practice for 3-5 minutes.

DOSHIC NOTES

Breathing:

May add a light Ujjayi sound

or

Smooth, even breath, synchronizing the movements with the breath.

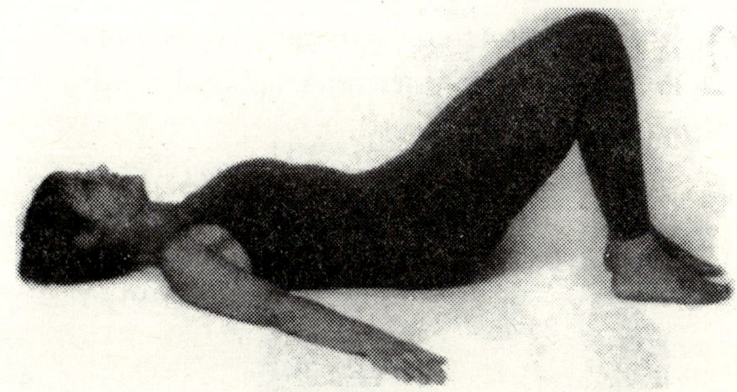

GENERAL PRECAUTIONS

If you experience knee pain, move your feet a little farther away from your buttocks.

Cat Stretch

Tri-Doshic

Relaxing and Restoring

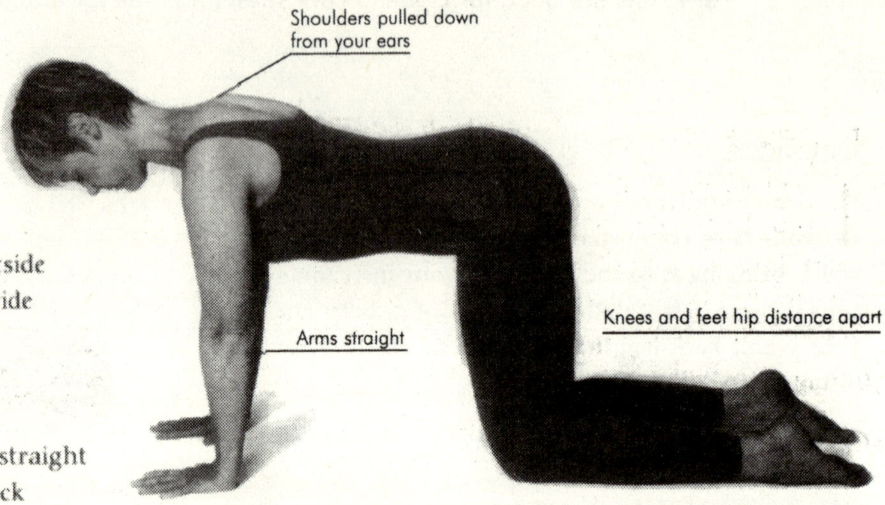

MOVING INTO THE POSE

With your hands, knees, and feet hip distance apart on the floor, make sure your knees are directly under your hip joints. The hands and straight arms are directly under the outside of your shoulders. Spread the fingers wide apart.

IN THE POSE

1 Inhale, keep your arms and thighs straight and vertical. Exhale and let your back become concave as it moves down toward the floor.

2 As you inhale, lift between your shoulder blades to push your spine upward toward the ceiling.

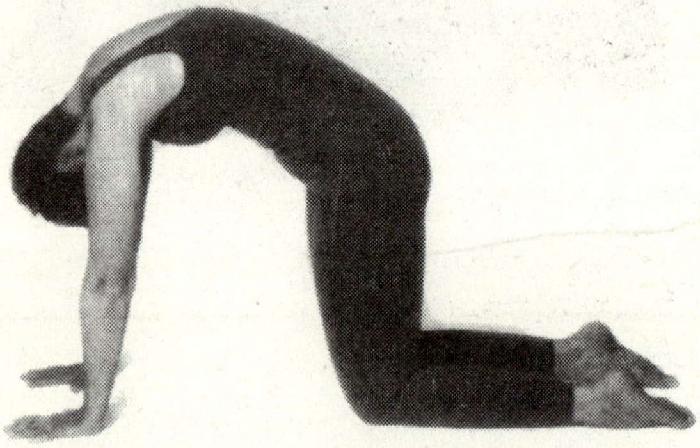

3 Continue moving your spine on each inhalation and exhalation for 1-3 minutes.

COMPLETING THE POSE

On an exhale, sit back onto your heels and place your forehead on the floor with your hands beside your feet palms up. Rest in this Child's Pose letting your breathing return to normal.

DOSHIC NOTES

Vata: Reduces excess Vata in the spine.

Pitta: Reduces Pitta by gently working the abdomen.

Kapha: Good beginning to get Kapha going.

GENERAL PRECAUTIONS

- *Those with knee problems should use soft padding under the knees or do this pose standing with the hands on a coffee table.*
- *For back or neck problems, go gently, easing the back only as far as it will comfortably move.*

Child's Pose

Tri-Doshic

Relaxing and Restoring
Parasympathetic Response, Cooling, Stilling, Grounding, Closing

MOVING INTO THE POSE

1 From Cat Stretch, sit back onto your heels and lay your chest on your legs placing your head on the floor.

2 Put your arms and hands on the floor with your palms facing up. Be comfortable. Relax.

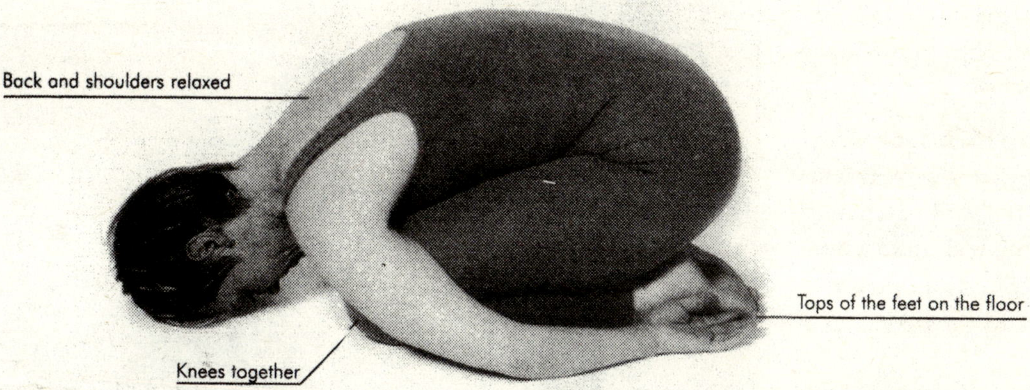

COMPLETING THE POSE

Slowly unroll your spine and come up to sitting on your heels with your spine straight.

LEARNING AT HOME: MODIFICATIONS

If you are uncomfortable, place folded blankets on your thighs and rest your chest on them. Support your forehead with another blanket.

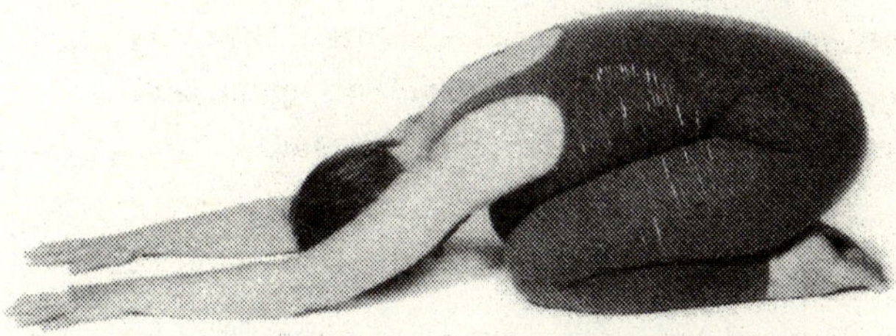

Variation

GENERAL PRECAUTIONS

For those with knee problems do not create any pain or pressure in the knee joint.

Chest Opening at the Wall

Tri-Doshic

Chest and Shoulder Opening, Back Strengthening, Stretching Warming, Sympathetic Response, Grounding, Opening Expansion

MOVING INTO THE POSITION

1 Stand two feet from the wall with your feet parallel. Stretch your arms fully up the wall, reaching toward the ceiling. Bend your elbows and bring your arms into a triangle position with your fingers interlocked.

2 Step back and exhale as you slide your chest down the wall. Step away from the wall until your legs are vertical, perpendicular to the floor.

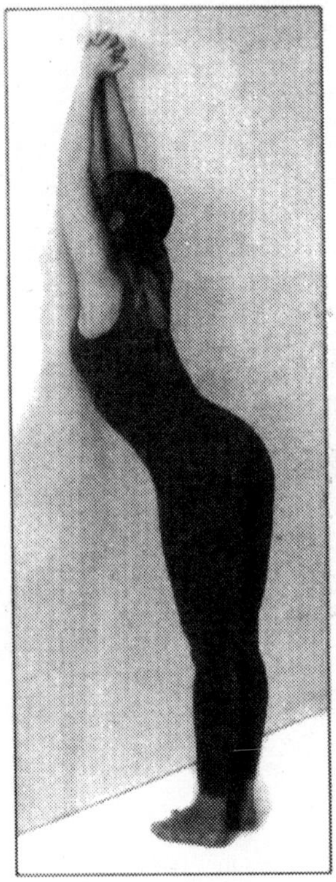

HOLDING THE POSITION

Maintain the triangle position of your arms with your forehead on the wall and release your upper spine toward the wall, moving it into your body. Breathe. Hold this shoulder stretching and chest opening position for 30-40 seconds.

COMPLETING THE POSITION

Step forward and relax your arms down. Roll your shoulders to release any tension in them.

LEARNING AT HOME: MODIFICATIONS

By working with your arms a little higher or lower on the wall, you change the place in your back and shoulders that is most affected by the pose. Explore.

IMPORTANT ACTIONS

- Shoulders and chest opening
- Knees held up strongly
- Neck extended
- Spine moving toward wall

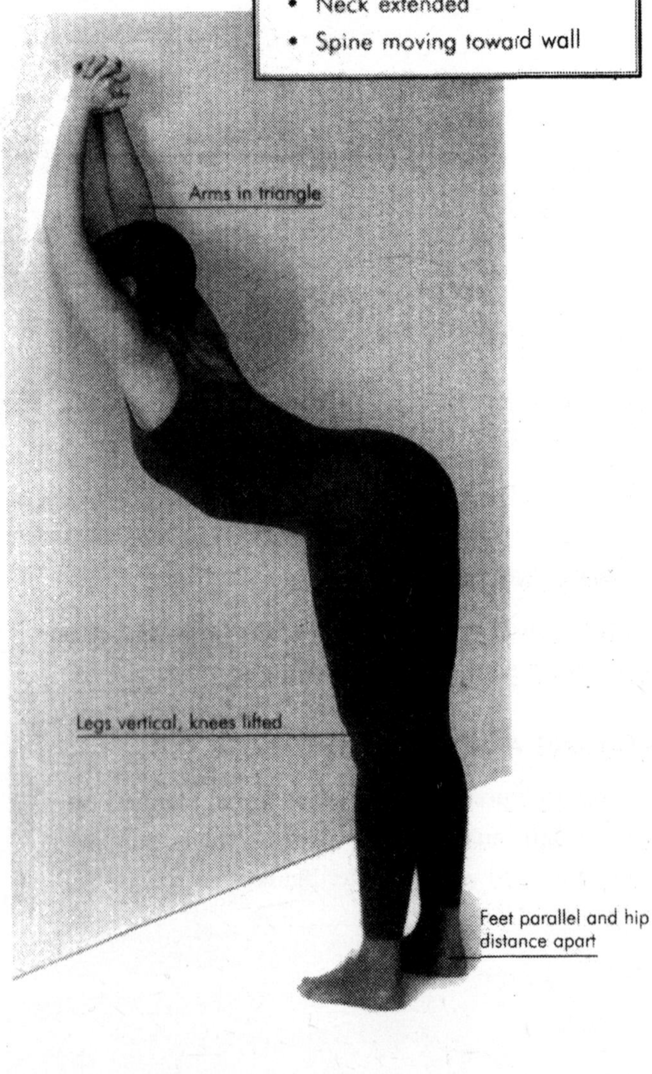

GENERAL PRECAUTIONS

Do not push the knees backward. Shoulders should feel opening, not pain.

Wall Push

Tri-Doshic

Thoracic Extension, Hamstring Stretching, Back Strengthening, Grounding, Strengthening, Stretching

MOVING INTO THE POSITION

1 Stand facing the wall. Place your hands on the wall shoulder distance apart at waist level.

2 Pressing the wall, step back until your arms and torso are fully stretched (parallel with the floor) and your legs are vertical. Feet are parallel and your knees are lifted.

IMPORTANT ACTIONS

- Torso and arms lengthen
- Sitting bones lift to increase leg stretch
- Lengthen arms, shoulders, and torso

HOLDING THE POSITION

With each inhalation, keep lengthening your arms, shoulders, and torso, pushing the wall with the palms of your hands. With every exhalation, lift your sitting bones, increasing the stretch in your hamstrings and calf muscles. Hold for 40-60 seconds or longer.

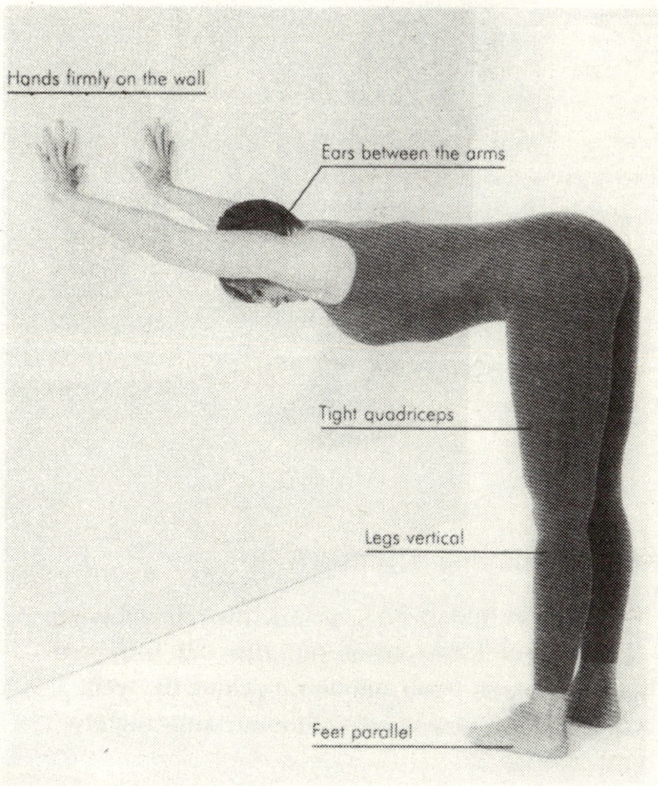

COMPLETING THE POSITION

Step forward and stand up. Roll your shoulders to release tension.

LEARNING AT HOME: MODIFICATIONS

Put your hands a little higher or lower on the wall. See how moving your hands changes the stretch. Explore.

GENERAL PRECAUTIONS

Do not push the knees backward. Keep the chest in line with the hands, arms, and sacrum and lengthen rather than pushing the chest down. Don't hyperextend the shoulder joints.

Wall Hang

Tri-Doshic

Hamstring Stretch, Back Lengthening, Grounding, Stilling, Stretching

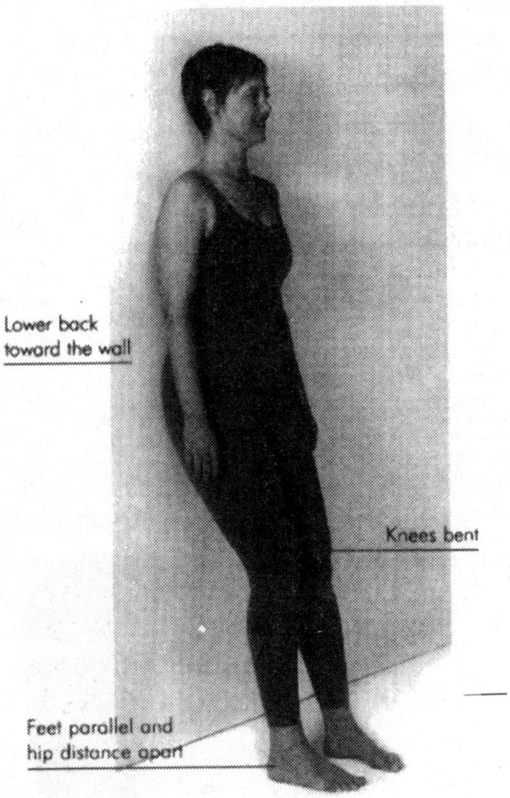

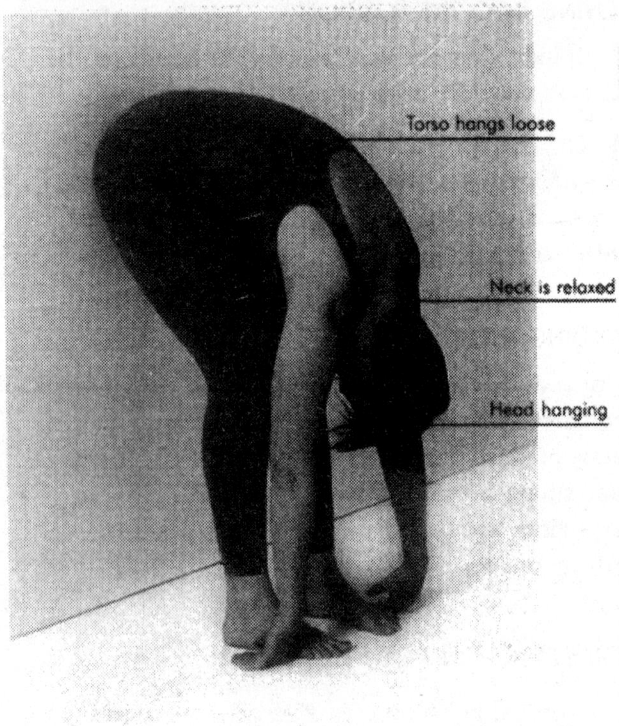

MOVING INTO THE POSITION

1 Stand with your back against the wall and your feet 12–18 inches away from the wall. Keep your back, shoulders, head, and hips touching the wall. Feet are hip distance apart with your knees slightly bent.

2 Bend your torso forward and let it hang toward the floor.

HOLDING THE POSE

1 Inhale and maintain your leg position and connection to the wall.

2 Exhale and relax your hanging torso (even more), releasing your neck and shoulders.

COMPLETING THE POSITION

1 With your arms hanging loose, keep your knees bent and tuck your tailbone under as you slowly unroll your spine up the wall (take 60 seconds).

2 Place each vertebra on the wall one at a time, stacking and lengthening them upward until your head is resting on the wall. Rest there for 30 or more seconds.

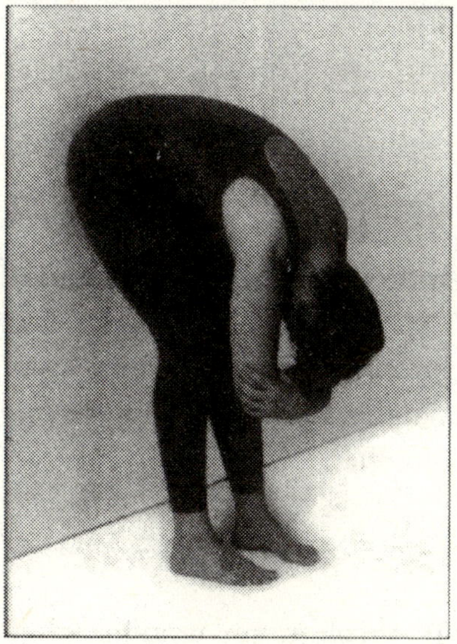

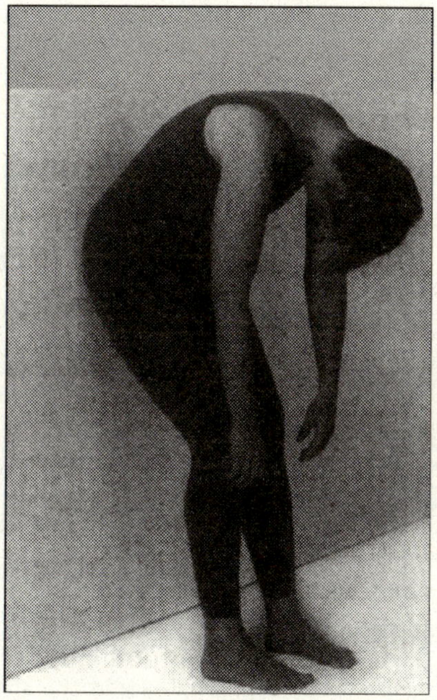

LEARNING AT HOME: MODIFICATIONS

If the position is too difficult, hold for only 15 seconds and repeat two or three times.

GENERAL PRECAUTIONS

- *Not for those with glaucoma.*
- *Not for sciatica or any disc problems.*

Surya Namaskar

SUN SALUTATION

Surya Namaskar is a twelve-pose series of asanas done together with the breath as flowing movement (Vinyasa). The Sun Salutation was traditionally practiced 12 times, once for each sign of the zodiac, while facing the East each morning as the sun rose. Surya Namaskar dispels the Doshas from the spine and stimulates Vyana Vayu. These movements improve digestion, reduce weight, and promote youth and vitality. Jumpings, a more vigorous style of practicing Sun Salutation, are best learned from an experienced teacher.

TECHNIQUE

1 **TADASANA:** Stand in Tadasana with your hands pressed into Namaskara (palms joined in front of the chest).

2 **THORACIC EXTENSION:** Inhale as you bring your arms out to the sides and up over your head in a big circular motion. Keep your elbows straight and behind your ears—palms facing each other. On each inhalation, ground your heels and move your navel back slightly to release the sacrum and tailbone downward. At the same time, lift your thoracic spine up and into your body, arching your chest upward. As your sacrum moves down and your chest lifts, shoulders and arms extend up and back.

3 **FORWARD BEND:** Exhale as you bend the knees and extend your torso forward and down toward to the floor (bringing your arms out to sides and down). Extend and straighten your spine.

4 **RUNNER'S LUNGE:** Inhale as you step your left leg and foot back 5 to 6 feet. Your right leg bends into a 90-degree angle. Open your chest forward and relax your hips down toward the floor.

5 **DOWNWARD DOG:** Exhale as you step your right foot back hip distance apart from the left foot. Stay on the balls of your feet as you lengthen the arms, shoulders, and torso into a straight line. Hold the sitting bones up as you lower your heels.

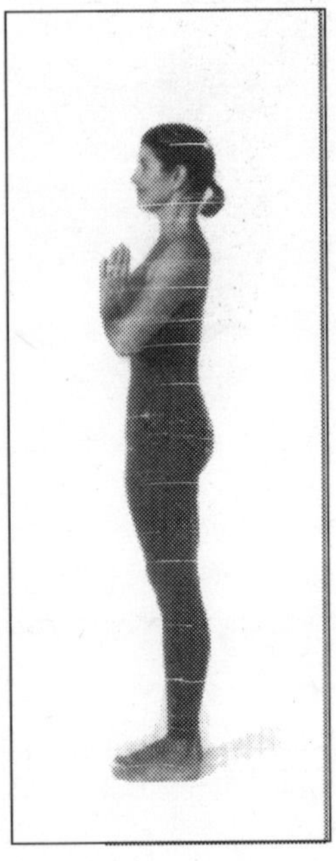

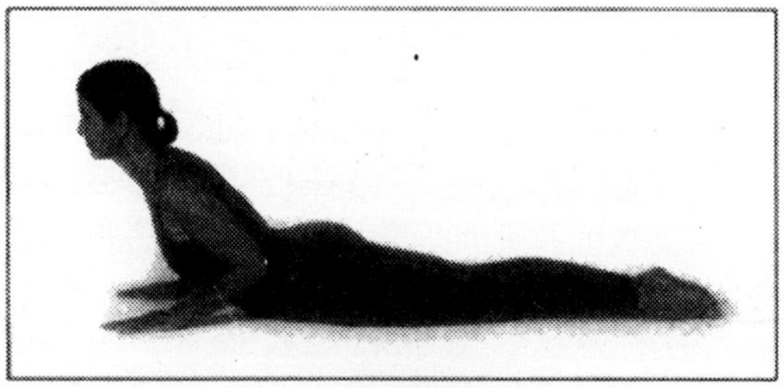

6 **PLANK POSE:** Inhale and bring your hips down until your torso is a straight line from head to feet. Arms are strong and straight.

7 **KNEES-CHEST-CHIN:** Exhale as you bend your knees, chest, and chin down to touch the ground. Buttocks remain in the air.

8 **UNSUPPORTED COBRA:** Inhale as you slide forward onto the floor. Strengthen your legs and buttocks. Keep elbows close to the body as you lift your head, neck, and chest off the floor, arching upward. Put no weight on your hands or arms.

9 **DOWNWARD DOG:** Exhale as you raise waist and hips up toward the ceiling (beginners come onto your hands and knees first) moving back into position 5—Dog Pose.

10 **RUNNER'S LUNGE:** With your hands in the same place, inhale and bring your left foot forward between your hands with your neck and head raised (same as position 4).

11 **FORWARD BEND:** Exhale as you bring your left foot forward, feet hip distance apart (same as position 3).

12 **THORACIC EXTENSION:** Inhale as you bring your arms and torso up to standing, keeping your knees slightly bent (same as position 2).

13 **TADASANA:** Exhale, returning to standing with your hands in **NAMASTE** (position 1).

Repeat, bringing the opposite leg backward and forward to keep the body balanced in positions 4 and 10. Doing the Sun Salutation twice, once on each side, completes one round. Practice two to twelve rounds.

ꕥ STANDING POSES ꕥ

FELICITY GREEN IN PARIVRTTA TRIKONASANA

Tadasana

MOUNTAIN POSE

VATA ↓↓↓ PITTA ↓ KAPHA ↓

	VATA ↓↓↓	PITTA ↓	KAPHA ↓
TIME	Long holds	Moderate holds without strain	Moderate holds and repetitions
BREATH	Long, smooth breath or Ujjayi	Long easy breath or light Ujjayi	Normal or Ujjayi
FOCUS	Strength, grounding, and stillness	Softness within strength	Lifting each part of the body
MOVE	Hold muscular strength & lift body	Internal lift on exhalations; light body	Lift and strengthen whole body

MOVING INTO THE POSE

1 Stand with your feet parallel. Stretch the soles of your feet so that as much of your foot as possible touches the floor. Each time you inhale become aware of the pull of gravity and feel firmly connected and grounded.

2 Holding this grounded awareness, strengthen your legs. Exhale, and begin to lift upwards. Lift your hips, rib cage, chest, neck, and head. With each exhalation lift every part of your spine upward, vertebrae by vertebrae.

HOLDING THE POSE

With each inhalation, lengthen your tailbone and sacrum downward. Focus on grounding and connecting with the earth. With every exhalation, extend your spine upward (from the waist). Relax your arms and hands, keep your neck and throat soft.

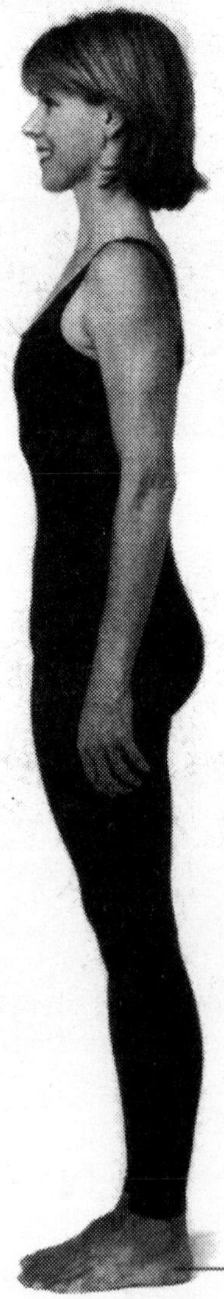

COMPLETING THE POSE

Mountain pose is the position from which all other standing poses begin and to which they return.

LEARNING AT HOME: MODIFICATIONS

Stand with your heels 2–4 inches from the wall. Your back, buttocks, shoulders and head are touching the wall. To lengthen your lower back, move your tailbone down the wall. At the same time, open your chest upward and forward, moving your upper spine into your body (away from the wall). Remember your heels remain rooted to the ground.

IMPORTANT ACTIONS

- All leg muscles lifted
- Hips lift up
- Spine lifts up out of the hips
- Rib cage lifts up
- Shoulders, arms, and hands hang relaxed
- Neck extends, lifting the head

GENERAL PRECAUTIONS

- *Knees are held up by strong thighs but be careful not to push the knees backward*
- *People with hyperextended knees should keep them slightly bent.*

Vrksasana

TREE POSE

	VATA ↓↓	PITTA ↓	KAPHA ↓
TIME	Longer holds for focus	Moderate holds	Moderate holds with repetitions
BREATH	Long, slow or Ujjayi for focus	Long easy breath or light Ujjayi	Normal or Ujjayi
FOCUS	Balance , stillness, groundedness	Be like a light, cool breeze (through leaves)	Pushing upward against gravity
MOVE	Strong lower body, lifting upper body	Back body extension from solid grounding	Lift, strengthen all internal muscles

MOVING INTO THE POSE

1 Stand in Tadasana - Mountain Pose (pg 70). As you inhale, focus on the ground and your connection to it. Exhale. Inhale and shift weight to your right leg. Hold your hips level. Exhale, lifting your left leg up, and place your left foot firmly on the inside of the right leg. With every inhalation stand strong on your right leg—balanced and grounded.

2 Hold your hips level and lower back lengthened as you open your left knee out to the side.

3 Turn your palms outward. Inhale and raise your straight arms (out to the sides) up over your head. Your shoulders move back and down from the ears as the inner arm extends up, palms facing.

HOLDING THE POSE

1 With every inhalation be aware of your foundation and balance. With each exhalation, extend your spine upward.

2 Work with your palms together or apart but keep the arms straight with your head between (or in front of) your arms.

COMPLETING THE POSE

With your full awareness, exhale and simultaneously bring your arms and your left leg down, returning to Tadasana. Re-establish Tadasana and notice any changes in how you feel. Then repeat on the other side.

IMPORTANT ACTIONS

- Tailbone moves down, lengthening the low back
- From a strong standing leg, lift the hips up
- Spine and rib cage lift up out of the hips
- Hips face forward as knee opens out
- Neck long-shoulders down

LEARNING AT HOME: MODIFICATIONS

Using the wall:

Stand with your torso and head against the wall and your heels 2-4 inches from the wall. Hold your hips level and facing forward as you press your lower back to the wall. As you hold your lower back toward the wall, lift your sternum up and move your middle spine away from the wall. Without moving the hips, open your bent knee back toward the wall. Keep your shoulders down as you bring your arms up. Extend your spine upward. Grow taller with each exhalation.

GENERAL PRECAUTIONS

Hold the standing knee strong by contracting quadriceps muscles. Do not push the knee back.

Trikonasana

TRIANGLE POSE

	VATA ↓	PITTA ↓	KAPHA ↓
TIME	Moderate holds with repetitions	Work without strain – short holds	Long holds with repetitions
BREATH	Smooth, even breath	Long easy breath or light Ujjayi	Normal or Ujjayi
FOCUS	Internal stillness, feeling grounded	Ground, stillness, easy extension	Intense strengthening and lifting
MOVE	Strengthen and rotate the legs open to extend the spine	Release the spine out of the hips, open the chest	Lift the knees, extend the torso, chest open, arms stretched

MOVING INTO THE POSE

1 Stand in Tadasana - Mountain Pose. Spread your legs 3-4 feet apart on an exhalation. Hold your hips facing forward as you turn your right leg and foot 90 degrees out to the right. Turn the ball of your (back) left foot 30 degrees in to the right.

2 Establish straight and strong legs by contracting your thigh muscles (quadriceps) to pull your knees up. Keep your weight evenly balanced between both legs. As you lift the arches of your feet, rotate both legs outward, opening them away from each other.

3 Inhale and lift your arms to shoulder height. Exhale, extending out horizontally from the shoulder blades to your fingertips. Inhale.

4 Exhale and extend your right arm and right side of your torso (shift your rib cage) to the right. The right side of your torso extends until it becomes parallel with the floor with a straight spine. Your right hand rests on your right leg or the floor. It is more important that your spine be straight than for your spine to be parallel with the floor.

IMPORTANT ACTIONS

- Legs open away from each other
- Arches are lifting
- Lengthen the spine and open the chest with each exhalation
- Lengthen the neck
- Stretch the arms

HOLDING THE POSE

1 With every inhalation focus on the strength and alignment of your feet and legs. Keep the outside of the left heel firmly grounded and rotate your left leg open (lifting the left hipbone).

2 If you can hold the ground ing and opening of the legs, your spine will naturally release and lengthen with each exhalation. As your spine grows longer, open and revolve your chest toward the ceiling (on every exhale).

COMPLETING THE POSE

Bring your torso up to standing. As you exhale, jump your legs and arms back to Tadasana (jumping can release the tension in the hip joints and legs). Re-establish Tadasana and be aware of how you feel. Then repeat on the other side.

DOSHIC NOTES

Kapha: Heavy Kapha Types should repeat the pose several times on each side for short durations, working strongly with the legs. Try not to rest any weight on your front hand or arm—instead work the muscles of your back to hold you up.

LEARNING AT HOME: MODIFICATIONS

- Stand with your back to the wall (feet 2-4 inches from wall). Keep your back, shoulders, head and arms on the wall. Keep your lower back pressing toward the wall as you open your chest and extend up through your head.
- With your back foot braced by the wall, bring awareness to your back leg and hip (also helps with balance). Try bending your left arm and placing that hand on your back to feel your muscles working.
- Work with the legs only for several weeks to learn the correct positioning and allow your hips time to open.

GENERAL PRECAUTIONS

- *Not for those with hip replacement surgery*
- *To avoid knee injury:*

  1. Keep the front knee facing out over the front ankle and always keep the legs straight.

  2. Look to see that you maintain the same position of the front leg as you go into and come out of the pose.

  3. Keep arches lifting and weight on outside of back heel.

  4. If you have hyperextended knees keep your front knee slightly bent. Keep your thigh muscles (quadriceps) very tight to support the knee.

Parivrtta Trikonasana

REVOLVING TRIANGLE

	VATA ↓↓	PITTA ↓	KAPHA ↓
TIME	Long holds with repetition	Hold without strain	Long holding times with repetitions
BREATH	Long, even breath	Long, easy breath or light Ujjayi	Normal or Ujjayi
FOCUS	Grounding and muscular strength	Grounding, easy extension	Intense strengthening & lengthening
MOVE	Strengthen the legs to extend the spine to rotate the chest open	Release the spine out of the hip. Keep the chest open	Lift the knees, work the legs, extend the torso opening the chest

MOVING INTO THE POSE

1 From Tadasana spread your legs 3-4 feet apart on an exhalation. Turn your legs, feet and torso to the right so your hips face your right leg. Establish straight and strong legs pulling your kneecaps up (contract thigh muscles). Your weight is evenly balanced between both legs with both heels on the floor.

2 Inhale and allow your arms to come up to shoulder level extending horizontally from your shoulder to your fingertips.

3 Exhale and turn your left hip, abdomen, and torso toward your right thigh. Press your left heel into the floor, pulling back on your right thigh until your hips are turned toward your right thigh. Lengthen your spine and turn your chest toward your right leg (torso is straight and parallel with the floor).

4 Inhale as you bring your left hand down to the floor (on the outside of your right foot) or on a prop).

IMPORTANT ACTIONS

- Relax the toes
- Heels on the floor
- Weight on outsides of feet
- Keep weight even on both feet
- Knees held up
- Extend the spine from the back heel
- Open the chest upward as spine extends

HOLDING THE POSE

Place your right hand on your back, elbow facing up.

1 With every inhalation re-establish your feet, legs, and groundedness.

2 With each exhalation press your left heel into the floor and spiral your left leg, hip and spine, opening your chest toward the ceiling. Continue the spinal extension out through the top of your head. Keep your chin in as you lengthen your neck.

COMPLETING THE POSE

As you inhale, with your left arm extended bring your torso up to standing. As you exhale, turn your feet forward and jump your legs and arms back to Tadasana (releases the tension in the hip joints). Re-establish Tadasana and be aware of how you feel. Then repeat on the other side.

DOSHIC NOTES

Kapha: Heavy Kapha Types repeat the pose several times on each side for short durations, working strongly with the legs.

LEARNING AT HOME: MODIFICATIONS

- Work with only your legs and hips for several weeks until you learn the correct positioning and prepare your body for the inward rotation and extension.
- Use a chair or block to support your hand and arm and make it easier for your hip joints to close.

GENERAL PRECAUTIONS

To avoid knee injury:

- *Keep the front knee facing out over the front ankle and always keep the legs straight*
- *With hyperextended knees, keep the front knee slightly bent and the thighs lifting*

Virabhadrasana II

WARRIOR POSE II

	VATA ↓	PITTA ↑	KAPHA ↓↓
TIME	Long holds	Work without strain –short holds	Long holds with repetitions
BREATH	Even slow breath or Ujjayi to focus	Long easy breath	Any breath
FOCUS	Stillness, extension, grounding	Lightness and extension	Staying strong and committed
MOVE	Strong legs, lift torso, extend arms	Lift and extend on the breath	Strengthen legs, lift torso, open chest

MOVING INTO THE POSE

1 From Tadasana exhale and spread your legs 4-5 feet apart. Turn your right foot and leg out 90 degrees to the right. Turn your left foot and leg 30 degrees in (to your right).

2 Keep your left leg straight and strong. Exhale, hold your right hipbone up as you bend your right knee until your right kneecap is over your right heel. If possible your right thigh becomes parallel with the floor. Your right shin is perpendicular to the floor. Keep your arches lifting and your knees opening away from each other. Lift your right hipbone as much as possible.

3 Inhale and allow your arms to come up to shoulder level. Keep extending your arms out from your torso through your fingertips, feeling your underarms lengthening. Turn your head and lean back slightly to look out over your hand.

IMPORTANT ACTIONS

- Rotate knees away from each other
- Open chest
- Lift rib cage up out of the hips
- Lift the spine upward
- Hold tailbone down to soften the low back

HOLDING THE POSE

With every inhalation, re-establish the Foundation Points (on photo). As you exhale focus on extension. Lift your hips out of your legs. Lift your spine, extending every vertebra up. Look out over your front fingers.

COMPLETING THE POSE

Repeat on the other side. Then return to Tadasana by jumping your legs back together.

LEARNING AT HOME: MODIFICATIONS

• Stand with your back to the wall (feet 2-4 inches from wall). Keep your back, hips, shoulders, head, and arms on the wall. Keep your lower back pressing toward the wall as you open your chest and extend your torso straight up the wall.

• Try standing with your back foot braced against the wall, bringing awareness to your back leg and hip. Also helps with balance.

• You may want to work with your legs only for several weeks or months to learn the correct positioning. Then try going only half way down to strengthen your legs and give your hips time to open.

GENERAL PRECAUTIONS

- *If you have very tight hamstrings or any back problems, use the hands on the wall or a countertop (at waist or hip height). Do not push the knees backward.*
- *Not for those with hip replacement surgery.*

Parsvakonasana

EXTENDED SIDE ANGLE POSE

	VATA ↓	PITTA ↑	KAPHA ↓↓
TIME	Moderate holds with repetition	Work without strain—short holds	Long holding times with repetitions
BREATH	Even breath or light Ujjayi sound	Slow even breath or light Ujjayi	Any breath
FOCUS	Breath, stillness, holding the pose	Breath, expansion, and lightness	Strength, extension and expansion
MOVE	Exhale, strengthen the legs and lengthen the spine	Stretch the torso up out of the hips	Strengthen legs, open knees apart, lengthen the spine opening the chest

MOVING INTO THE POSE

1 Establish Warrior II (page 78) pose. Exhale as you extend your right arm and torso to the right. Move your right femur (thighbone) horizontally into your right hip socket (not letting the thigh move down). Extend fully to the right until your right torso comes down to touch your right thigh. Place your right hand on the floor behind and beside your right foot.

2 Keep weight on your left (back) foot. Extend your left arm over your head making a straight line of your body from your left foot to your left hand. Look up at the extended hand.

HOLDING THE POSE

1 With every inhalation, focus on the foundational points (on photo). Feel the outside of your left heel firmly weighted into the floor. Keep weight on your left leg. Both legs rotate open and away from each other. Your right knee must remain over your right heel.

2 As you exhale focus on the Important Actions. Open and rotate your back leg toward the ceiling. Continue this spiral rotation from your left heel all the way through your left hand.

IMPORTANT ACTIONS

- Lift arches and inner ankles
- Open knees out away from each other
- Open the left hipbone toward the ceiling
- Hold the right thigh parallel with the floor
- Ground the back heel
- Rotate the back leg up
- Rotate hips, chest, shoulders, left arm
- Keep weight on outsides of the feet

COMPLETING THE POSE

On the inhalation, hold your legs firm as you bring your torso up, returning to Warrior II (Virabhadrasana II) pose. After establishing Warrior II, inhale and straighten your front leg and turn your feet to face forward. Exhale, jump your legs back into Mountain Pose. Re-establish Tadasana and see how you feel. Then repeat on the other side.

LEARNING AT HOME: MODIFICATIONS

- Use the wall for support, for balance, or to focus on technique. Work with your back, shoulders, head, and extended hand on the wall (with your feet about 2-3 inches from the wall). Hold your right knee firmly over your right foot as you rotate your legs open.
- Use a block under the supporting hand, or put the supporting hand in front of your bent leg so the back of the right arm braces the position of the right, bent leg. This will help hold your knee open and in place.
- By bending your elbow and placing your hand on your mid-back (with the fingertips touching your spine), you can feel the movement of your spine. With each exhalation, feel the spine move into the body and lengthen.

GENERAL PRECAUTIONS

- *Avoid knee injury: Keep the front knee in alignment over the front ankle*
- *Always keep the back leg straight and strong to protect the knee*
- *Always keep the front knee facing the front ankle as you move in or out of the pose*
- *Not for those with hip replacement surgery*

Utkatasana

POWER CHAIR POSE

	VATA ↓↓↓	PITTA ↑↑	KAPHA ↓
TIME	Long holds	Very short holds	Long holding times with repetitions
BREATH	Full, even breathing	Easy, full breathing	Full breathing
FOCUS	Holding still in the pose	Ease in the pose	Strengthening, holding the pose
MOVE	Lift the spine as legs, hold steady	Strong legs with a lifting spine	Holding strong, chest open

MOVING INTO THE POSE

1 Stand in Tadasana. As you inhale stretch your arms out to your sides and over your head so that your ears are touching the insides of your upper arms.

2 Exhale and bend your knees, squatting down until your thighs are parallel with the floor (as if sitting on a chair).

3 Keep your chest as vertical as possible and your lower spine in neutral. Sit back and down as much as possible keeping your heels on the floor.

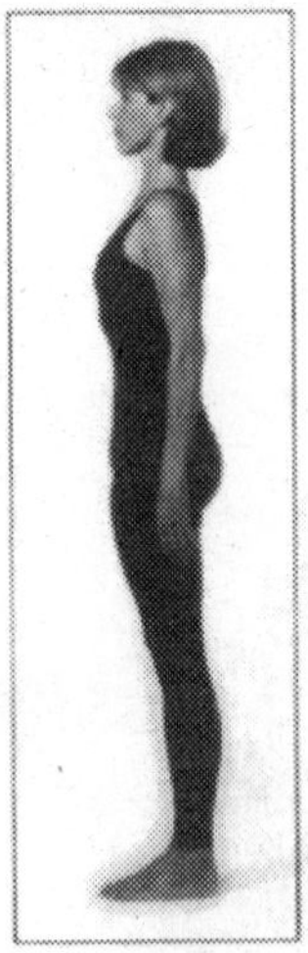

IMPORTANT ACTIONS

- Keep the chest open
- The back is as vertical as possible
- Shoulders are down from the ears
- Upper arms move back behind the ears

HOLDING THE POSE

With each inhalation focus on stability and adjustment. With each exhalation strengthen and extend. Hold the pose for 10-30 seconds.

COMPLETING THE POSE

On an exhalation, lower your arms and straighten your legs returning to Mountain Pose.

GENERAL PRECAUTIONS

Can help weak knees but take it easy at first.

Padottanasana

SPREAD LEGS FORWARD BEND

	VATA ↓↓	PITTA ↓↓↓	KAPHA ↓
TIME	Long holds and repetitions	Longer holds or comfortable holds	Shorter holds
BREATH	Even slow breath or Ujjayi for focus	Long easy breath	Normal
FOCUS	Stillness, stability and leg strength	Releasing, gentle practice	Strengthening legs; extending spine
MOVE	Lift the sitting bones and open the chest toward your feet	Strong legs, lengthen the spine, relax the neck	Lengthen and lift back legs to extend the front torso forward, open chest

MOVING INTO THE POSE

1 Establish Mountain Pose (pg 70). Exhale and spread your legs 4-5 feet apart. Ground your feet and lift your kneecaps. Inhale.

2 Exhale, extend your front torso forward, lifting and separating your sitting bones. Place your hands on the floor (or a prop) under your shoulders.

HOLDING THE POSE

1 Inhale. With your hands on the floor, raise your head, neck and shoulders until your arms are straight and your back is concave.

2 Exhale, lift your sitting bones and lengthen your spine, chest, neck, and head down toward the floor.

COMPLETING THE POSE

With hands on your waist, come up (on an exhalation) with a straight spine by pivoting at your hip joints. Jump your legs back to Tadasana.

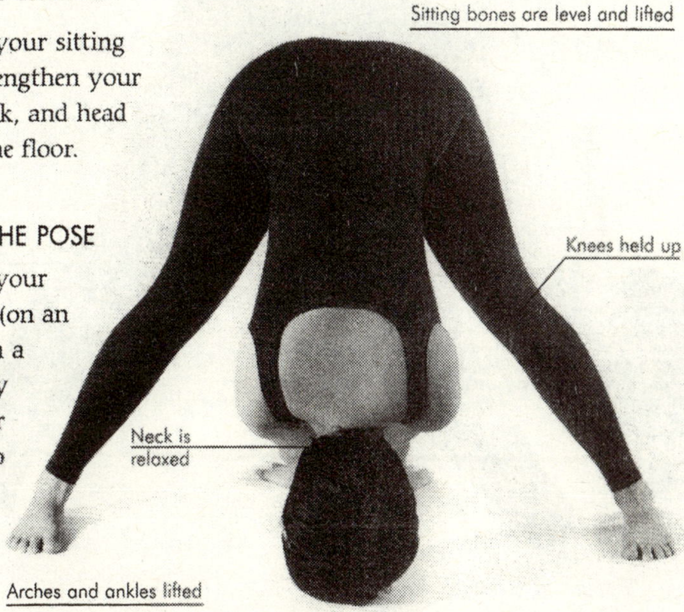

IMPORTANT ACTIONS

- Back lower leg moves down
- Back upper leg lifts
- Sitting bones widen as you bend
- Lengthen spine toward the floor
- Chest stays open - shoulders back
- Relax the neck and head

LEARNING AT HOME: MODIFICATIONS

Place your hands on the wall or a chair to work with straight arms and a straight spine.

GENERAL PRECAUTIONS

Not for those with hip replacement surgery.

Parsvottanasana

INTENSE SIDEWAYS STRETCH POSE

	VATA ↓↓	PITTA ↓	KAPHA ↓
TIME	Moderate holds	Short holds	Long holds and repetitions
BREATH	Even slow breath or Ujjayi for focus	Long easy breath	Normal
FOCUS	Stillness, stability, and leg strength	Releasing, gentle practice	Strengthening legs and extension
MOVE	Lift the sitting bones and open the chest toward your feet	Stretch the hamstrings and lengthen the spine, relaxing the neck	Lengthen and lift the back legs to extend the front torso, open chest

MOVING INTO THE POSE

1 After establishing Mountain Pose (pg 70), inhale and keep the chest open as you bring the hands to the waist. After you are familiar with the leg positions and your shoulders are supple, bring your hands into Namaste (prayer position) behind your back. Exhale and spread your legs 4-5 feet apart.

2 Inhale and turn your left leg 90 degrees to the left and turn your right (back) leg 60-70 degrees in (to the left).

3 On an exhalation turn your hips, torso, shoulders, and arms to the left so you face your left foot. As you inhale, strengthen your straight legs and lift your arches.

4 Exhale and bend at the hips, bringing your torso over your left leg. Keep your back straight and your weight evenly balanced on both feet.

IMPORTANT ACTIONS

- Toes relaxed
- Shoulders stay back
- Press palms together
- Open chest
- Lengthen the neck and head toward the foot

Virabhadrasana I

WARRIOR POSE I

VATA ↓↓	PITTA ↑↑	KAPHA ↓↓
Long holds with repetitions	Short holds	Long holds with repetitions
Long, smooth breath or Light Ujjayi	Long easy breathing	Any breath
Groundedness, breath, stillness	Lightness of the upper body	Lifting up and out of the legs
Lift torso out of strong legs	Upper body rises from strong legs	Strong legs, lift upper body and open chest

TO THE POSE

ı Mountain Pose (pg
th an exhalation, spread
-5 feet apart. Inhale and
straight arms out to the
over the head. Your
ove down from the ears
arm extends up, arms
ars, palms facing. Turn
foot and leg 90 degrees
ight and turn your left
in 60 degrees to the

xhale, turn your
rso, shoulders and
right, facing your
As you inhale,
ft arch pressing
of your left heel
the floor.

3 Exhale and bend your right knee until it is over or be- hind your right heel. The right shin is perpendicular to the floor, and if possible, the right thigh is parallel with the floor. It is more important that you are able to keep your back leg straight than it is to bring your front thigh down. Keep your weight evenly balanced over both legs.

IMPORTANT ACTIONS

- Shift weight into straight leg
- Keep your tailbone down
- Lift pubis up
- Lift rib cage up out of the hips
- Open the chest
- Shoulders back and down, arms straight reaching up
- Arms straight and behind ears
- Lengthen neck

HOLDING THE POSE

1 Inhale, firmly ground your feet, strengthen your legs, and keep your kneecaps lifted. Keep your chest and shoulders open as you move forward with each exhalation. Extend your spine, chest, and head toward the floor, lengthening your torso along the front of your left leg.

2 Exhale as you bring your torso back up to parallel with the floor (as above). Turn your feet and legs first to the front and then to the right side.

3 Repeat step 1 to your right side as you exhale, extending your torso forward and over your right leg.

COMPLETING THE POSE

Exhale as you lift your to
straight spine by pivoting
and face front and jump y

LEARNING AT HOME: MO

Put your hands on a wall,
chair to work with a strai

GENERAL PRECAUTIONS

- *For back problems and tig*
  to work with a straight s
  or a counter (at waist or
  straight as you work the
- *Do not push the knees bac*

TIME
BREATH
FOCUS
MOVE

MOVING I

1 Establi
70). W
your legs
bring your
sides and u
shoulders
as the insi
behind the
your righ
out to the
(back) foo
right.

2 On an
hips, t
arms to t
right foot.
lift your
the outsid
down int

Front kne
over fron

Right shin bo
is perpendic

HOLDING THE POSE

1 With every inhalation re-establish the Foundation Points (marked on photo). Be aware of your lifting arches, the balanced weight between two strong legs, and your straight back knee.

2 With every exhalation, lift your torso up (focus on the Important Actions). Lift your hips out of your legs by lifting your pubis up as your tailbone moves down. Extend your thoracic spine up. Move your shoulders down as you extend your arms and hands up.

COMPLETING THE POSE

As you inhale, straighten your right leg and turn your feet back toward the front. As you exhale, jump your legs back to Tadasana and be aware of how you feel. Then repeat on the other side.

LEARNING AT HOME: MODIFICATIONS

- With your back foot braced against the wall, bring awareness to your back leg and hip. Using the wall will also help with balance.
- Work with your legs only for several weeks or months to learn the correct positioning and prepare the legs, hips and groin muscles.

GENERAL PRECAUTIONS

Avoid knee injury:

- *Keep the bent knee behind the heel of that foot (shin vertical). The back knee must always be straight.*
- *Keep the front right knee facing over the ankle as you go into and come out of the pose.*

Virabhadrasana III

WARRIOR POSE III

	VATA ↓↓	PITTA ↑↑	KAPHA ↓↓↓
TIME	Moderate holds (use wall for balance)	Short holds (use wall for ease)	Long holds with repetitions
BREATH	Smooth, even breathing or Light Ujjayi	Long, easy breathing	Any breath
FOCUS	Breath and groundedness	Stability & lightness of the pose	Extension and control
MOVE	Move down through standing leg as you lengthen the body	Plant the standing leg and lengthen the body as you exhale	Strengthen and extend both legs, torso, arms, and open the chest

MOVING INTO THE POSE

1 Starting from Tadasana (pg 70) establish Virabhadrasana I (pg 86) to the right. Exhale and extend your torso and arms forward bringing your chest toward your front right thigh. Inhale. Exhale as you shift your weight over your right leg. Arms remain extended and beside your ears.

2 Inhale and gain your balance. Exhale and straighten your right standing leg. Bring your arms, head, torso, and back leg up into one straight line parallel with the floor.

IMPORTANT ACTIONS

- Legs are straight and strong
- Keep hips level
- Right hipbone lengthens down and pulls back away from the waist
- Chest moves down as the arms lift and lengthen

HOLDING THE POSE

1 With every inhalation re-establish the foundation points (see photo).

2 With every exhalation, employ the Important Actions list. Remember to extend through the back of the lifted leg, the heel, the spine, arms, and hands.

COMPLETING THE POSE

1 As you exhale, bend your right leg and lower your straight left leg until your foot touches the ground. Place your foot back in its former position. Inhale and bring your weight evenly on to both legs. Exhale and bring your torso, shoulders, and arms back up into Virabhadrasana I.

2 Take a few breaths in this position. Then exhale and straighten your right leg. Inhale turning your feet to face front, jump your legs back to Tadasana. In Tadasana be aware of how you feel. Repeat on the other side.

LEARNING AT HOME: MODIFICATIONS

- Place your hands on the wall and come into Wall Push, pg 63. Push away from the wall until your arms and torso are in a straight line. Lift your back leg and work on leveling your hips and lengthening your spine.
- When the hamstrings are tight place the hands higher on the wall. Keep your arms, torso, and leg still in one straight line but in a more open angle.

GENERAL PRECAUTIONS

- *If you have hyperextended knees then keep the standing knee slightly bent with the quadriceps contracted. Do not push the standing knee back.*
- *Keep the front knee facing over the center of the foot as you go into and come out of the pose. Do not allow the knee to turn as you move.*

Ardha Chandrasana

HALF MOON POSE

	VATA ↓	PITTA ↓	KAPHA ↓↓↓
TIME	Moderate - long holds	Short - moderate holds (no strain)	Long holds with repetitions
BREATH	Light Ujjayi breath for focus	Normal or Ujjayi sound	Any breath
FOCUS	Staying steady and strong	Expand in all directions like light	Strength, lift, and expansion
MOVE	Down through standing leg, then extend body in all directions	Lift inner standing leg, extend and open body into the pose	Strengthen and elongate legs, extend torso, and open chest

MOVING INTO THE POSE

1 From Tadasana (pg 70) move into Trikonasana on your right side and establish the pose (pg 74).

2 Then exhale and bend your right knee placing your right hand on the floor about 12 inches in front and a few inches to the outside (back) of your right foot. Breathe comfortably until you feel stable.

IMPORTANT ACTIONS

- Keep both legs strong
- Shoulders and arms are straight and lengthened
- Lift the torso up out of the supporting shoulder and arm
- Keep extending from the lifted heel through the top of the head
- Elongate the spine and rotate the chest toward the ceiling
- Extend and lengthen in all directions

3 As you exhale, shift some of your weight onto your hand and straighten your front standing leg. As your weight shifts, raise your left (back) leg into the air and fully strengthen and straighten both legs. At the same time, straighten your arms and open your chest (rotate it toward the ceiling).

HOLDING THE POSE

1 With every inhalation feel your standing (right) foot firmly grounded and lift up your inner right leg to maintain strength and stability of the posture.

2 With each exhalation, extend in all directions. Grow out through your arms and legs, and extend your spinal column, lengthening out through your neck and head. As the spine extends, rotate the chest toward the ceiling.

COMPLETING THE POSE

Exhale as you bend your right knee and bring your back foot (leg stays straight) down to the ground. Straighten your front leg and come back into Trikonasana. Breathe. On an exhalation, bring your torso up, turn your feet and legs forward, and jump back to Mountain Pose on an exhalation. Re-establish Tadasana and see how you feel. Then repeat on the other side.

LEARNING AT HOME: MODIFICATIONS

- Use the wall for support, balance, or to focus on technique. Work with your back, shoulders, head, and back heel on the wall with your standing foot about 2-3 inches from the wall.
- Use a block, chair, or bench, for your supporting hand.
- Use your upper hand to feel the movement of your spine by bending your elbow and placing your upper hand on your mid-back with your fingertips touching the spine.
- You may want to lay your upper arm straight and on top of the side of your body with your hand down on your thigh.

GENERAL PRECAUTIONS

- *Not for those with hip replacement surgery.*
- *Keep the standing leg straight with the thigh pulled up but not pushed back. The knee should not hyperextend.*
- *To avoid falling, use props and the wall.*
- *To avoid knee discomfort, keep rotating the standing leg out (away from the middle) so the knee remains facing the toes of that foot.*

Padangusthasana

FOOT BIG TOE POSE

	VATA ↓↓	PITTA ↓↓	KAPHA ↓
TIME	Long holds with repetition	Moderate holds	Moderate holds
BREATH	Light Ujjayi or even slow breath	Long easy breath	Normal
FOCUS	Stillness, grounding, breath	Comfort, extension, and grounding	Strengthening, extending, working
MOVE	Hold strength in the legs, internal extension of torso	Strengthen legs and internal extension of torso (no strain)	Strong legs, lift sit bones, extend torso, and open chest

MOVING INTO THE POSE

1 Stand in Tadasana - Mountain Pose (pg 70). Inhale and focus on your connection to the ground. Exhale and focus on growing the spine upward.

2 Inhale and keep the chest open as you bring your arms out to the sides and up over your head. Keep your feet firmly grounded and your back straight as you bend your torso forward from the hip joints. Extend the arms, torso, and chest forward to move. Maintain a Neutral lower back. Lift and separate the sitting bones to extend the torso to the floor. With the palms facing each other, wrap the first two fingers of each hand around the big toes.

IMPORTANT ACTIONS

- Extend the straight spine as you bend forward from the hips
- Sitting bones move away from each other and lift
- Straighten the knees without pushing them backward
- Belly stays relaxed and drops toward the chest
- Lengthen the neck and head toward the feet

HOLDING THE POSE

1 Inhale, straighten the arms and lift the head. Stretch the spine, chest, and neck, as you concave the back and bring the bottom ribs forward. Legs stay strong.

2 Holding the extension of the spine, exhale and lengthen the front torso toward the floor as you are bending the elbows out to the sides. Bring the chest and head down toward the ankles. Relax the belly and neck. Maintain the stretch. Repeat 1 & 2 as desired.

COMPLETING THE POSE

Exhale as you lift by pivoting the torso at the hip joints and come up with the back, arms, neck, and head straight. When standing, relax the arms out to the sides and down. Re-establish Tadasana and see how you feel.

LEARNING AT HOME: MODIFICATIONS

- If you have tight hamstrings, put your hands on a block or a chair so you can work with a straight spine and lengthened arms.
- Beginners should put the hands on their waists or open their arms out to the sides when bending forward or coming up in this pose.

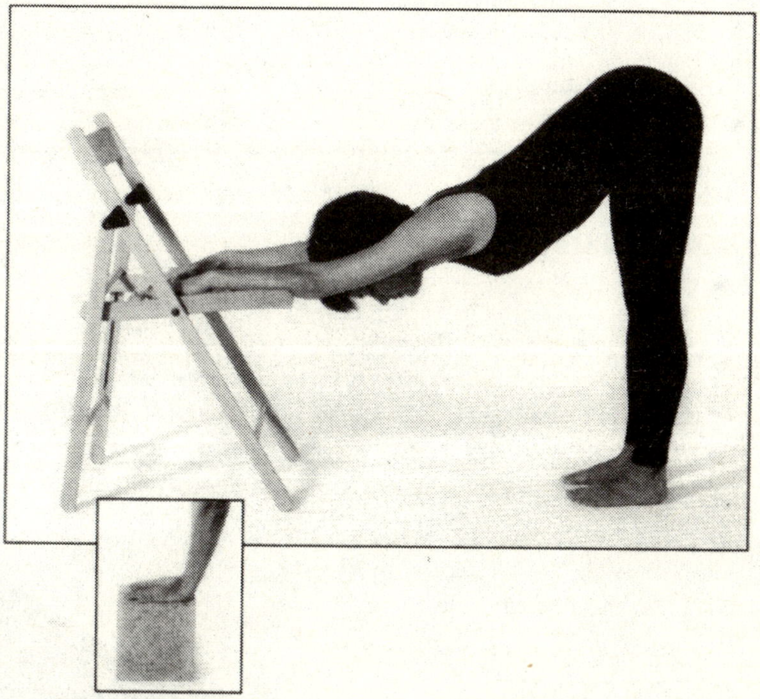

GENERAL PRECAUTIONS

- *Not for people with Sciatica*
- *Do not push the knees back. Keep the weight forward on the feet to prevent overstretching the back of the knees.*

Urdhva Prasarita Ekapadasana

UPWARD LEG FORWARD BEND

	VATA ↓↓↓	PITTA ↓	KAPHA ↓
TIME	Long holds with repetition	Moderate holds	Moderate holds
BREATH	Ujjayi or smooth, even breathing	Long easy breath or light Ujjayi	Any breath
FOCUS	Stability, grounding, and stillness	Stillness, extension, and grounding	Strength and extension
MOVE	Hold strength in both legs and lengthen the spine	Stretching and extending, releasing the spine without strain	Lengthen, strengthen, lift the leg, and open chest

MOVING INTO THE POSE

1 Stand in Tadasana (pg 70). Inhale, bring the arms out to the sides and up over the head.

2 With the back straight bend forward from the hip joints. Extend the arms and torso toward the floor. Keeping the feet firmly grounded, take hold of the right ankle with the left hand. The right hand is on the floor fingers beside the toes.

3 As you exhale, lift the left leg behind you as high as possible. Hold. Keep both legs straight with the knees lifted.

HOLDING THE POSE

1 With each inhalation, ground, relax the belly and neck and strengthen the right standing leg.

2 With every exhalation extend the spine, chest, and neck toward the floor as you lift the leg higher.

Optional: With the right hand on the floor and the left around the right ankle lift the chest up as you inhale. Extend the chest and belly downward as you exhale.

IMPORTANT ACTIONS

- Standing leg stays vertical
- Toes are relaxed
- Keep the standing leg strong
- Extend the spine, chest, and neck
- Belly relaxes
- Extend through ball of the foot (lifted leg)

COMPLETING THE POSE

Bring the lifted leg back down onto the floor into Uttanasana. As you exhale bring your straight torso up pivoting at the hip joints. For the first year, keep the arms out to the sides when you come up . Re-establish Tadasana. Repeat on the other side.

LEARNING AT HOME: MODIFICATIONS

Use the wall or a chair for your hands so you can work with a straight spine.

GENERAL PRECAUTIONS

- *Not for those with sciatic pain*
- *If you have any back problems or tight hamstrings use the hands on a chair at hip height.*
- *If your back is weak, bring your arms out to the sides as you bend forward and come back up.*

Padahastasana

HANDS UNDER FEET POSE

	VATA ↓↓↓	PITTA ↓↓	KAPHA ↓
TIME	Long holds with repetitions	Long holds with repetition	Shorter holds
BREATH	Even, smooth breath or Ujjayi	Long, easy breath or light Ujjayi	Any breath
FOCUS	Stillness, extension, and stability	Grounding and lengthening	Strengthening, extending, working
MOVE	Ground feet, lift sitting bones, and extend spine	Lift sitting bones up and release the spine	Strengthen and lift legs, extend the spine, and open the chest

MOVING INTO THE POSE

1 Stand in Tadasana (pg 70). Keep the chest open as you inhale and bring your arms out to the sides and up over your head.

2 Keep your feet firmly grounded and your back straight as you bend your torso forward from the hip joints. Extend the arms, torso, and chest toward the floor. Lift and separate the sitting bones as you extend. Keep the weight toward the balls of the feet.

3 Place your hands, palms up, under your feet (fingertips to front of heel) and stand with the balls of your feet on the palms of your hands. Keep the weight evenly balanced on both feet.

HOLDING THE POSE

1 Inhale as you straighten the arms and lift the head. Stretch the spine as you bring the bottom ribs forward and the back to concave. The sitting bones should be level and lifting.

2 Holding the extension of the spine, bend the elbows and bring the chest and head toward the ankles as you exhale. Relax the belly and neck. Strengthen the legs.

COMPLETING THE POSE

Place the hands beside the feet, palms pressing the floor. Exhale and lift the arms, shoulders and torso by pivoting at the hip joints. Come all the way up to Tadasana and see how you feel.

IMPORTANT ACTIONS

- Arches, ankles, and inner legs lifting
- Hold the knees strong but not pushed back
- Back of lower leg moves down
- Back of upper leg moves up
- Belly releases
- Lengthen the neck

Uttanasana

INTENSE EXTENSION POSE

	VATA ↓↓↓	PITTA ↓↓	KAPHA ↓
TIME	Long holds with repetitions	Long holds with some repetition	Shorter holds
BREATH	Even, smooth breath or Ujjayi	Long easy breath or light Ujjayi	Any breath
FOCUS	Stillness, extension, and stability	Easy lengthening	Strengthening, extending, working
MOVE	Legs strong, lift sitting bones, extend spine	Lift legs, release spine, open chest	Lift legs, extend spine, open chest

MOVING INTO THE POSE

1 Stand in Tadasana (pg 70). Keep the chest open as you inhale and bring your arms out to the sides and up over your head.

2 Keep your back straight as you bend from the hip joints. Extend the arms, torso, and chest forward and down toward the floor. Lift and separate the sitting bones. Keep weight toward the balls of the feet to prevent hyperextension of the knees.

3 Place your palms on the floor beside the feet.

HOLDING THE POSE

1 With each inhalation, ground and strengthen your legs, and relax your belly and neck.

2 With every exhalation, extend the spine, chest, neck, and head, lengthening the front torso.

COMPLETING THE POSE

Exhale and lift the torso by pivoting at the hip joints. Keep the back, arms, neck and head straight as you come up to Tadasana. (Beginners and weaker backs come up with the arms out to the sides)

LEARNING AT HOME: MODIFICATIONS

Place your hands on a prop or a chair and work with a straight spine and arms.

GENERAL PRECAUTIONS

Not for those with sciatic pain

INVERTED POSES

RICHARD ROSEN IN EKA PADA SARVANGASANA

Adho Mukha Svanasana

DOWNWARD FACING DOG

VATA ↓↓↓ PITTA ↑ or ↓ KAPHA ↓↓

	VATA ↓↓↓	PITTA ↑ or ↓	KAPHA ↓↓
TIME	Long holds with repetition	Short holds (work without strain)	Long holds with repetitions
BREATH	Slow, even breathing or Ujjayi	Easy breath or light Ujjayi	Normal
FOCUS	Extension and stillness	Grounding and easy stretch	Lengthening, lifting, extending
MOVE	Extend arms and torso, stretch legs	Extend arms and torso, stretch legs	Lift thighs and sitting bones, extend torso and legs

MOVING INTO THE POSE

1 From Cat Stretch (pg 60), the knees are under the hip joints, feet hip-distance apart, toes turned under. The hands are under the outside of the shoulders. Now move the hands one hand-length forward (fingers spread wide apart). Keeping the arms straight, inhale and drop the chest toward the floor as in Cat Pose.

2 As you exhale, come onto the balls of the feet and straighten the legs. Keep the heels up as you lengthen (from the index finger) the arms, shoulders, torso and sitting bones up to the ceiling making a straight line from hands to tailbone.

3 Holding the straight line of the upper body and the sitting bones up, let the heels slowly descend. Lower the heels only if you can keep the sitting bones lifted.

HOLDING THE POSE

1 As you inhale feel the breath move into the body and re-establish the Foundation Points (on photo). The head, neck, and belly hang relaxed.

2 With each exhalation, lift the sitting bones and let the heels move down. Hold the pose 30-40 seconds to begin and gradually increase the holding time as the arms and shoulders strengthen.

IMPORTANT ACTIONS

- Lift the inner groins up
- Open the chest toward the feet
- Lift the back thighs up as the back calves move down
- Head, neck, and belly are relaxed

COMPLETING THE POSE

Exhale as you bend the knees to the floor, sit back onto your heels, and rest in Child's Pose (pg 61).

LEARNING AT HOME: MODIFICATIONS

• To increase the stretch in the legs, work with the back of the heels braced against the wall and the bottoms of the heels firmly on the floor.

• To learn the movement of the lower back relative to the position of the legs, practice Wall Push, (pg 63). This will teach the movement of the sitting bones as they lift and how to draw the spine into the body. Knees are always lifted.

• *Dog Pose Variation:* Use Wall Push to learn the movement of the sitting bones and how to hold the hips level as you raise the extended leg. Practice the extension of the body from palms to tailbone.

DOSHIC NOTES

• Stay longer in the pose to reduce fatigue.

• Relieves stiffness in shoulders and tight hamstrings.

GENERAL PRECAUTIONS

- *Those with a 'carrying angle' and/or hyperextended arms will benefit from shortening the distance between the hands and feet by 4-9" depending on your size. This relieves strain on the elbows.*
- *This pose is good for the heart and usually safe for high blood pressure.*

Adho Mukha Svanasana Variation

DOWNWARD FACING DOG LEG EXTENDED

MOVING INTO THE POSE

1 From Downward Facing Dog inhale and shift the weight onto the right foot.

2 Exhale, keeping the hips level, push through the back of the left leg (and heel) and raise it until there is a straight line from index finger to left heel.

IMPORTANT ACTIONS

- Keep the pelvis level
- Lengthen and strengthen the extended leg
- Neck relaxed

HOLDING THE POSE

1 Hold the pose 10-20 seconds to begin. Gradually increase the time as you strengthen the shoulders and arms.

2 Exhale coming back into Dog Pose. Repeat on the other side.

Sarvangasana I & II

HALF SHOULDERSTAND I & II

	VATA ↓↓↓	PITTA ↓	KAPHA ↓↓
TIME	Moderate-Long holds	Short-moderate hold - no strain	Long holds
BREATH	Long smooth breath	Smooth easy breath	Normal
FOCUS	Stability and holding still	Comfort and lifting	Lifting and working the pose
MOVE	Lengthen the spine, strengthen the legs—use wall for stability	Lengthen spine and legs—use wall for ease	Open chest, extend the torso, and strengthen and lengthen legs

3 Take one leg off the wall and straighten it at an angle, as shown. Take the other leg off the wall and balance. Breathe.

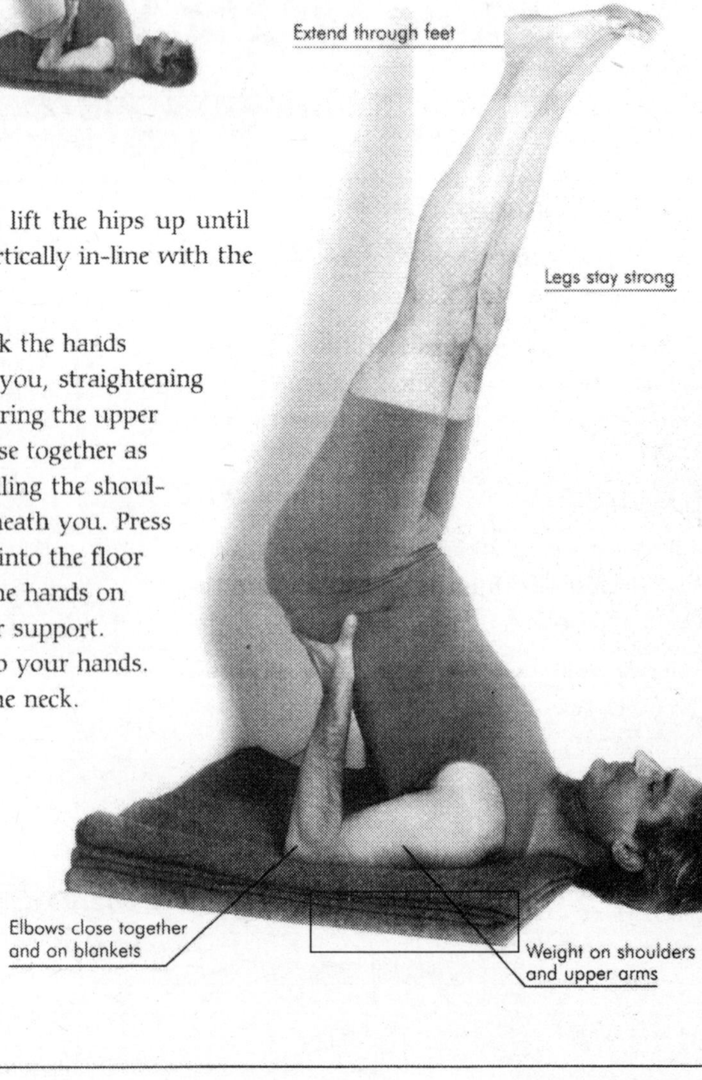

MOVING INTO THE POSE

Practice Neck Stretch, pg 57, to prepare the neck. Use 2-4 folded blankets to create space for the neck. To begin, fold and stack the blankets so that they will fit evenly under the hips, torso, shoulders and upper arms. Make the sharp edge of the blankets on the side used for the shoulders. Lying on the blankets, move the shoulders down from the ears (and two inches down from the edge of the blankets) and together underneath the back. Lengthen the neck.

Sarvangasana I

1 Place the blankets at the wall. Lie on the blankets with legs extended up the wall and sitting bones touching it. Head is on the floor. Bend your knees until the feet just touch the wall. Push against the wall to lift the hips up until they are vertically in-line with the shoulders.

2 Interlock the hands behind you, straightening the arms. Bring the upper arms as close together as possible pulling the shoulders underneath you. Press the elbows into the floor and place the hands on the back for support. Hips sit into your hands. Lengthen the neck.

Sarvangasana II

1 Place the blankets one arm's length from the wall. Bend the knees, feet close to the buttocks. Press arms and hands into the floor. Roll the body up bringing the feet over the head and onto the wall or chair behind you.

2 Interlock the hands behind you, straightening the arms. Bring the arms as close together as possible, pulling the shoulders underneath you. Press the elbows into the floor and place the hands on the upper back for support. Straighten your spine.

3 Take one leg off the wall and then the other. Keep the legs straight, balance and breathe.

HOLDING THE POSE — I & II

Press the hands into the back, lifting the spine up into the body and opening the chest. Hold the posture breathing comfortably for 1-2 minutes to begin. Gradually increase the time.

COMPLETING THE POSE

Bend the knees toward the ears. Straighten the arms placing the hands on the floor behind you. Use the arms for support as you slowly unroll the spine vertebrae by vertebrae back to the ground. You may lift the chin but do not lift the head or shoulders off the floor as you come down. Slide off the blankets onto the floor and rest.

DOSHIC NOTES

Excellent for Kapha practice, although excess weight could be difficult. Counters high Pitta unless held too long. Excellent for Vata.

GENERAL PRECAUTIONS

- *If you have glaucoma or unmedicated high blood pressure do not practice this posture.*
- *Practice 2 hours after eating.*
- *If you experience any pressure in the eyes, ears, head, neck, or breathing, come down and consult an experienced teacher.*

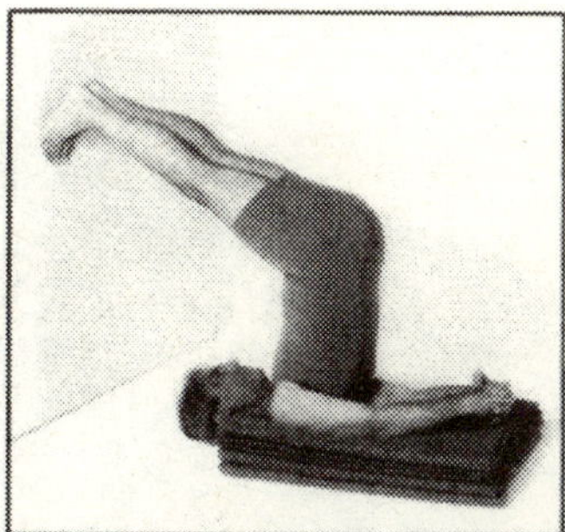

IMPORTANT ACTIONS

- Spine is straight from shoulders to buttocks
- Chest comes toward the chin
- Neck is soft
- Eyes, neck, face stay relaxed
- Stay on the tops of shoulders
- Lift the inner thighs
- Extend the legs through balls of feet

Sarvangasana III

FULL SHOULDERSTAND

	VATA ↓↓↓	PITTA ↓	KAPHA ↓↓
TIME	Moderate-Long holds	Short holds – no strain	Long holds
BREATH	Long, smooth breath	Smooth, easy breath	Normal
FOCUS	Holding still and stable	Comfort and steadiness	Lifting, working the pose
MOVE	Lengthen and lift spine and legs	Lengthen the spine and legs	Open chest, extend the torso and legs

MOVING INTO THE POSE

Before you begin, practice Neck Stretch, pg 57. Use 2-4 folded blankets as in Shoulderstand I and II, pgs 102-103.

1 Lie on the folded blankets with the neck and head on the floor. The shoulders are 2 inches in from the edge of the blankets—shoulder blades tucked under. Elbows are beside the body and the neck is relaxed.

2 Bend the knees, press the palms against the floor and roll the body up, bringing the feet over the head and onto the floor behind you.

3 Interlock the hands behind you, straightening the arms. Bring the arms as close together as possible, pulling the shoulders underneath you. Press the elbows into the floor and place the hands on the upper back. Straighten the legs up to the ceiling, pushing through the heels, thighs rolling inward.

4 Press the elbows into the floor as you lift the torso and legs upward. Relax the neck and head. Breathe.

HOLDING THE POSE

1 Stay on the tops of the shoulders. Press the hands into the back, lift the spine and move the chest toward the chin.

2 Separate the legs 6" apart, extend the inner legs upward. Hold this extension as you bring the legs together.

3 Hold the posture, breathing comfortably for 1-3 minutes to begin. Gradually stay in the pose longer as is appropriate for your dosha.

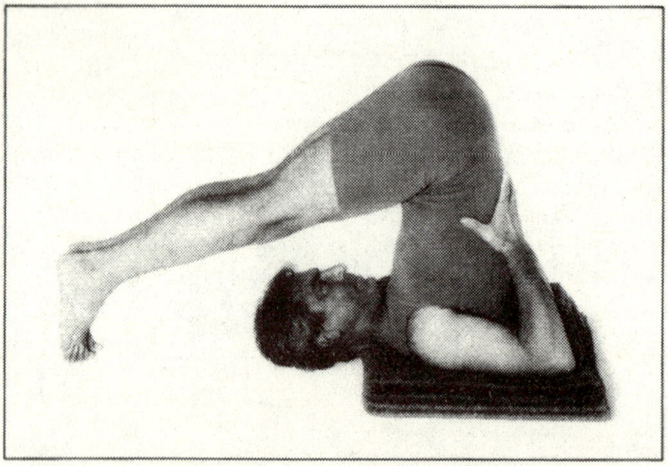

IMPORTANT ACTIONS

- No pressure on the head
- Press your hands into your back to lift the spine
- Chest comes toward the chin
- Draw the tailbone in and up
- Lift the inner thighs
- Extend through the balls of the feet

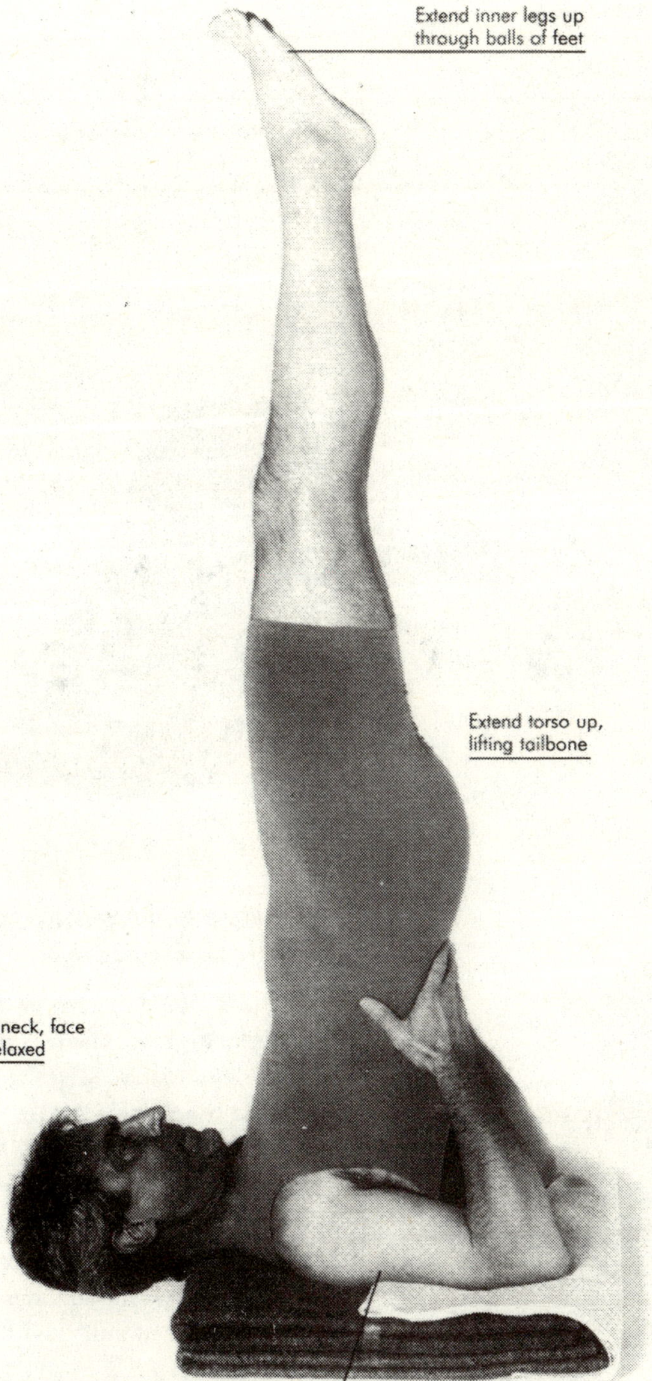

COMPLETING THE POSE

Bend the knees toward the ears. Straighten the arms placing the hands on the floor behind you. Slowly unroll the spine vertebrae by vertebrae back to the ground. Lift the chin (as you roll down) but not the head or shoulders. Slide off the blankets onto the floor and relax.

LEARNING AT HOME: MODIFICATIONS

- If you have been having trouble with the arms widening, use a belt or tie above the crease of the elbows to hold the arms shoulder width apart.
- Use a metal chair or bench to learn the pose with support and to allow concentration on chest opening. This is best learned from your asana teacher.

DOSHIC NOTES

Purifies the blood and nourishes the brain, throat and lungs. Regulates Udāna Vayu and Kapha in the region of the chest. *Pitta:* Counters high Pitta unless held too long or strained. *Kapha:* Excess weight can make this pose unsafe, but is excellent for Kapha.

GENERAL PRECAUTIONS

- *If you have glaucoma or unmedicated high blood pressure do not practice this posture. With low blood pressure, medicated high blood pressure, or heart problems, consult your physician and yoga teacher.*
- *Practice this pose 2 hours or more after eating.*
- *If you experience any pressure in the eyes, ears, head, neck, or breathing, come down and consult an experienced teacher.*

Three Sarvangasana Variations

THREE FULL SHOULDERSTAND VARIATIONS

	VATA ↓↓	PITTA ↑ or ↓	KAPHA ↓↓
TIME	Moderate – long holds	Short holds – without strain	Moderate – long holds
BREATH	Long, smooth breath	Smooth, easy breath	Normal
FOCUS	Holding still and stable	Comfort and steadiness	Lifting, working the pose
MOVE	Lengthen and lift spine and legs	Support the torso, lengthen spine and legs	Open chest, extend the torso and legs

1 EKA PADA SARVANGASANA: *One Leg Extended Shoulderstand*

Establish Sarvangasana III, the full shoulderstand position, pg 104. Hold the left leg up and straight. Exhale extending through the back of the right leg and heel as you bring it down to touch the floor or a chair (as in Halasana). Keep lifting the spine, moving the sitting bones to the ceiling. Breathe and hold 20 or more seconds. Extend through the back of both legs as you bring the right leg back up into Sarvangasana. Repeat other side.

2 SUPTA KONASANA SARVANGASANA: *Open Angle Shoulderstand*

Bring the legs into Halasana, pg 108. From Halasana spread the legs as wide apart as possible. Keep the legs straight and the tops of the toes touching the floor. Keep the spine and sitting bones lifting and the chest as open as possible. Breathe and hold 20 or more seconds. Bring the legs back into Halasana and return to Shoulderstand.

• *Modification:* Use a bench or chair so you can work with the feet higher.

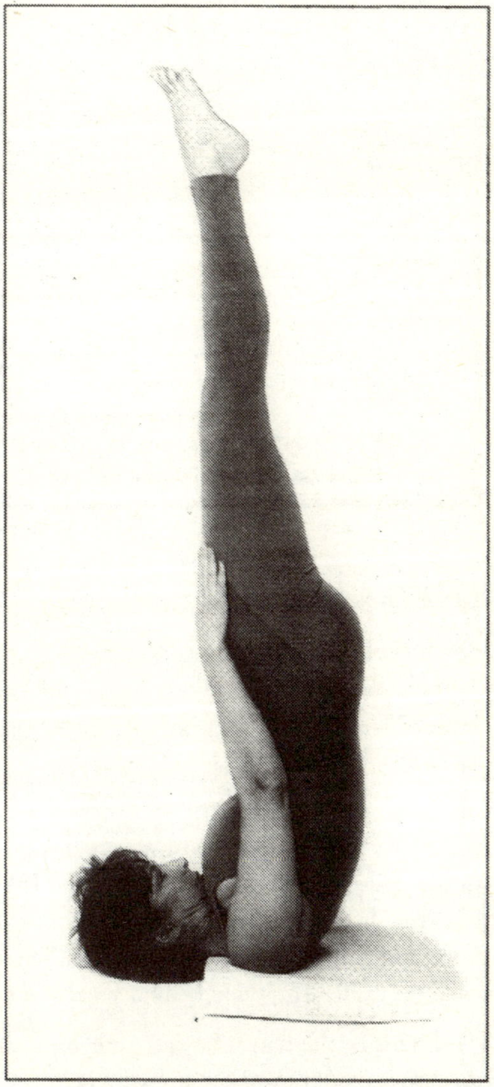

Niralamba Sarvangasana
Unsupported Shoulderstand
Variation

3 SETU BANDHA SARVANGASANA: *Bridge Pose from Shoulderstand*

With the spine lifted and the palms firmly on the back, scissor the right leg backward and the left forward. Begin arching the upper back by moving the spine up and into the body, opening the chest. Hold the lower back strongly in Neutral (tailbone lifting) as you stretch the right thigh, bend the right knee and reach the toes toward the floor. Arch the spine up into the body as the leg comes down. Hold the tailbone up and bring the left foot to the floor. Hold for 30-60 seconds to begin.

To return to shoulderstand strengthen the left leg and lift the spine into the body. Open the chest and lift the right leg straight up. Lift the tailbone and push up onto the ball of the left foot. At the same time, shift the hips up above the shoulders. Adjust the arms and shoulders and lift and straighten the torso and legs. Repeat alternate side.

Halasana

PLOW POSE

	VATA ↓↓↓	PITTA ↓	KAPHA ↓
TIME	Moderate to long holds	Short to moderate holds – no strain	Short holds
BREATH	Long, easy breath	Easy breath	Normal
FOCUS	Holding still and stable	Comfort and steadiness	Lifting, working the pose
MOVE	Lengthen the spine, strengthen the legs, use the wall for stability	Lengthen the spine and legs, use wall for ease of practice	Lift the chest, extend the torso up and the legs down

MOVING INTO THE POSE

Before you begin, practice Neck Stretch, pg 57. Use 2-4 folded blankets as in Shoulderstand I and II, pgs 102-103.

1 Lie on the folded blankets with the neck, and head on the floor. The shoulders are 2 inches from the edge of the blankets—shoulder blades tucked under. Elbows are beside the body and the neck is relaxed. Bend the knees, press the palms into the floor, and roll the body up bringing the feet over the head and onto the floor behind you.

2 Interlock the hands behind your back, straightening the arms. Bring the arms as close together as possible and pull the shoulders underneath you. Press the elbows into the floor and place the hands on the upper back.

3 As you press the elbows into the floor, straighten your back, lifting your sitting bones toward the ceiling (chest opens toward the chin). Straighten the legs pushing through the heels, thighs rolling inward. Inhale and Relax the neck and head (without turning them).

HOLDING THE POSE

With every inhalation focus on grounding. With each exhalation focus on the Important Actions. Breathe comfortably in Halasana for 30-60 seconds to begin.

IMPORTANT ACTIONS

- Keep the elbows close together
- Press the hands into the back, lifting the spine
- Press the sitting bones up
- Strengthen the legs
- Chest open and toward the chin

COMPLETING THE POSE

Place your arms on the floor with the hands pressing down. Bend the knees. Using the arms and hands for support, slowly unroll the spine, vertebrae by vertebrae, until your back and feet rest on the floor. As you roll down, the head and shoulders must stay on the floor. Keep your legs lengthened as much as you can.

LEARNING AT HOME: MODIFICATIONS

- Use a belt or tie to hold the elbows firmly in place.
- Use a metal chair, bench, or block to support the legs and feet (as shown).
- Try working with your arms stretched over your head, relaxed on the floor.

DOSHIC NOTES

Nourishes the brain, throat and lungs.

Vata: Remain still in the pose for extended periods.

Pitta: Counters high Pitta (unless held too long).

Kapha: Excess weight could make this pose difficult to do safely but it is good for Kapha.

GENERAL PRECAUTIONS

- *If you have glaucoma or unmedicated high blood pressure do not practice this posture. With low blood pressure, medicated high blood pressure, or heart problems, consult your physician and yoga teacher.*
- *Practice this pose at least two hours after eating.*
- *If you feel pressure in the eyes, ears, head, neck, come down and consult an experienced teacher.*

Depada Pidam

BRIDGE POSE

	VATA ↓↓	PITTA ↓	KAPHA ↓↓
TIME	Moderate to long holds	Moderate holds	Long holds with repetitions
BREATH	Even, slow or Ujjayi	Long, easy breath	Normal or Ujjayi
FOCUS	Strength, stillness, ground	Ground, lightness, ease	Strength, lift
MOVE	Draw the spine into body and hold	Internal lift and holding without strain	Lift the spine and strengthen the legs

MOVING INTO THE POSE

1 Lie on the back with the knees bent, feet close to the buttocks and hip distance apart. Turn the toes in slightly with the knees directly over the feet.

3 Strengthen the feet and legs and lift the tailbone and hips up until you rest on the tops of the shoulders. Keep the lower back in Neutral.

2 Lengthen the neck and tuck the shoulders under so the shoulder blades are flat on the floor. Stretch the arms down beside you with the palms pressing the floor. Inhale and center the head on the floor.

HOLDING THE POSE

1 Focus on opening the chest and keeping the knees over the heels with each inhalation. Relax the neck, head, and face.

2 Exhale as you lift the spine up into the body, arching the upper back. See Important Actions. Hold 20-30 seconds to begin. Gradually increase to 2 minutes.

COMPLETING THE POSE

Inhale and slowly roll the spine down, placing each vertebrae on the floor one at a time. Remember the tailbone is always the highest point both in the posture and as you unroll the spine. Breathe and relax.

IMPORTANT ACTIONS

- Press the feet, arms and shoulders down to lift the spine up into the body, arching the upper back
- Keep the face and throat relaxed
- Lift the upper back
- Tailbone is highest point, always lifting

LEARNING AT HOME: MODIFICATIONS

Another way to practice this pose, especially good for Pitta and Kapha or very provoked Vata, is to move up into the Bridge and back to the floor as you breathe. Lift the tailbone and hips up into Bridge with every exhalation. Return to the floor with every inhalation. This practice is a continuous marriage of measured movement and breath.

PROPS: You can belt the legs just above the knees to keep the knees over the feet as you lift and hold the pose.

GENERAL PRECAUTIONS

- *For back or neck problems, go gently and only as far as the neck will comfortably allow. You can use folded blankets under shoulders, back, and hips. With the head and neck on the floor and the torso on blankets, space is created for the neck.*
- *Use extra blankets under the shoulders, torso and hips if you need more space for the neck to remain soft.*

Preparation for Sirsasana

PREPARATION FOR HEADSTAND

	VATA ↓↓↓	PITTA ↑↑	KAPHA ↓↓↓
TIME	Moderate holds with repetition	Short holds	Long holds with repetitions
BREATH	Smooth or Ujjayi	Easy, full breath	Normal or Ujjayi
FOCUS	Holding strong and stable	Stability and extension	Working, lifting, extending
MOVE	Hold shoulders and torso up	Lift shoulders, lengthen spine	Lift the shoulders and torso

2 Push the forearms against the floor and straighten the legs, lifting the hips upward. Stay up on the toes and continue pushing away from the floor lengthening your torso until your arms, shoulders, and torso are a straight line.

3 Hold the length in your torso as you tiptoe your straight legs in toward your hands. Be sure your torso stays straight. Tiptoe in until your back is vertical. Breathe. Keep the head off the floor by constantly lifting the shoulders.

MOVING INTO THE POSE

1 With your hands and knees on a mat place your forearms on the floor. Interlock your fingers and make an equilateral triangle from your elbows to your interlocked fingers. Move the muscles in your lower arm toward the inside of the triangle so you rest securely on the bones. The elbows are under the shoulder joints—not wider. It is important to keep the wrists vertical and pinned to the floor. The weight is evenly distributed between the wrists and the forearms (no white knuckles—use the wrists). The shoulders must always lift up and away from the floor.

HOLDING THE POSE

1 Hold the shoulders and torso up as you lengthen the neck just enough to touch the top of the head to the floor for one second.

2 Exhale as you lift the head and shoulders up away from the floor. Extend the spine up from shoulders to tailbone.

3 Repeat #1 and #2 to build strength and experience in the shoulders and arms. Never put any weight on the head.

COMPLETING THE POSE

Hold the shoulders up as you tiptoe the feet slowly back out to where you started. Bend the knees and sit back on the heels in Child's Pose to rest.

LEARNING AT HOME: MODIFICATIONS

The upper arms can be belted to hold the position, but this should not become a habit.

IMPORTANT ACTIONS

- Lengthen the torso
- Lift the sitting bones to ceiling
- Chest remains open
- Legs as straight as possible
- Head stays up off floor
- Keep lifting the shoulders up

DOSHIC NOTES

Kaphas with excess weight should practice short repetitions to build strength. Excellent for reducing excess Vata.

GENERAL PRECAUTIONS

Not good for high blood pressure, heart problems or glaucoma.

Adho Mukha Vrksasana

HANDSTAND

	VATA ↑ or ↓	PITTA ↑ or ↓	KAPHA ↓↓↓
TIME	Long holds at wall	Moderate holds –no strain	Long holds with repetitions
BREATH	Normal, even	Easy breath	Normal
FOCUS	Strength and holding still	Lightness and lift	Strong, full length extension
MOVE	Strengthen arms, lift shoulders and torso, extend legs	Strengthen arms, lift shoulders and torso, use wall for ease	Strengthen arms, lift shoulders and torso, push upward to balance

MOVING INTO THE POSE

1 On the hands and knees, place the hands under the shoulders (about one foot from the wall), and spread the fingers. The elbows must remain straight. Straighten the legs and lengthen the arms, shoulders, and torso as in Dog Pose (pg 100).

2 Inhale, step the right foot forward (knee bent) under the chest. The left leg is straight and behind you. Quickly push up with the right leg (bounce up by straightening the right leg) and immediately kick the straight left leg up to touch the wall. The torso becomes vertical as you quickly bring the right leg up to touch the left on the wall.

HOLDING THE POSE

1 With every inhalation strengthen the arms and check your Foundation Points.

2 With every exhalation extend the entire body upward. Move the upper spine into the body opening the chest as you keep the low back in 'neutral'. (see Important Actions). Extend through the arches and balls of the feet.

3 Holding the vertical alignment of the body, bend the right knee and put the toes on the wall for balance as you take the left off the wall and straighten it. Take the right leg off the wall and balance.

COMPLETING THE POSE

On an exhalation, bend at the hips to bring the left leg straight down to the floor, quickly followed by the right. Bend the knees and sit in Basic Virasana, pg 142.

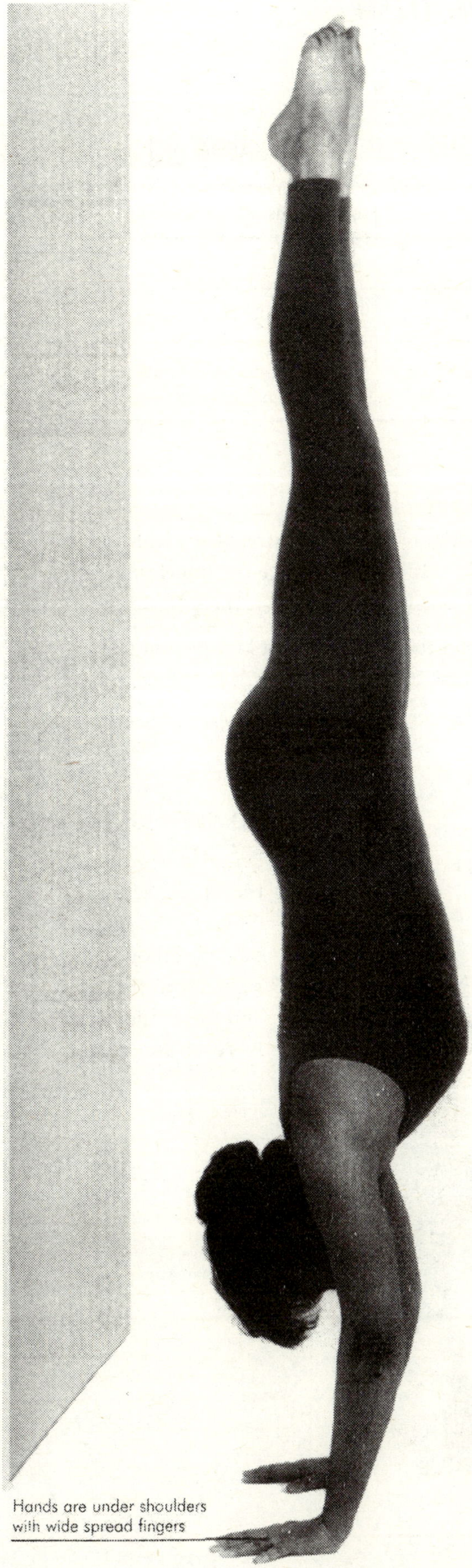

Hands are under shoulders with wide spread fingers

LEARNING AT HOME: MODIFICATIONS

To begin, practice bouncing. To 'bounce,' the right leg bends and then forcefully straightens, pushing you up. As your right leg quickly pushes you upward, the hips shift up and the left leg leaves the floor as if you are going up, but you don't. You bounce up and come back down. Repeat to gain the experience of moving into the pose.

GENERAL PRECAUTIONS

Those with wrist, elbow or shoulder problems should work carefully after consulting a physician and an experienced teacher.

IMPORTANT ACTIONS

- Arms and elbows always remain strong and straight
- Push up to lift the shoulders
- Lower front ribs move back
- Tailbone lifts up
- Extend through the inner legs and feet
- Spine is lifting

Pincha Mayurasana

ARM STAND

	VATA ↓↓	PITTA ↑↑	KAPHA ↓↓↓
TIME	Long holds at wall	Shorter holds	Long holds with repetitions
BREATH	Smooth, even breath	Easy, smooth breath	Normal
FOCUS	Strength, stability	Lightness, lift, breath	Strong lifting
MOVE	Strengthen arms, extend torso up, open chest, balance	Strengthen and extend all parts up, balance	Strengthen arms, lift shoulders and torso, extend upward

MOVING INTO THE POSE

1 From hands and knees, place the hands, wrists, and forearms parallel with each other on the floor. Spread the thumb and fingers wide braced against the wall or a block. Move the flesh of the forearm inward so your weight rests firmly on the forearm bones. Keep the elbows and shoulders vertical.

2 Inhale, step the right foot forward (knee bent) under the chest. The left leg is straight and behind you. *Remember, the head never touches the floor.*

3 Exhale as you quickly push up with the left leg (bounce up by straightening the left leg) and immediately kick the straight right leg up to touch the wall. The torso becomes vertical as you quickly bring the left leg up to touch the right on the wall.

HOLDING THE POSE

1 With the feet together, stretch the legs and inner thighs straight up. Move the upper spine into the body opening the chest on the inhalation.

2 Extend the shoulders, torso, legs and feet upward on every exhalation. Remain in the pose as is appropriate for your dosha.

COMPLETING THE POSE

On an exhalation, bring the left leg straight down to the floor quickly followed by the right. Bend the knees and sit on the heels in Basic Virasana Pose.

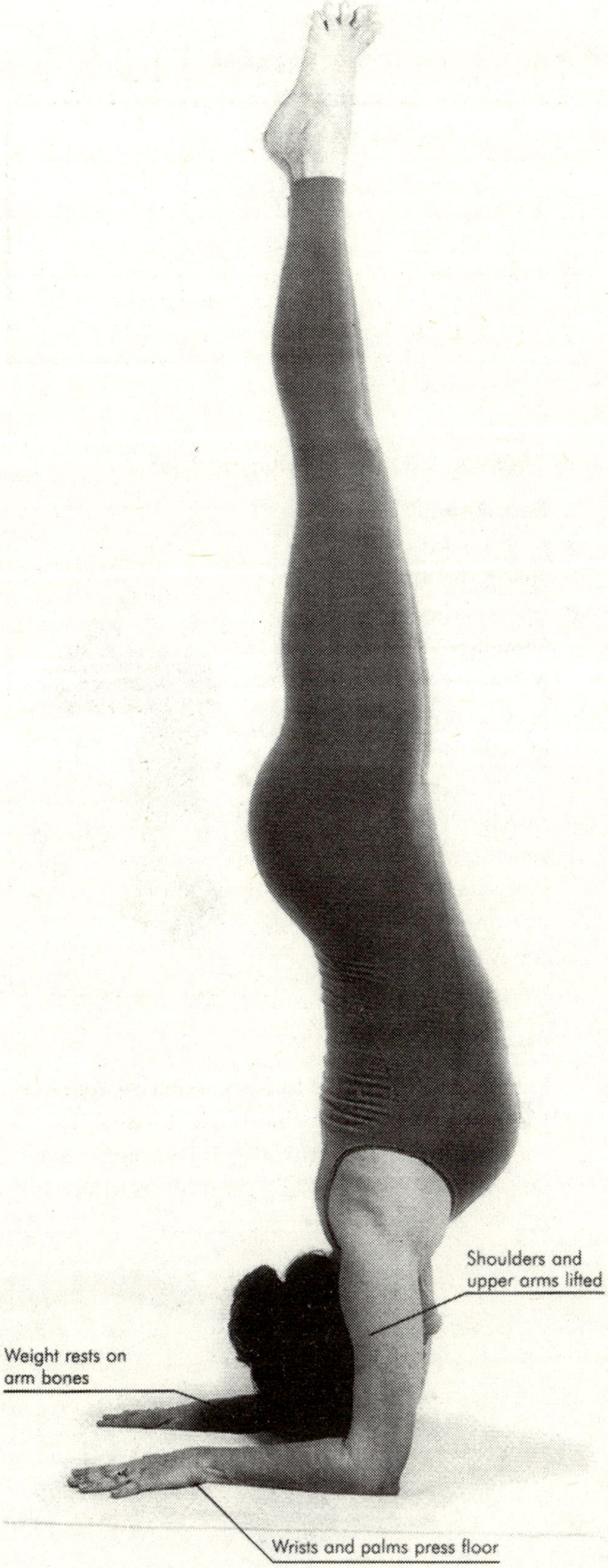

LEARNING AT HOME: MODIFICATIONS

• ARMS VARIATION: This variation may be easier for beginners. Work in a corner. Make an equilateral triangle of the arms with a straight line from fingers to elbows (see arms in Preparation for Headstand, pg 112. Continue as above using these arms.

• PROPS: Use a block or a thick book the length of your forearms to brace your hands against. This will help you keep the hands from sliding together.

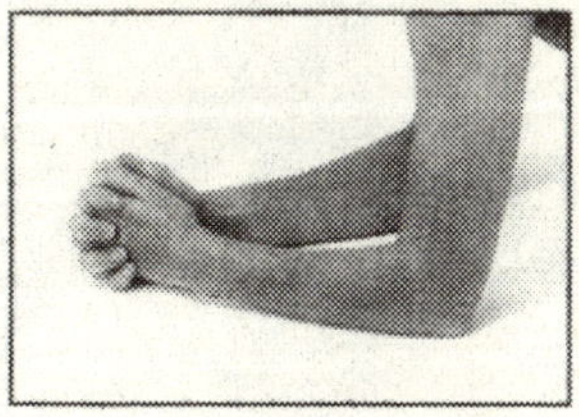

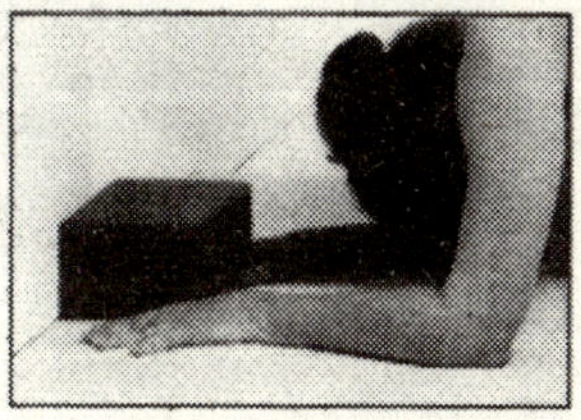

GENERAL PRECAUTIONS

Those with elbow or shoulder problems should consult an experienced teacher and a physician.

IMPORTANT ACTIONS

- The front lower ribs move back as armpits open forward
- Spine is lifting
- Extend through the inner legs and feet
- Press the hands and wrists into the floor

Sirsasana

HEADSTAND

	VATA ↓↓↓	PITTA ↑↑↑	KAPHA ↓↓↓
TIME	Moderate holds	Shorter holds – no strain	Long holds with repetitions
BREATH	Smooth and full	Easy, full breath	Smooth or Ujjayi
FOCUS	Stable and still, balanced	Lightness and lift	Strong extension, balance
MOVE	Strengthen arms, lift shoulders, torso, and legs; wall is helpful	Strengthen arms, extend shoulders and torso up, balance; wall is helpful	Strengthen arms, lift shoulders, torso, and legs as much as possible

PREPARING

1 Use the wall or a corner until you are stable. See Preparation for Headstand, pg 112. Interlock the fingers and make an equilateral triangle so there is a straight line from fingers to elbows. Move the flesh of the forearm to the center of the triangle and rest firmly on the bones of the forearms. The elbows are under the shoulder joints—not wider. Keep the wrists vertically pinned to the floor and distribute the weight between the wrists and forearms.

2 Inhale and push the forearms and wrists against the floor. Exhale and tiptoe the straight legs in toward you as far as possible until the upper body is vertical. The shoulders keep lifting.

3 Place your head (halfway between the crown and forehead) onto the floor with the back of the head touching the hands but not pressing them open. Inhale.

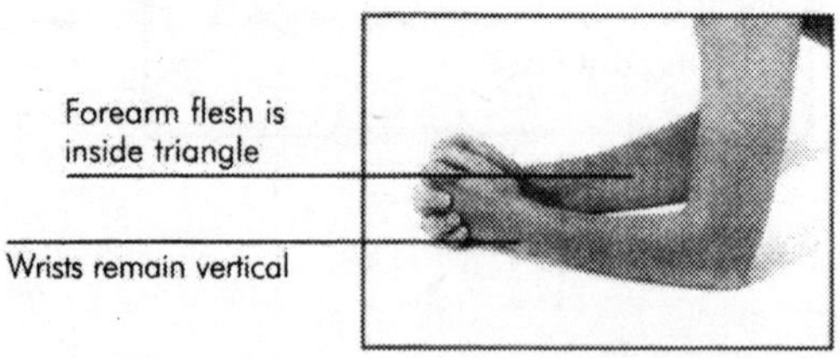

TWO WAYS TO MOVE INTO THE POSE

Bent knees: Exhale, bend the knees and swing the legs gently up over the hips and shoulders. Inhale. Balance with the knees bent before straightening the legs. Exhale and straighten the legs slowly. Beginners keep touching the wall as you straighten the legs one at a time up the wall. Find your balance in the pose.

Straight legs:
Exhale, walking in as far as possible so that the torso is vertical. Shift the weight toward the back body and push through the straight legs and heels to raise the legs straight up to vertical.

HOLDING THE POSE

1 Separate the legs 6". Exhale and extend the inner legs upward. Hold that extension as you close the legs together.

2 Inhale and keep the majority of your weight evenly distributed between the wrists, forearms, and elbows. With each exhalation, lift the shoulders, torso, lower back and legs. Hold for 30-60 seconds to begin.

COMPLETING THE POSE

As you exhale, lower the legs back the same way you lifted them. Keep the shoulders and back lifted as you bring the legs down. Sit back on the heels into Child's Pose (pg 61) to rest.

Note: The Shoulderstand will soften the energy created in headstand and should follow it.

IMPORTANT ACTIONS

- Keep wrists vertically pinned to the floor
- Ears and eyes are level with each other
- Keep the bottom ribs pulled in
- Open the armpits and chest
- Low back remains in 'Neutral'
- Inner legs are lifting
- Push up through balls of feet

GENERAL PRECAUTIONS

- *Practice 2 hours or more after eating.*
- *Not good for high blood pressure, heart problems or eye problems.*
- *If you feel pressure in the neck, eyes or head, stop and talk with a teacher.*
- *Practice this pose after you are proficient in Shoulderstand and Preparation for Headstand.*

DOSHIC NOTES

Kapha: Excellent for lowering Kapha. Excess body weight should not be put on the neck or head. Work with Preparation for Headstand first.

LEARNING AT HOME: MODIFICATIONS

- Beginners should practice Preparation to Headstand for 1-3 months first. Use the wall or corner with hands about 6-8" from the wall so your feet can touch.
- PROPS: The upper arms can be belted (not always) to hold the elbow position.

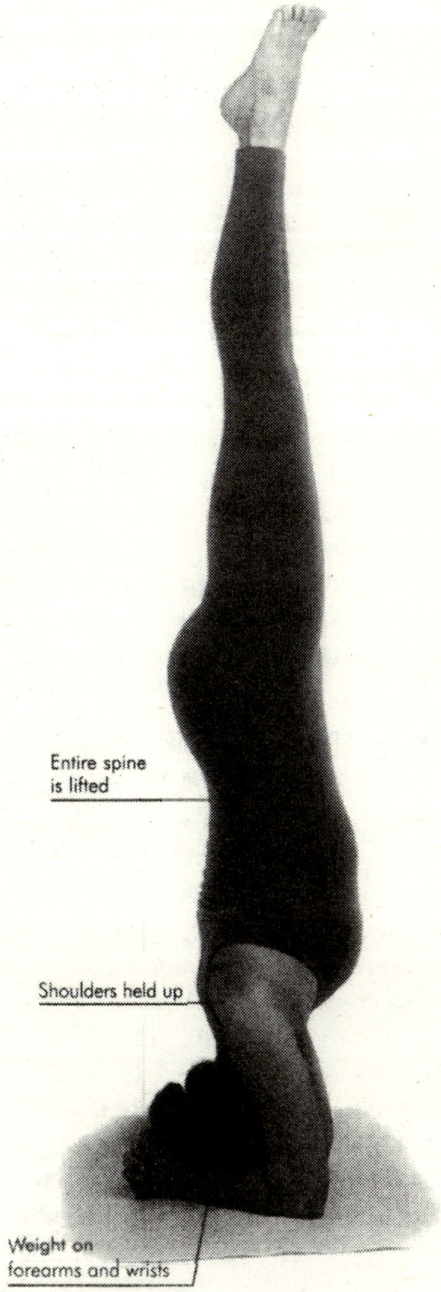

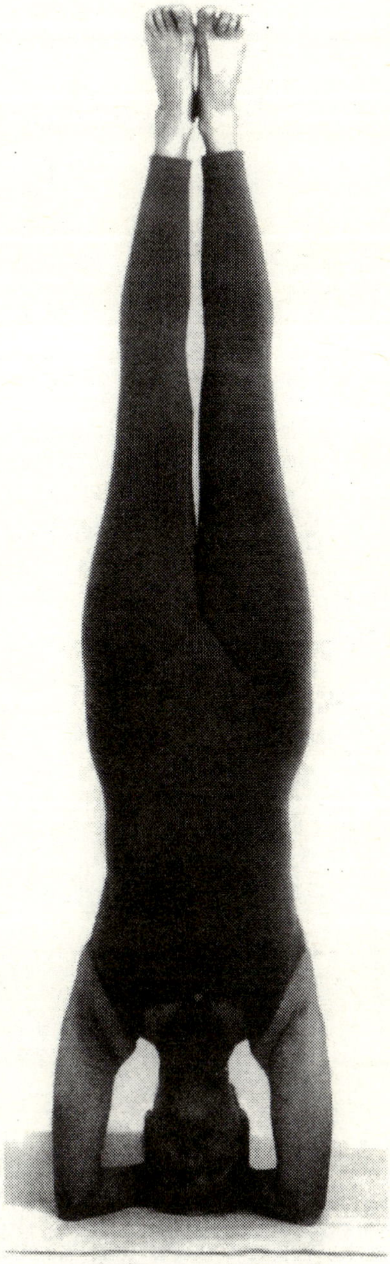

Two Sirsasana Variations

TWO HEADSTAND VARIATIONS

	VATA ↓↓↓	PITTA ↑↑↑	KAPHA ↓↓↓
TIME	Moderate holds	Short holds – no strain	Long holds with repetitions
BREATH	Smooth and full	Easy, full breath	Any breath
FOCUS	Grounded balance	Lightness and lift	Strong extension, balance
MOVE	Lifting the shoulders and spine, extending through legs and feet	Lifting the shoulders and spine, extending through legs and feet	Maximum lift of shoulders, chest, tailbone, and legs

Note: Remain in Sirsasana for 5 minutes before practicing variations.

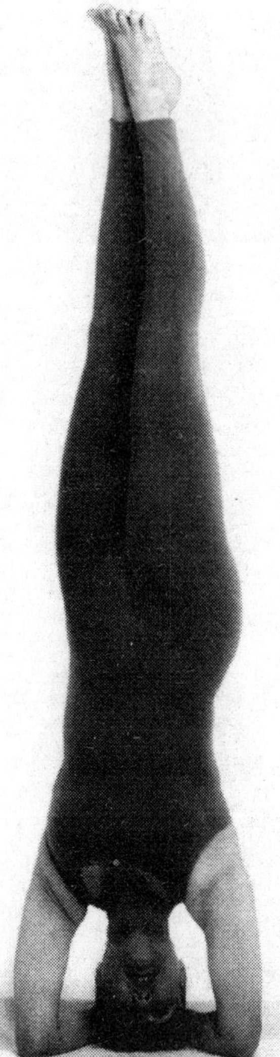

1 PARSVA SIRSASANA: *Rotated Legs in Headstand*

Hold your torso vertical as you rotate your spine, hips and legs to the right— a little more with every exhalation. As you inhale hold your rotation, and focus your attention on balance and grounding. When you can no longer rotate, hold for 20 seconds (to begin). Inhale and return to center. Establish Headstand before repeating on the other side.

2 PARIVRTTAIKA PADA SIRSASANA: *Rotated Open Legs in Headstand*

Holding the spine erect in Sirsasana, exhale and scissor open the legs, right leg forward and left leg back. Keep the legs straight and evenly open. Inhale focusing on holding your foundation (arms, shoulders, wrists etc.). Exhale as you rotate your hips and straight, opened legs to the right. Hold for 5 to 20 seconds to begin. Inhale and rotate back to center. Exhale as you close your legs back into headstand. Establish Headstand before repeating on the other side.

GENERAL PRECAUTIONS

Those with spinal disc problems should avoid these positions.

Viparita Karani

SPECIAL INVERSION

	VATA ↓↓↓	PITTA ↓↓	KAPHA ↓
TIME	Long holding	Long holding	Moderate or short holding times
BREATH	Natural relaxed	Natural relaxed	Natural relaxed
FOCUS	Stillness and inner quiet	Easy relaxation	Restful practice
MOVE	Hold strong legs, relax upper body	Release and relax upper body	Hold strong legs, relax upper body

MOVING INTO THE POSE

Place 4-6 folded blankets or a bolster (depending on your size) at the wall to support your hips. Place two other blankets in front of those to support your shoulders. Sit sideways on the edge of the blankets with the sitting bones on the wall. Use your hands to roll yourself onto your back, on the blankets. Your sitting bones should touch the wall. Straighten your legs vertically up the wall. Relax your upper body.

IMPORTANT ACTIONS

- Eyes are closed and relaxed
- Legs straighten up the wall
- Lengthen the neck
- Relax the face, jaw, and shoulders

HOLDING THE POSE

The arms are comfortably out to the sides or overhead—palms up. Close your eyes, breathe, and rest completely.

COMPLETING THE POSE

Bend your knees and push your feet against the wall to slide the body away from the wall. Then turn on to the right side and use your arms to push yourself up to sitting.

LEARNING AT HOME: MODIFICATIONS

Place a small soft neck roll under your neck if you have any neck strain. Using fewer blankets to reduce height may also ease your neck.

GENERAL PRECAUTIONS

- *Practice Inversions on an empty stomach, 2 hours or more after eating.*
- *This pose is contraindicated (as are all inversions) for glaucoma and other eye disorders and during menses.*
- *Check with a physician before practicing this pose if you have uncontrolled hypertension*

BACKBENDS

PATRICIA WALDEN IN PADANGUSTHASANA DHANURASANA

Back Vinyasa

MOVEMENT SERIES FOR THE BACK

	VATA ↓	PITTA ↓↓	KAPHA ↓↓
TIME	Fewer repetitions	Repetitions as comfortable	More repetitions
BREATH	Smooth and even, or Ujjayi	Even and slow or Ujjayi	Long, smooth breath or Ujjayi
FOCUS	Stable grounding, lengthen breath	Move as you breathe	Lengthening to lift
MOVE	Shoulders down, lift back of knees	Lifts on exhalations, buttocks tight	Maximum lift and extension

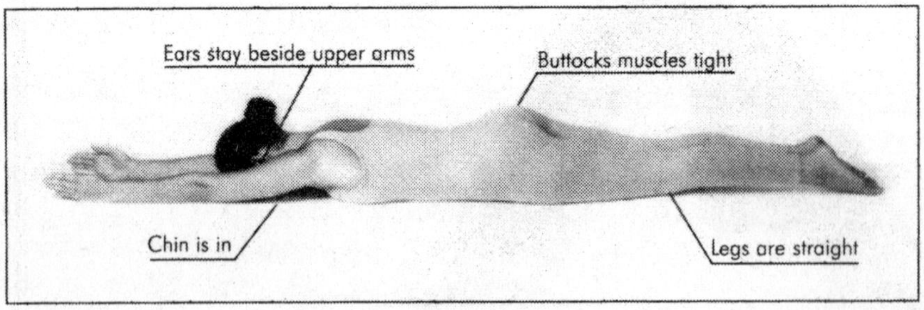

IMPORTANT ACTIONS

- Lift from the back of the knee
- Hold Neutral and keep the tailbone pressing down
- Open the chest as you lift
- Shoulders are back and down
- Arms and back of neck are lengthened
- Coordinate the movement with the breath so they take the same amount of time

BASIC POSITION & BREATH

Lie face down on the floor with the legs together and the tops of the feet on the floor. Tighten the buttocks and the backs of the legs. Stretch the arms forward along the floor, lengthening from the shoulders out through the fingers. Note: The exhalation is for the most difficult work, the lifting. The inhalation is used for receiving Pranic energy—use during the more passive movements (as when lowering).

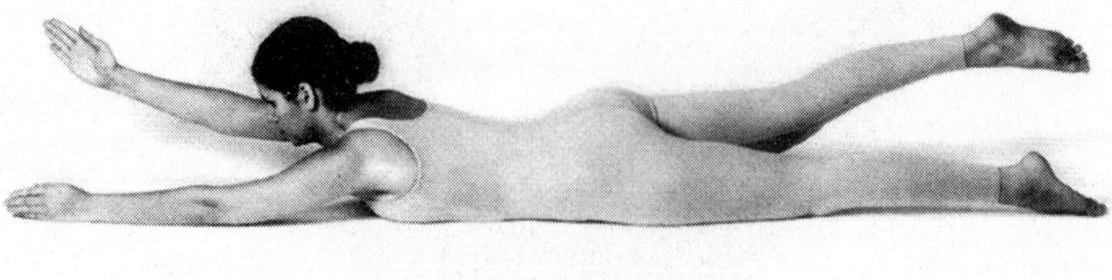

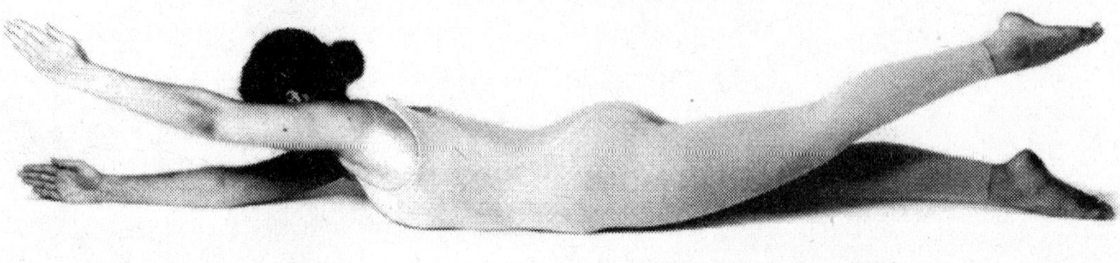

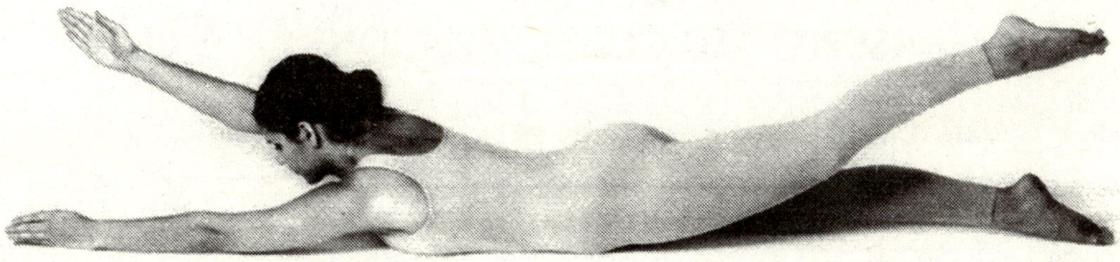

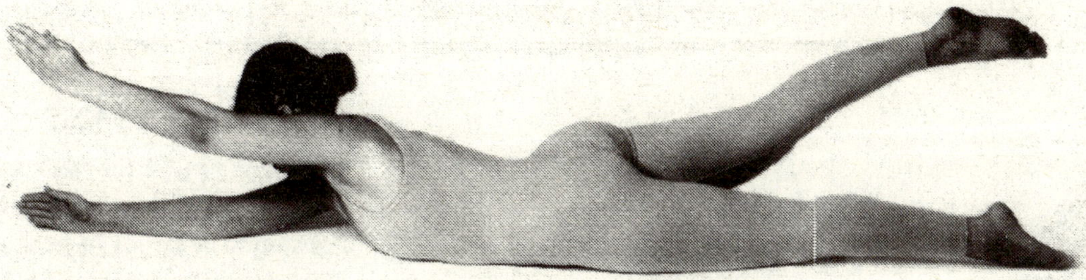

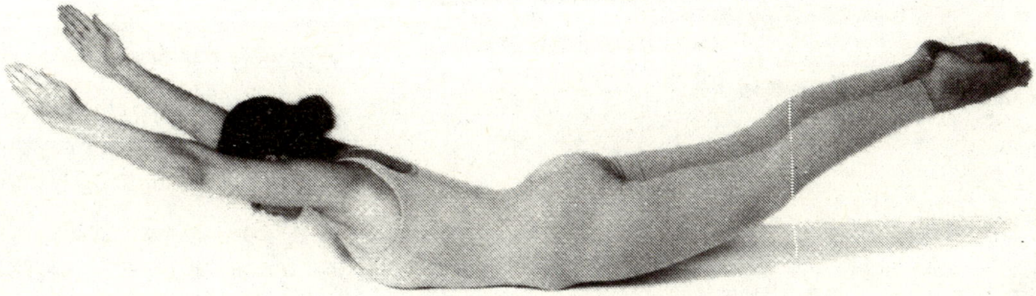

MOVEMENT AND BREATH

1 Exhale as you lift your right side: arm, head, shoulder, leg and foot up. Keep your arms and legs straight and extended. The head always remains beside the moving arm. Slow your movement so you move for the length of each breath.

2 Inhale as you slowly lower your right side to the floor.

3 Exhale as you slowly lift your left side (arm, head and leg).

4 Inhale as you slowly lower the left side to the floor.

5 Exhale as you slowly lift the right arm and left leg.

6 Inhale as you slowly lower the right arm and left leg.

7 Exhale as you slowly lift the left arm and right leg.

8 Inhale as you slowly lower the left arm and right leg.

9 Exhale as you slowly lift everything up: arms, head, shoulders, and legs. Take 3 long, smooth breaths holding this position, then slowly lower to the floor on your fourth inhalation.

COMPLETING THE POSE

Turn your head to the side and relax completely or move into Child's Pose sitting on your heels to rest.

Niralamba Bhujangasana I, II & III

UNSUPPORTED COBRA VARIATIONS I, II & III

	VATA ↑ or ↓	PITTA ↓	KAPHA ↓
TIME	Short holds	Moderate holds - no strain	Long holds with repetitions
BREATH	Even, slow breath or Ujjayi	Smooth, even breath or Ujjayi	Normal or Ujjayi
FOCUS	Holding still and strong	Light lifting and smooth breath	Strengthening and working the pose
MOVE	Hold grounded legs, lift upper torso	Grow upward from strong foundation	Maximum grounding and lift

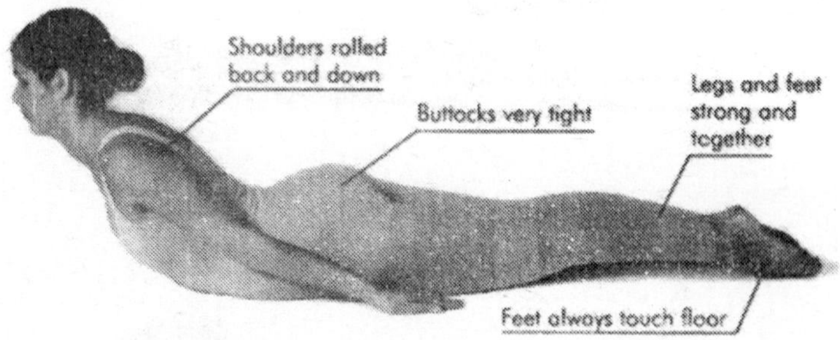

Unsupported Cobra Variation I - Arms Back

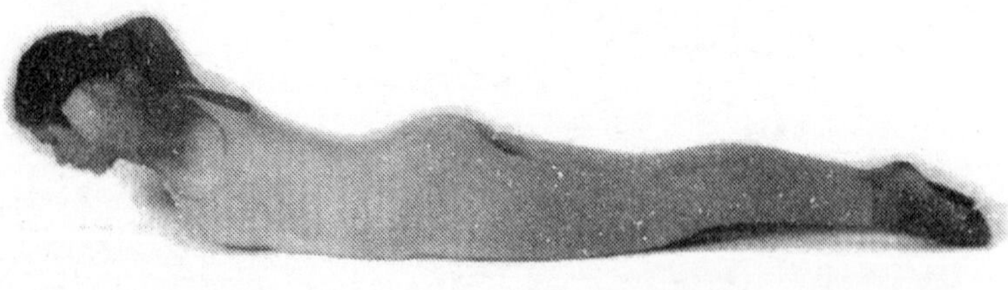

Unsupported Cobra Variation II - Pressing the Head Into the Hands

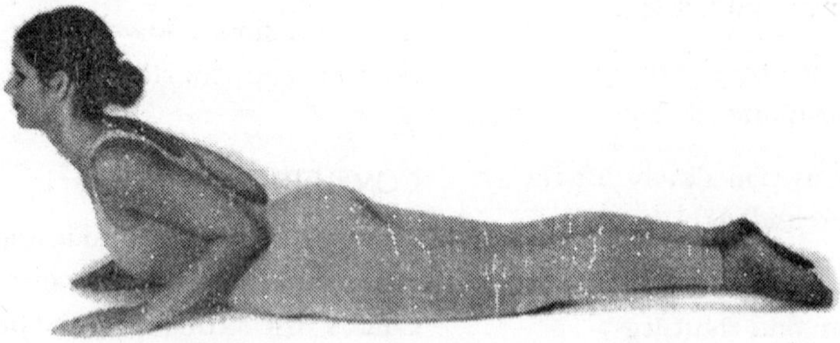

Unsupported Cobra Variation III - No Weight on the Hands

MOVING INTO THE POSE

Lie face down on the floor with the legs together. Begin with the forehead on the floor and the hands in position I, II, or III. Tighten the buttocks and leg muscles, pressing the tops of the feet onto the floor. Lift the face, draw the shoulders back, lift the head and shoulders.

HOLDING THE POSE

1 For III, keep the elbows bent close to the body. There is never any weight on the hands in this variation. Breathe.

2 With every inhalation focus on the foundation points on photo. On every exhalation strengthen the Important Actions list. Hold for 20-30 seconds to begin. Gradually increase the time.

COMPLETING THE POSE

Slowly unroll the spine down, lengthening the front body forward. Relax. Practice these three back strengthening Cobra variations for one month before continuing on to more difficult backbending.

IMPORTANT ACTIONS

- Tailbone presses down
- Extend spine upward arching upper back
- Open the chest
- Chin held in

Salabhasana I, II & III

LOCUST VARIATIONS I, II & III

	VATA ↑ or ↓	PITTA ↑ or ↓	KAPHA ↓↓
TIME	Short holds	Short holds repeat as desired	Long holds with repetitions
BREATH	Even, slow breath or light Ujjayi	Smooth, even breath or Ujjayi	Normal or Ujjayi
FOCUS	Core strength and stillness	Strong foundation, easy lift	Strengthening and working
MOVE	Ground, extend up and hold	Easing up on each exhalation	Maximum lift and extension

MOVING INTO THE POSE

1 Lie face down on the floor with the legs and feet together, forehead touching the floor. Place arms in position I, II, or III. As you inhale, tighten the buttocks and legs and press the tailbone toward the floor. Keep the legs and feet touching.

2 On the exhalation: Locust I lifts the face, draws the shoulders back, and lifts the head, arms, shoulders, and legs up. Locust II lifts the legs up by lifting from the back of the knees. Locust III: Lift the front thighs up off the floor.

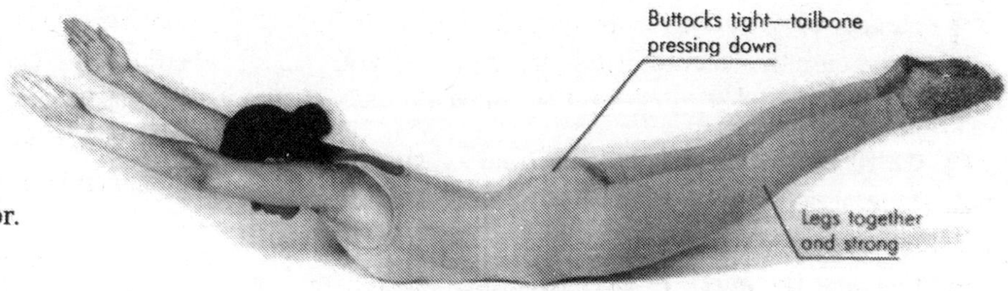

Locust Variation I: Fully Extended and Lifted Arms and Legs

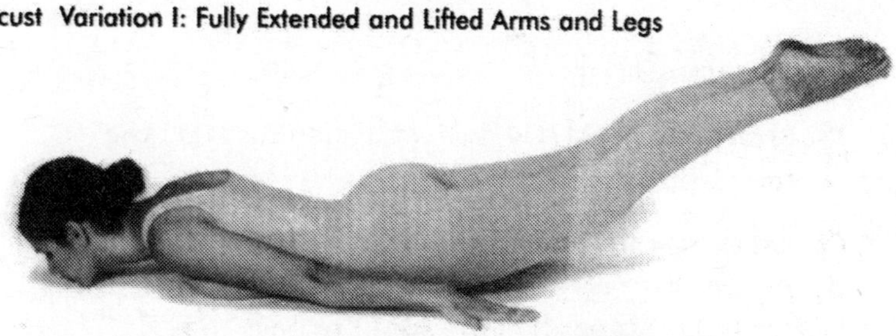

Locust Variation II: Legs Only Lift

HOLDING THE POSE

On every inhalation receive the breath. On every exhalation, tighten the buttocks even more and extend legs out through the feet. Hold this position for 20-30 seconds to begin.

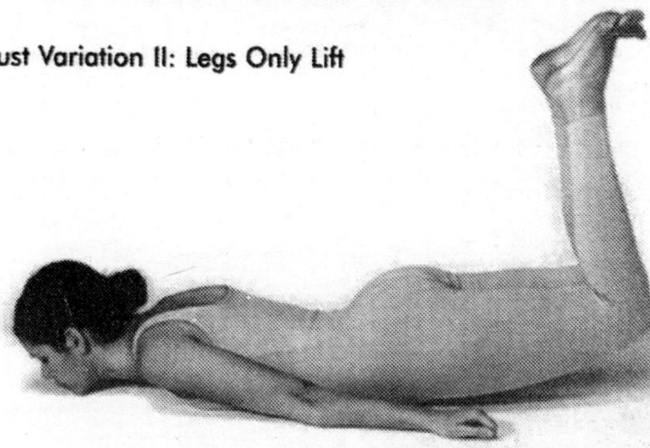

Locust Variation III: Legs Only Lift - Bent Knees

COMPLETING THE POSE

As you exhale, lengthen along the floor to come down. Relax.

GENERAL PRECAUTIONS

If there is existing back pain consult a physician or yoga therapist.

Makarasana

LOCUST VARIATION

	VATA ↑ or ↓	PITTA ↑ or ↓	KAPHA ↓↓
TIME	Moderate holds	Short to moderate holds - no strain	Long holds with repetitions
BREATH	Smooth, slow breathing or Ujjayi	Even smooth breath or light Ujjayi	Any breath
FOCUS	Holding still and breathing evenly	Breath and lightness	Strengthening and lifting
MOVE	Extend and hold, solid grounding	Light lifting from strong foundation	Maximum lift and extension

MOVING INTO THE POSE

1 Lie face down on the floor with the legs together. Hands are interlocked behind the head. As you inhale, tighten the buttocks and leg muscles.

2 On the exhalation draw the shoulders and elbows back and lift the head, elbows, shoulders and straight legs up. Keep the elbows wide and push the head against the hands to strengthen the back of the neck.

HOLDING THE POSE

1 Breathe and hold. On each inhalation focus on the foundation points.

2 On every exhalation focus on the Important Actions list. Keep the head and feet at the same height. Hold this position for 20-30 seconds to begin.

COMPLETING THE POSE

On an exhale, unroll the front body down to the floor as you lower the legs. Relax.

LEARNING AT HOME: MODIFICATIONS

Another way to practice this pose is with the knees bent, lifting the thighs as in Locust Variation III, page 127. Make sure that the tailbone is always pressing down and that the buttocks muscles remain tight while bending the legs.

GENERAL PRECAUTIONS

If there is existing back pain, consult a physician and yoga therapist before working this pose.

IMPORTANT ACTIONS

- Tailbone is always moving down
- Backs of the knees lift
- Shoulders move back and down
- Chest is open

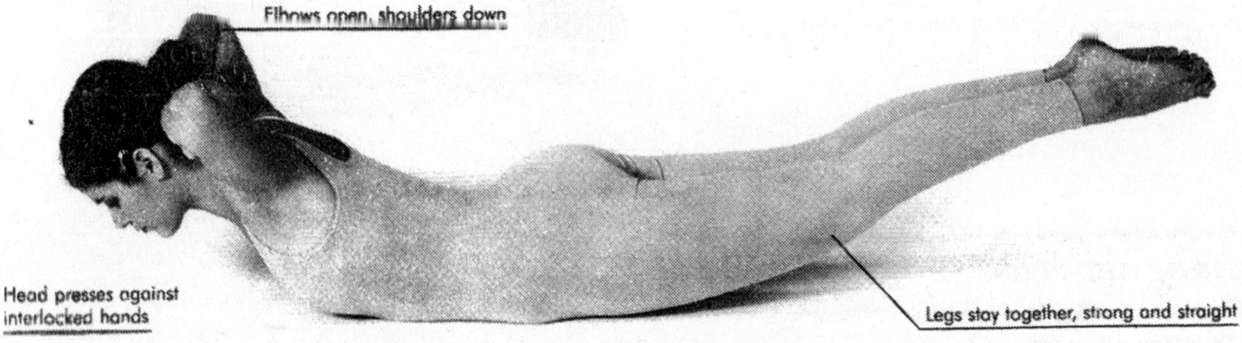

Dhanurasana

BOW POSE

	VATA ↑↑	PITTA ↑ or ↓	KAPHA ↓↓↓
TIME	Short holds	Short holds with repititons – no strain	Long holds with repetitions
BREATH	Smooth, even breath or Ujjayi	Even, smooth breath or light Ujjayi	Normal or Ujjayi
FOCUS	Strong, quiet holding	Light lifting from strong foundation	Open chest, lift legs
MOVE	Hold Neutral Spine, lift the legs	Lift legs and open chest	Straighten the legs and lift spine

MOVING INTO THE POSE

1 Lie face down with the legs together and tailbone pressed down. Continuously hold tightened buttocks muscles. As you inhale, bend both knees and take hold of the ankles with your hands, keeping the arms straight. Keep the legs together.

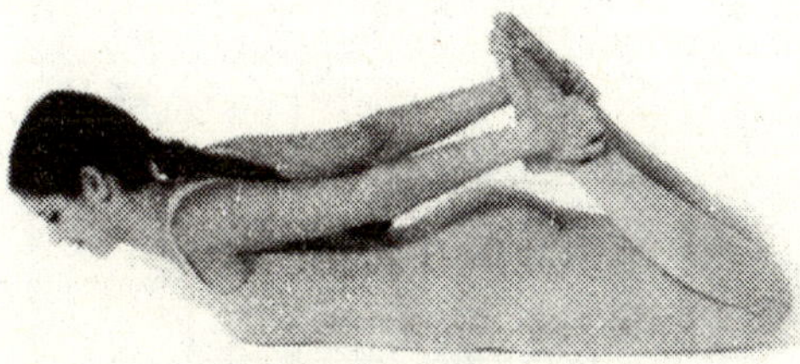

2 On the exhalation lift the feet toward the ceiling. If you try to straighten your knees as you lift, your thighs, chest and back will move upward. Remember, keep the buttocks strong, knees 4-6" apart, and press tailbone down to hold 'Neutral.'

HOLDING THE POSE

1 Breathe and hold. On each inhalation remember your alignment.

2 On every exhalation lift the spine and legs upward. Hold 10-30 seconds to begin.

COMPLETING THE POSE

As you exhale release the ankles and bring the body down to the floor. Turn the head to the side and relax.

IMPORTANT ACTIONS

- Spine moves into the back to open chest
- Tailbone is pressing down
- Feet are stretching upward
- Shoulders pulled back and down

LEARNING AT HOME: MODIFICATIONS

In the beginning work with Pelvic Tilts to increase the low back awareness and strength. Work with bridge pose, cobras, and locusts to prepare the back for this pose.

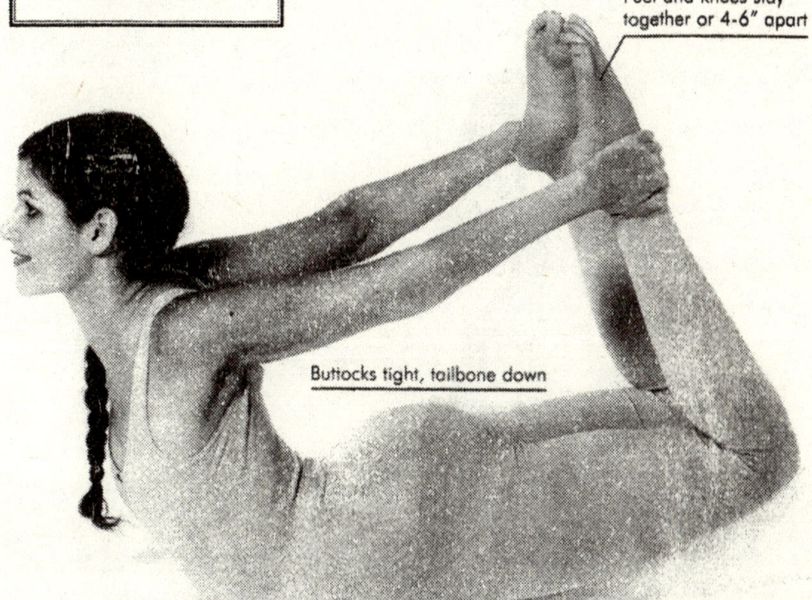

GENERAL PRECAUTIONS

If you experience discomfort, consult a therapist and recheck your technique for back, knees, and feet.

Bhujangasana

FULL COBRA POSE

	VATA ↑	PITTA ↑ or ↓	KAPHA ↓↓↓
TIME	Short holds	Easy holds and repetitions	Long holding with repetitions
BREATH	Long, smooth breath or Ujjayi	Smooth, even breath or Ujjayi	Long, smooth, even, or Ujjayi
FOCUS	Core strength and stillness	Spine rising on breath	Strengthening and working
MOVE	Strong legs, strong lift, even breath	Strong grounding, easy lift	Maximum grounding, lift and extension

MOVING INTO THE POSE

1 Lie face down with the legs together, tops of the feet on the floor. The forehead is on the floor with the hands under the shoulders (fingers facing forward) and the elbows close to the body. As you inhale tighten the buttocks and legs, and press the tailbone down.

2 As you exhale, draw your shoulders back and lift your upper body as if you are standing on your tailbone. Keep the legs and buttocks strong at all times. Arms stay close to the body.

HOLDING THE POSE

1 Breathe and hold the pose. On each inhalation strengthen the buttocks and legs.

2 On each exhalation focus on the Important Actions list. Hold for 20-30 seconds to begin.

IMPORTANT ACTIONS

- Legs strong, together, and straight
- Tailbone presses down
- Extend up to arch thoracic spine
- Chest is open

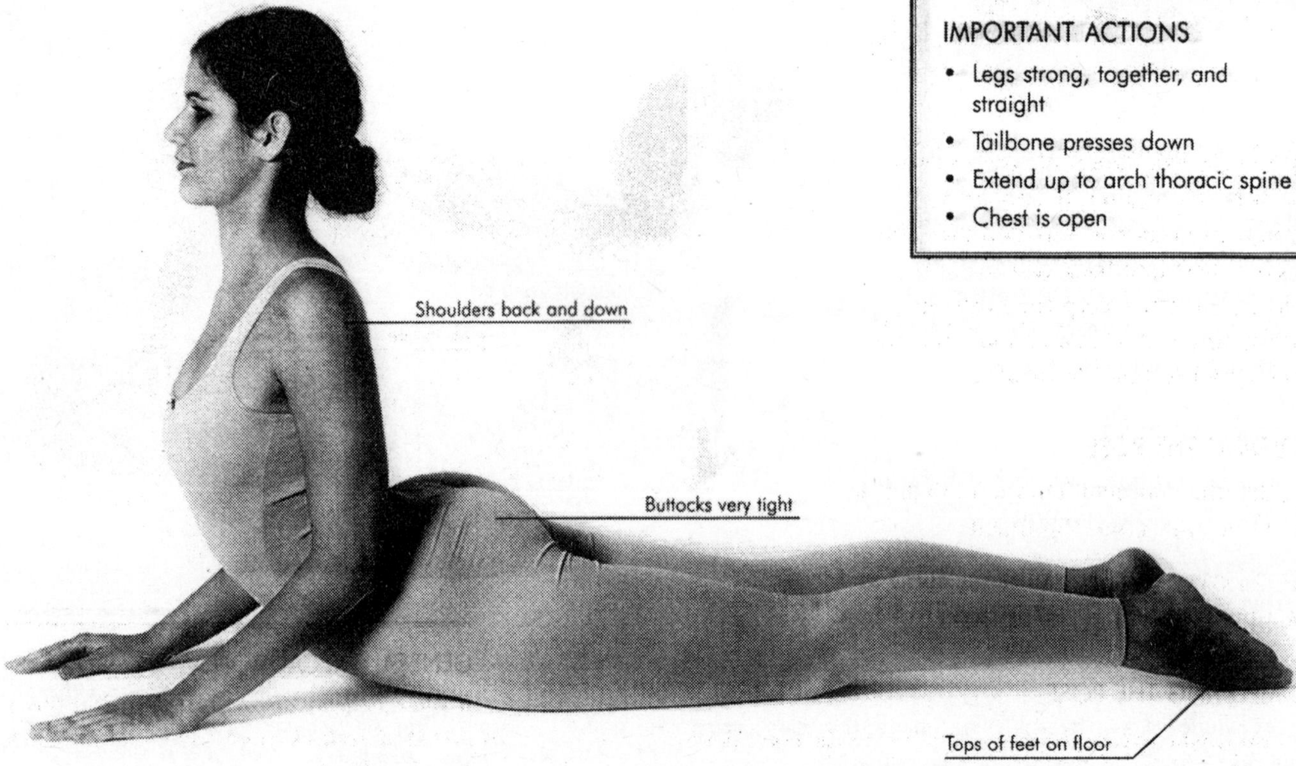

COMPLETING THE POSE

Keep the buttocks tight and the lower back in neutral as you exhale and lower the front body forward and down to the floor, lengthening the spine. Relax

LEARNING AT HOME: MODIFICATIONS

After a firm practice of this pose has been established, gradually move the hands back 2-6" toward the waist for a more advanced practice.

GENERAL PRECAUTIONS

- *If there is existing back pain, consult a physician and yoga therapist.*
- *Prepare the body with cobra variations I-III.*

Note: *There should be no sensation of any kind in the lower back. If there is, come down immediately and redouble your efforts to press your tailbone down and tighten your buttocks.*

Urdhva Dhanurasana

UPWARD BOW POSE

	VATA ↑↑↑	PITTA ↑ or ↓	KAPHA ↓↓↓
TIME	Short, easy, gentle holds	Short, easy holds with repetitions	Long holds with repetitions
BREATH	Smooth, even breath or Ujjayi	Even, easy breath	Normal breath
FOCUS	Strong grounding and holding still	Ease of action – quiet holding	Strengthening and opening
MOVE	Maintain tight buttocks and strong legs	Strong legs and arms, lift and open upper spine	Strong legs and arms, maximum spinal extension and lift

MOVING INTO THE POSE

1 Lie on your back with your knees slightly bent, feet pigeon-toed, hip distance apart and close to your buttocks. Bend the elbows and place palms under the shoulders, hands firmly on floor, fingers spread and facing feet. As you inhale tighten the buttocks and hold the spine in neutral.

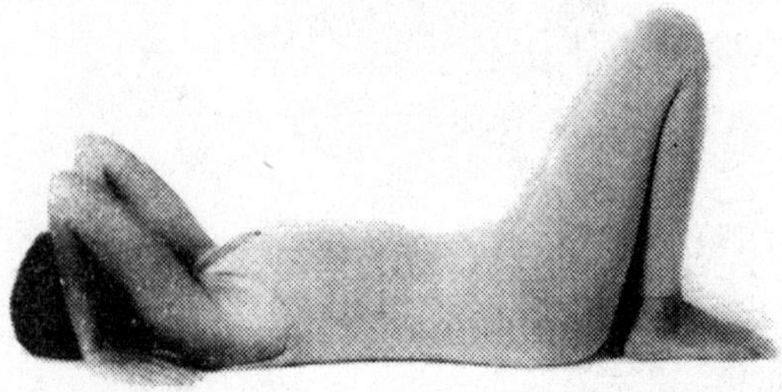

2 On an exhalation lift the tailbone up, pushing evenly with the arms and legs until the arms are straight.

HOLDING THE POSE

1 On each inhalation focus on the foundation points, strengthen the legs, and hold the lower back in Neutral.

2 On every exhalation focus on all Important Actions. Open the shoulders and chest, tighten the buttocks and extend the spine upward.

COMPLETING THE POSE

As you exhale, bend the arms and legs and bring the back down to the floor (maintain a neutral spine as you lower). Relax.

LEARNING AT HOME: MODIFICATIONS

Work with Pelvic Tilts to increase low back awareness and strength. Work with Bridge, all Cobra variations, Makarasana, Locust variations, and Bow to prepare the back, legs, and arms for this pose.

IMPORTANT ACTIONS

- Roll outsides of knees up and in
- Lengthen arms and shoulders
- Lift armpits and chest forward
- Tailbone always lifts

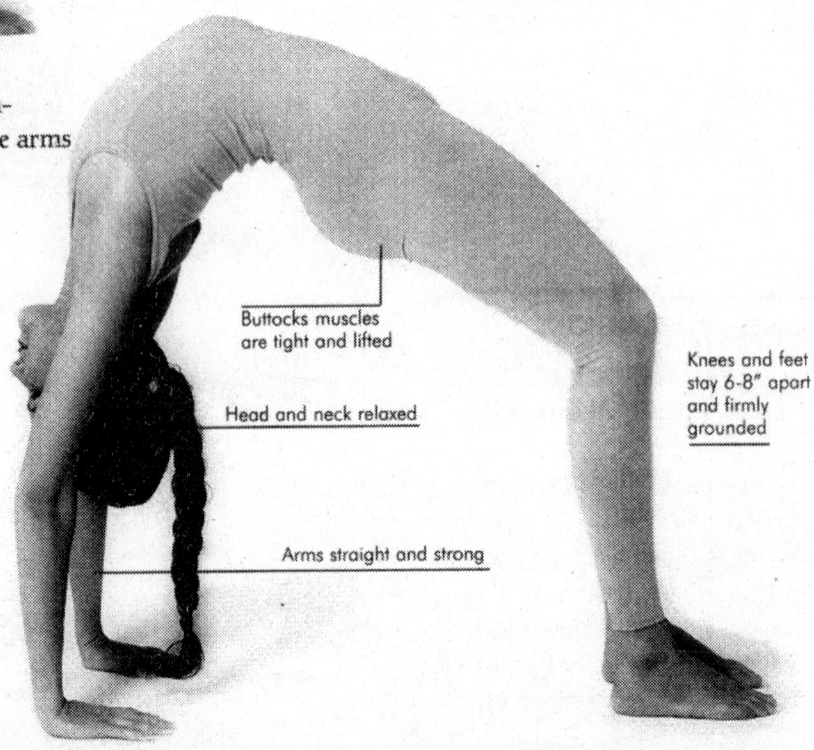

Eka Pada Urdhva Dhanurasana

UPWARD BOW ONE LEG EXTENDED POSE

VATA ↑↑↑ PITTA ↑↑ KAPHA ↓↓↓

MOVING INTO THE POSE

Exhale and come up into Urdhva Dhanurasana, pg 132. Inhale and ground the feet and hands firmly on the floor. Bring the weight onto the right leg. Exhale as you bend the left leg bringing the knee up toward the chest. Inhale. Hold the hips level as you exhale and straighten the left leg.

IMPORTANT ACTIONS

- Hands firmly on floor, fingers spread
- Roll the outsides of the standing leg knee up and in
- Buttocks muscles tight
- Lengthen arms and shoulders
- Keep lifting the left hip to support the extended left leg
- Hold hips level
- Extend through the ball of the foot

HOLDING THE POSE

1 On each inhalation focus on the Foundation Points. Strengthen the arms and tighten the buttocks.

2 On every exhalation focus on the Important Actions list.

COMPLETING THE POSE

Come back to Urdhva Dhanurasana by bending the left knee toward the chest and placing the foot on the floor. Keep the lower back in Neutral as you come down. Repeat on the other side.

LEARNING AT HOME: MODIFICATIONS

See Urdhva Dhanurasana

GENERAL PRECAUTIONS

- *This pose is not appropriate for high blood pressure, glaucoma, back or neck pain, or Vata provocation.*
- *Remember to keep the buttocks strong and tailbone lifting.*
- *Prepare the body with other poses first.*

Eka Pada Rajakapotasana

PIGEON POSE STRETCH

	VATA ↑↑	PITTA ↑↑ or ↓	KAPHA ↓↓↓
TIME	Short–moderate holds	Any holding time–no strain	Moderate–long holds with repetitions
BREATH	Slow, even breath	Smooth, even breath	Normal
FOCUS	Remaining still – quiet holds	Opening upward and breath	Strengthen spine, open chest
MOVE	Hold grounding and extend spine	Lifting from firm grounding	Maximum extension and stretch

MOVING INTO THE POSE

1 From Dog Pose (pg 100) inhale, bend the right knee and bring it forward between the hands. Exhale and stretch the left thigh back, placing the left knee and leg down on the floor. Inhale, lay the right leg down on the floor so the knee is facing the right and the down heel is close to the left groin.

2 Exhale, and lengthen the front of the left leg back along the floor. The torso remains straight and tall.

HOLDING THE POSE

Pigeon Stretch – Level I

When you feel balanced, take the hands to your waist. Exhale and press the tailbone down as you draw the spine up and into the body opening the chest. Hold 20-30 seconds to begin.

Pigeon Stretch – Level II

From Pigeon Stretch Level I, inhale and bend the left leg. Exhale and take hold of the left foot or ankle with the left hand. Hold the tailbone down as you take the right hand back to hold the ankle. Hold 20-30 seconds to begin.

Pigeon Stretch – Level II

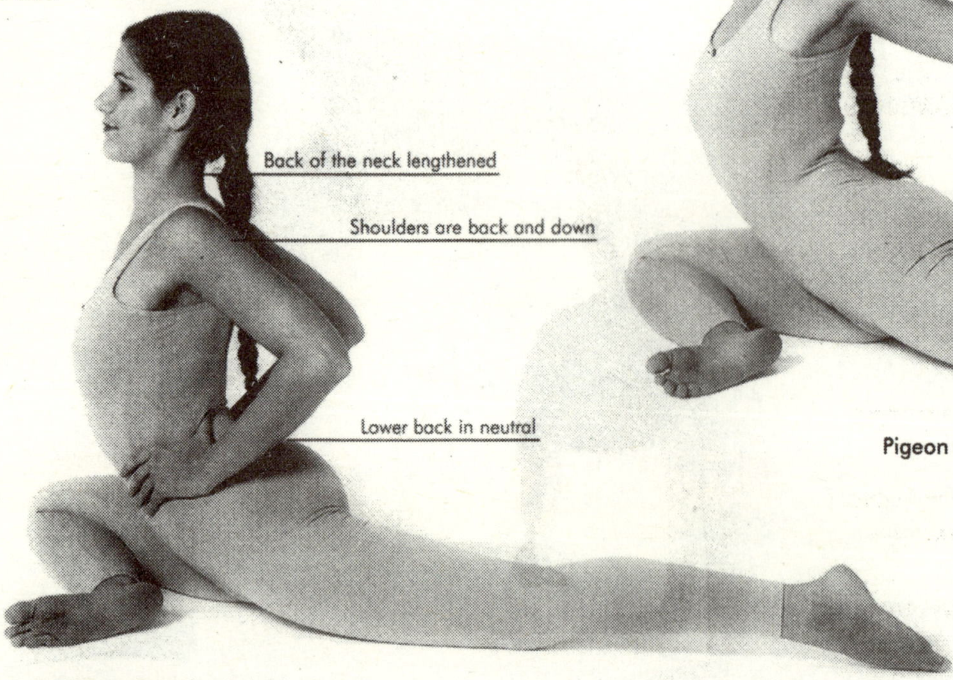

Pigeon Stretch – Level I

Eka Pada Rajakapotasana I

PIGEON POSE I

MOVING INTO THE POSE

Practice this pose after warming up with the Level I and II preparatory poses for some time.

1 Place the hands back on the floor, bend the left knee, tighten the left buttocks, and bring the foot up to face the ceiling (perpendicular to the floor). Exhale as you stretch the right arm up and back and take hold of the left foot. Breathe. Exhale as you stretch the left arm up and back to take hold of the foot.

2 Push the thorasic spine forward to expand the chest and bring the elbows back. Keep the left buttocks tight with the front hip bones lifting. Breathe as normally as possible. Hold for 5-10 seconds to begin.

IMPORTANT ACTIONS

- Lengthen the back thigh along the floor
- Open the armpits and chest
- Thoracic spine arches upward
- Keep tailbone down

COMPLETING THE POSE

1 Release the ankle and place your hands back on the floor. Rest for a while.

2 Push yourself back up into Dog Pose and then repeat to the other side. After both sides have been completed, rest in Child's Pose.

Dwi Pada Viparita Dandasana

INVERTED ARCH POSE

	VATA ↑↑	PITTA ↑↑	KAPHA ↓↓↓
TIME	Short holds	Short holds without strain	Long holds with repetitions
BREATH	Smooth, even breath	Even, smooth breath	Normal
FOCUS	Strong grounding and quiet holding	Easy lifting from strong foundation	Lifting upward
MOVE	Strong legs, buttocks, arms, and shoulders. Lift thoracic spine	Maximum support in arms, shoulders, and legs for thoracic lift and chest expansion	Maximum support in arms, shoulders and legs for lift. Strengthen spine and open chest

MOVING INTO THE POSE

1 Lie on the back with the knees bent, feet hip distance apart, close to the buttocks. Bend the elbows and place the palms down under the shoulders. As you inhale, tighten the buttocks, holding the spine in Neutral.

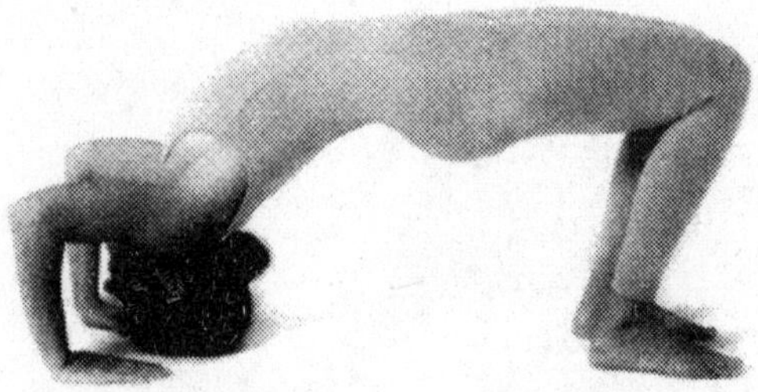

2 As you exhale, push up with the arms and legs and place the top of the head on the floor. Place the forearms, wrists, and interlocked hands on the floor. Bring the elbows in and make a triangle of the arms (see Preparation for Headstand, pg 112). Lift the shoulders, neck and head up.

3 You can hold this pose, with the knees bent and hip distance apart. Or you can straighten the legs: hips stay lifted as you slowly straighten the legs one at a time.

HOLDING THE POSE

On each inhalation strengthen and lift the shoulders to open the armpits. Hold the legs straight, strong, and together. On every exhalation lift the armpits, spine, and hips, and work with the Important Actions list. Breathe. Hold for 10-20 seconds initially.

COMPLETING THE POSE

Bend the knees, release the hands, and lower yourself to the floor. Relax.

LEARNING AT HOME: MODIFICATIONS

Work with your elbows braced against the wall.

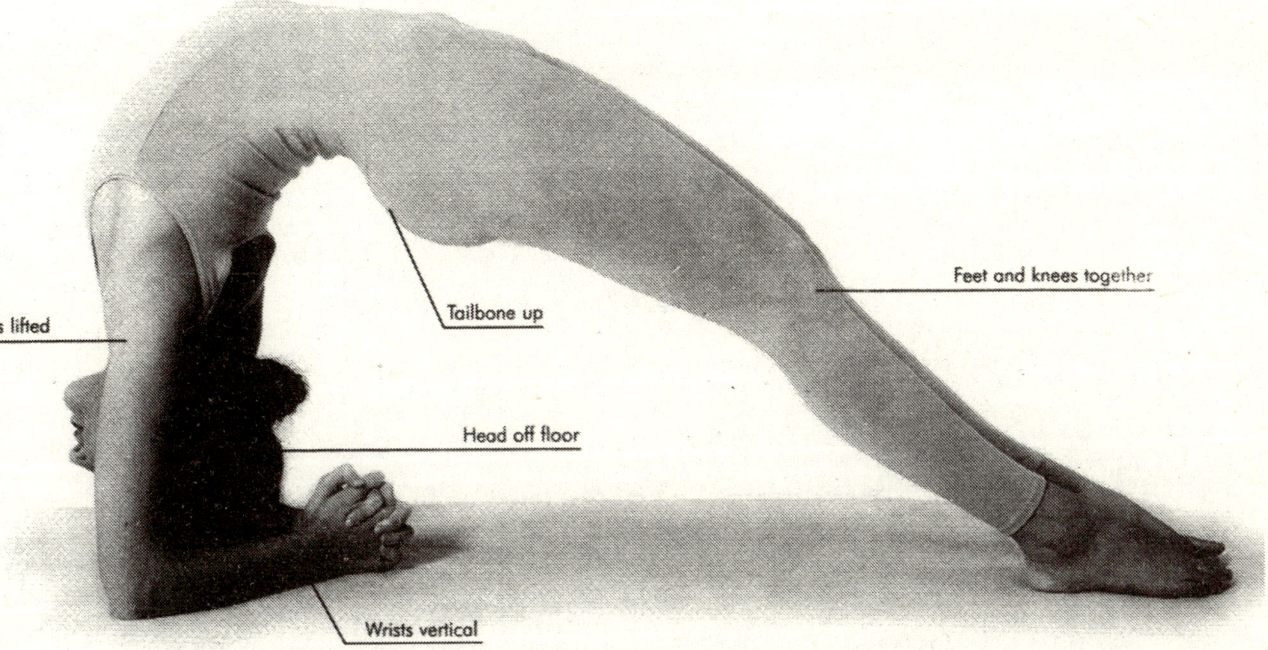

IMPORTANT ACTIONS

- Roll the outsides of the knees in
- Buttocks muscles are always tight
- Lower back stays in neutral
- Press the spine up and into the body
- Open the armpits and chest forward

Eka Pada Viparita Dandasa
One Leg Variation – Inverted Arch Pose

GENERAL PRECAUTIONS

This pose is not appropriate for high blood pressure, glaucoma, back or neck pain.

FLOOR POSES

DAVID LIFE AND SHARON GANNON IN PARIPURNA NAVASANA

Baddha Konasana

BOUND ANGLE SITTING POSE

	VATA ↓↓	PITTA ↓↓	KAPHA ↓
TIME	Longer holds with repetitions	Any holding time	Shorter holds
BREATH	Long, smooth breath or Ujjayi	Long, easy breath or light Ujjayi	Ujjayi
FOCUS	Breath and stillness	Breath, softening and opening	Stretching and extending on breath
MOVE	Extend spine up, release legs	Legs open and spine rises	Move knees down as the spine lifts

MOVING INTO THE POSE

1 Bend the knees and press the soles of the feet together. Pull both feet toward you as much as possible and press the knees open out to the sides. Keep the head, neck, and back vertical with the shoulders back and down.

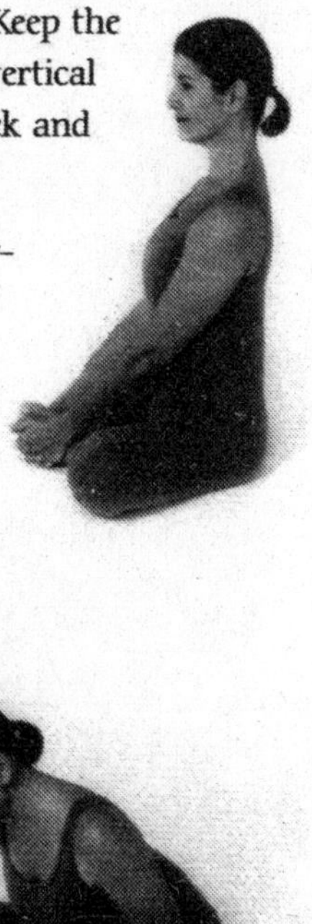

2 With fingers interlocked, the hands hold the feet or ankles. With every exhalation, open the knees.

HOLDING THE POSE

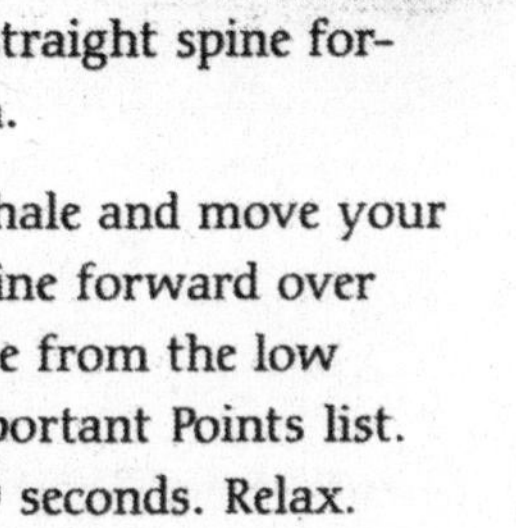

1 As you inhale, see nourishing breath come into the body. As you exhale, bend from the hips and bring the straight spine forward as shown.

2 Inhale. Exhale and move your straight spine forward over your feet (move from the low spine). Use Important Points list. Hold for 30-60 seconds. Relax.

DOSHIC NOTES

In general all of the quiet sitting poses reduce Vata, control Apana and keep Prana moving upward. They do not aggravate the other Doshas.

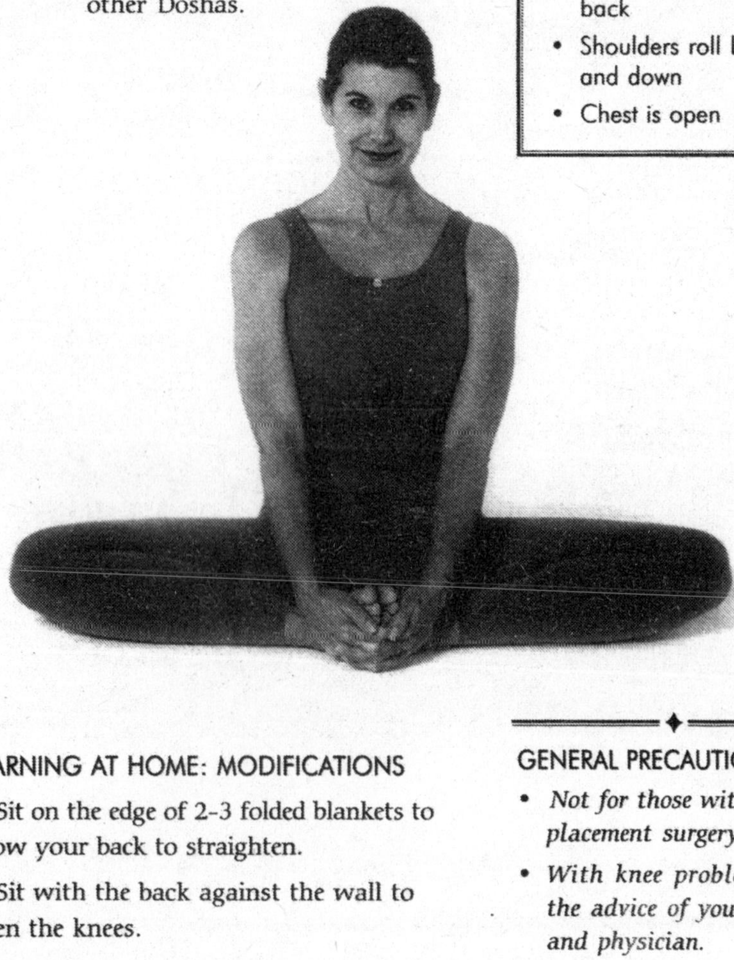

IMPORTANT POINTS

- Press feet together
- Spinal column vertical
- Knees open toward the floor
- Bottom front ribs stay back
- Shoulders roll back and down
- Chest is open

LEARNING AT HOME: MODIFICATIONS

- Sit on the edge of 2-3 folded blankets to allow your back to straighten.
- Sit with the back against the wall to open the knees.

GENERAL PRECAUTIONS

- *Not for those with hip replacement surgery.*
- *With knee problems, ask the advice of your teacher and physician.*

Siddhasana

PERFECT SITTING POSE

	VATA ↓↓	PITTA ↓↓	KAPHA ↓
TIME	Longer holds and repetitions	Any holding time	Shorter holds
BREATH	Long, smooth breath or Ujjayi	Long, easy breath or light Ujjayi	Ujjayi
FOCUS	Breath and stillness	Breath	Breath
MOVE	Ground sit bones, lift the spine	Ground sit bones, lift the spine	Ground sit bones, lift the spine

For most bodies, this sitting pose is the best posture for meditation. It promotes spiritual knowledge.

MOVING INTO THE POSE

1 From Dandasana, bend the right knee and place the right foot under the perineum. Place the left heel on top of the right heel and against the pubic bone. Keep the neck and back straight. Shoulders relaxed.

2 Place the hands on the knees, palms open, or make Jnana Mudra (optional), the sign of knowledge, by touching the thumb to the index finger, keeping the other three fingers straight.

HOLDING THE POSE

1 On each inhalation, see nourishing breath coming into the body.

2 On each exhalation, see the body being cleansed by the breath. Fix the gaze at the third eye (between the eyebrows). Remain in the pose as long as you like. For meditation, remain for 15-30 minutes.

DOSHIC NOTES

It calms Vata, controls Apana and keeps Prana moving upward. It does not aggravate the other Doshas.

IMPORTANT POINTS

- Spinal column is vertical and straight
- Shoulders back and down
- Chest is open
- Bottom front ribs move back slightly
- Arms relaxed on the legs, palms up

LEARNING AT HOME: MODIFICATIONS

- Sit in easy sitting pose (simple crossed legs), Sukhasana, until Siddhasanas is comfortable.
- Sitting on the edge of 2-3 folded blankets will allow your back to straighten.

GENERAL PRECAUTIONS

- *Not for those with hip or knee replacements.*
- *With knee problems, ask the advice of your teacher and doctor.*

Basic Virasana

BASIC HERO POSE

	VATA ↓↓	PITTA ↓↓	KAPHA ↓
TIME	Longer holds and repetitions	Any holding time	Shorter holds
BREATH	Long, smooth breath or Ujjayi	Long, easy breath or light Ujjayi	Ujjayi
FOCUS	Breath and stillness	Breath	Breath
MOVE	Sit into heels and hold spine up	Sit into heels and hold spine up	Sit into heels and hold spine up

Basic Virasana is a good sitting pose for the practice of meditation and simple twisting movements. Foundation Points, Important Actions, Holding the Pose, Learning at Home: Modifications, and General Precautions are the same for both Basic Virasana and Virasana.

MOVING INTO THE POSE

With the knees together on the floor, sit on the heels. The weight is evenly balanced on each foot. The shoulder joints are directly over the hip joints and pulled back and down from the ears. Lift the front of the hips (the hipbones) slightly, allowing the tailbone to descend.

HOLDING THE POSE

1 Inhale as you lift the front of the hipbones slightly. As you exhale, the tailbone descends as you extend the rest of the spine upward.

2 If this position is difficult, hold for 20-30 seconds. If you are comfortable, hold for 2-5 minutes.

GENERAL PRECAUTIONS

Consult a physician if you have knee problems and seek a knowledgeable teacher.

COMPLETING THE POSE

Straighten the legs and rest.

LEARNING AT HOME: MODIFICATIONS

If you are uncomfortable, place a cushion or folded blanket between your feet and buttocks.

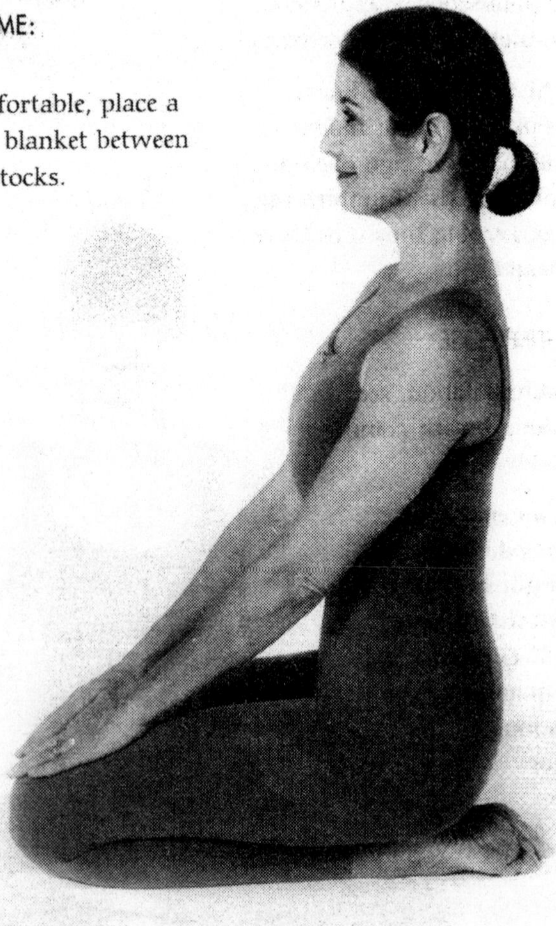

Virasana

HERO POSE

	VATA ↓↓	PITTA ↓↓	KAPHA ↓
TIME	Longer holds and repetitions	Any holding time	Shorter holds
BREATH	Long, smooth breath or Ujjayi	Long, easy breath or light Ujjayi	Ujjayi
FOCUS	Breath and stillness	Breath	Breath
MOVE	Sit into heels and hold spine up	Sit into heels and hold spine up	Sit into heels and hold spine up

MOVING INTO THE POSE

From Basic Viraśana, come up onto your knees. Inhale as you separate the feet to hip width. Exhale and pull the calf muscles to the outsides of the legs as you sit down between them on the floor. Keep the feet beside the hips. The shoulders are relaxed down from the ears. Keep the shoulders directly above the hip joints.

IMPORTANT ACTIONS

- Tailbone descends
- Lengthen the back of the neck
- Shoulders move back and down
- Bottom front ribs are held in
- Knees stay close together

HOLDING THE POSE

Same as Basic Virasana

LEARNING AT HOME: MODIFICATIONS

Same for Basic Virasana

- To relieve pressure in the knee: Kneeling, roll a small piece of tissue into a tight ball. Press the tissue ball into the back of the knee as you bend the leg to sit all the way down.
- If the front of the lower leg or the ankles are stiff, sit on 2–3 folded blankets with the toes hanging over the edge.

Supta Virasana

RECLINING HERO POSE

	VATA ↓↓	PITTA ↓↓	KAPHA ↓
TIME	Longer holds	Longer holds	Moderate holds
BREATH	Slow and even or Ujjayi	Long and easy or Ujjayi	Normal or Ujjayi
FOCUS	Strength and stillness, grounding	Ground, extension, ease	Strengthening, lifting, working the pose
MOVE	Internal lift with Neutral spine	Internal lift with Neutral spine	Lift, work, and extension

MOVING INTO THE POSE

1 From Virasana, lean backward onto your elbows and hands. Inhale and tuck your tailbone under keeping the lower back in 'Neutral,' pg 58. Exhale, lengthen the spine as you ease yourself carefully down onto your elbows.

2 After comfort has been established, exhale and ease yourself down onto your back with the arms stretched over your head.

HOLDING THE POSE

With each exhalation lengthen the tailbone toward the knees so that the low back moves toward the floor. Breathe and hold.

COMPLETING THE POSE

Keeping the spine in Neutral, lift up onto your elbows. Use your hands to support you as you return to Virasana.

LEARNING AT HOME: MODIFICATIONS

- Use a bolster under your back and head until the front thighs are stretched and you can come down to the floor.
- To relieve pressure in the knee: Kneeling, roll a small piece of tissue into a tight ball. Press the tissue ball into the back of the knee as you bend the leg and sit all the way down.

GENERAL PRECAUTIONS

Those with knee problems should consult a physician and experienced yoga teacher.

IMPORTANT ACTIONS

- Keep knees together
- Tailbone lengthens
- Lengthen upper spine
- Lengthen the neck
- Lower back stays in Neutral

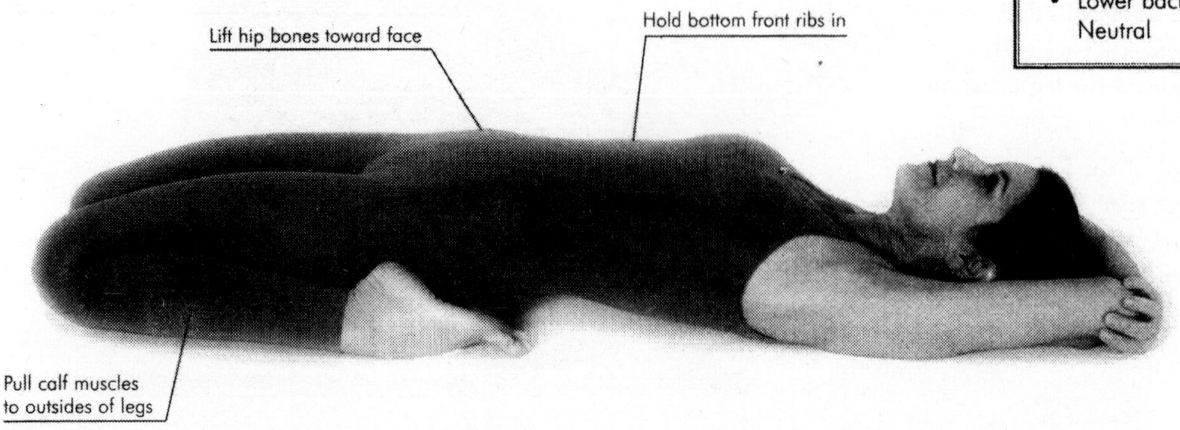

Navasana

BOAT POSE

	VATA ↓↓↓	PITTA ↑ or ↓	KAPHA ↓↓
TIME	Moderate-Long holds and repetition	Short holds – no strain	Long holds and repetitions
BREATH	Smooth, even breath or Ujjayi	Even breath or light Ujjayi	Normal or Ujjayi
FOCUS	Balance and holding lift	Balance and breath	Strengthening and lifting
MOVE	Ground and extend through legs	Lift and extend from firm foundation	Maximum lift and extension

MOVING INTO THE POSE

1 From Dandasána, pg 156, bend the knees. Hold the back of the knees with your hands. Lean back with a

straight spine until the arms become straight. Hold a straight line from the top of the head to the tailbone. Balancing on the sitting bones, raise the lower legs until they are parallel with the floor.

2 Straighten the legs and let go of the knees. Hold the arms and hands parallel with the floor. Use the abdominal muscles to lessen the strain in the low back.

HOLDING THE POSE

Inhale and balance. Exhale and draw the spine up into the body. Extend through the legs. Use the Important Actions list. Hold this position for 10-30 seconds to begin.

COMPLETING THE POSE

Bend the knees. Re-establish Dandasana.

IMPORTANT ACTIONS

- Legs and spine straight
- Use the abdominal muscles
- Keep the neck long
- Keep spine straight and extended
- Press through the heels
- Balance on the buttocks

LEARNING AT HOME: MODIFICATIONS

Balance with hands holding the legs.

GENERAL PRECAUTIONS

Should not be practiced with any hip flexor injuries or serious disk problems.

Ubhya Padangusthasana

BALANCING FOOT BIG TOE POSE

	VATA ↓↓	PITTA ↓	KAPHA ↓
TIME	Moderate-Long holds	Short-Moderate holds	Any hold with repetitions
BREATH	Smooth, even breath or Ujjayi	Even breath or light Ujjayi	Normal or Ujjayi
FOCUS	Balance and holding lift	Balance and breath	Strengthening and lifting
MOVE	Ground and extend through legs	Lift and extend from firm foundation	Maximum lift and extension

MOVING INTO THE POSE

From Dandasana, pg 156, exhale and bend the knees toward the chest. Balance back on the sitting bones as you did in Navasana. Take hold of the feet with the hands. Move the spine in and straighten it. Hold the spine straight and lifted as you straighten the legs.

HOLDING THE POSE

Inhale and balance. Exhale and use the Important Actions list. Hold for 20-30 seconds to begin.

IMPORTANT ACTIONS

- Draw the spine up and in
- Abdominal muscles strong
- Lengthen the back of your neck
- Keep spine long and straight
- Press through the feet
- Legs extended and straight

COMPLETING THE POSE

Bend the knees. Re-establish Dandasana and see how you feel.

LEARNING AT HOME: MODIFICATIONS

1 Hold onto a belt (placed around the feet) to help you straighten the back and legs.

2 Try placing the feet at eye level on the wall, legs straight. Use a belt or rope around the feet if you cannot reach the toes. Only use this idea occasionally.

GENERAL PRECAUTIONS

- *Should not be practiced with any hip flexor injury or serious disk problems.*
- *Use the abdominal muscles as much as possible to take the strain out of the back.*

Anantasana

SERPENT STRETCH

	VATA ↓↓	PITTA ↓↓	KAPHA
TIME	Longer holds and repetitions	Longer holds and repetitions	Short - moderate holds
BREATH	Smooth, even breath	Even, slow breath	Smooth, even breath
FOCUS	Balance and breath	Balance and breath (no pressure)	Balance and commitment
MOVE	Tighten abdominals, extend legs	Tighten abdominals, extend legs	Tighten abdominals, extend legs

MOVING INTO THE POSE

Lie on the right side with the right hand supporting the head. Inhale, bend the left knee and take hold of the left foot with the left hand. Exhale and straighten the left leg, foot stretching up to the ceiling.

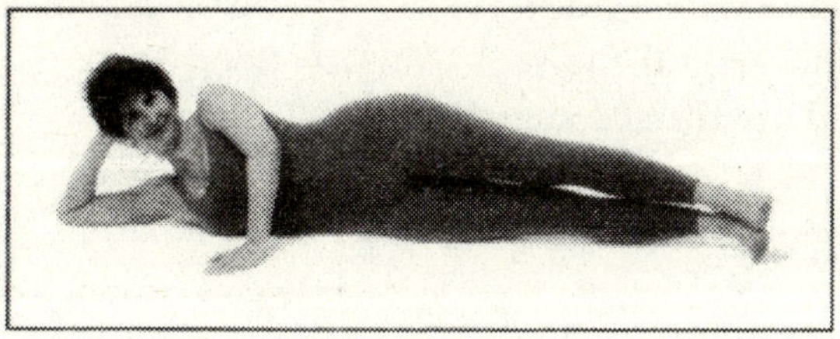

IMPORTANT POINTS

- Hold the abdominal muscles in
- Extend through both legs
- Elbows in straight line with body

HOLDING THE POSE

Hold for 20-30 seconds grounding as you inhale and extending as you exhale.

COMPLETING THE POSE

Exhale as you return. Repeat on the other side.

LEARNING AT HOME: MODIFICATIONS

With shorter hamstrings, use a belt around the extended foot.

GENERAL PRECAUTIONS

Not for those with hip replacement surgery.

Urdhva Prasarita Padasasana

UPWARD EXTENDED FEET POSE

	VATA ↓↓	PITTA ↓	KAPHA ↓
TIME	Moderate-Long holds	Short-Moderate holds	Any hold with repetitions
BREATH	Smooth, even breath or Ujjayi	Even breath or light Ujjayi	Normal or Ujjayi
FOCUS	Stillness and breath	Breath and ease of hold	Strengthening and commitment
MOVE	Tight abdominals, legs extend	Tight abdominals, legs extend	Tight abdominals, legs extend

MOVING INTO THE POSE

Lie on the back, straighten and stretch the legs, and reach the arms over the head. Lengthen the body. Press the lower back toward the floor (Neutral Spine) and use the abdominal muscles throughout the entire pose.

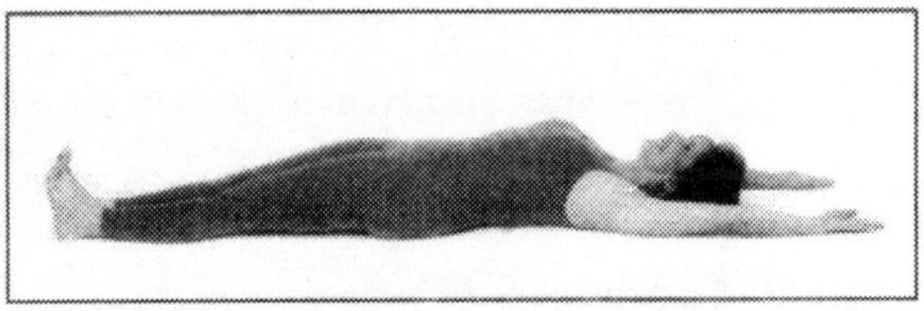

HOLDING THE POSE

1 With each inhalation, strengthen and lengthen the legs, extending out through the heels. Exhale, raising the straight legs to 90 degrees. Breathe and hold for 20-30 seconds. Exhale lowering the legs back down to the floor. Do not let the lower back lift as you bring the legs down.

2 As you exhale, hold the lower back to the floor and raise straight legs to 30 degrees. Hold 5-15 seconds.

3 As you inhale, raise the legs to 60 degrees. Hold 5-15 seconds.

4 As you exhale, raise the legs to 90 degrees and hold 5-15 seconds.

5 On an exhale, lower the legs back to the floor. Relax.

LEARNING AT HOME: MODIFICATIONS

- If you cannot keep the low back down while raising or lowering the legs, begin by lifting only one leg at a time.
- Try just raising and lowering the legs without stopping or holding.

IMPORTANT ACTIONS

- Extend the legs out through the heels
- Hold the chin in
- Hold the abdominal muscles in

GENERAL PRECAUTIONS

- *Do not let the back lift up.*
- *If there is existing back pain do not practice until you have consulted a physician.*

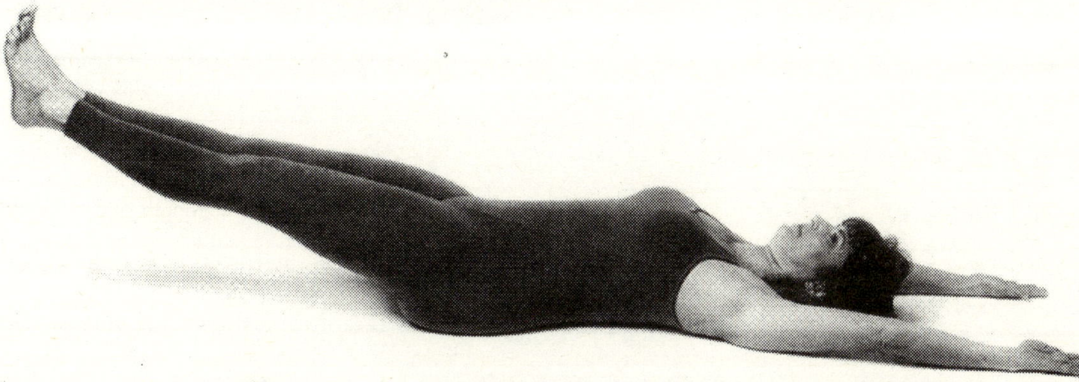

Legs strong and straight
Arms touching the floor
Lower back on floor

Chaturanga Dandasana

PLANK POSE

(Sun Salutation Position #6)

VATA ↓↓↓ PITTA ↑ KAPHA ↓↓

	VATA ↓↓↓	PITTA ↑	KAPHA ↓↓
TIME	Long holds	Short holds	Long holds with repetitions
BREATH	Smooth, even breath or Ujjayi	Even, breath or light Ujjayi	Normal or Ujjayi
FOCUS	Holding still and strong	Stillness and breath	Strength and commitment
MOVE	Strengthen and extend arms, legs, torso	Strong grounding, open torso	Strengthen and extend arms, legs, torso

MOVING INTO THE POSE

Begin by lying face down on the floor. Inhale and bring the hands under the shoulders near the armpits. Spread the fingers and press the palms on the floor. Keep the elbows close to the body. Exhale, turn the toes under and straighten the arms pushing the body evenly up. Move the abdomen into the body to lift the torso.

IMPORTANT POINTS

- Feet, legs, torso, head in straight line
- Arms straight and strong
- Chest open
- Low spine in Neutral

HOLDING THE POSE

Inhale. Exhale straightening the body from head to feet. Press through the arms, bring the shoulders back and open the chest. Hold for 20-40 seconds to begin. Rest in Child's Pose.

Vasisthasana

SIDE PLANK POSE

	VATA ↓↓	PITTA ↑	KAPHA ↓↓
TIME	Long holds	Short holds	Long holds with repetitions
BREATH	Smooth, even breath or Ujjayi	Even breath or light Ujjayi	Normal or Ujjayi
FOCUS	Holding still and strong	Stillness and breath	Strength and commitment
MOVE	Strengthen and extend arms, legs, torso	Strong grounding, open torso	Strengthen and extend arms, legs, torso

MOVING INTO THE POSE

1 From Plank Pose (Chaturanga Dandasana) pg 150, exhale and turn to the right, placing the weight on the left hand and arm. Keep the torso lifted as you roll onto the outside of the left foot.

2 Inhale, strengthen your bal ance. Exhale and extend the right hand straight up into the air. Inhale, straightening the body from feet to head. Exhale and press down with the right hand, extend out through the legs and roll the shoulders back. Open the chest and lengthen the back.

COMPLETING THE POSE

Turn back to Plank Pose. Bend your knees and sit back on your heels in Basic Virasana. Relax. Repeat on the other side.

IMPORTANT POINTS

- Feet together as if standing on them
- Right arm straight and strong
- Low spine in Neutral
- Chest open

LEARNING AT HOME: MODIFICATIONS

Variation: On knees instead of toes.

HOLDING THE POSE

Inhale, turn the head to look up at the hand. Exhale, extend the length of the body so feet, legs, torso, and head are in a straight line. Hold this position for 10-30 seconds to begin.

Purvottanasana

INTENSE FRONT EXTENSION POSE

	VATA ↓	PITTA ↑	KAPHA ↓↓↓
TIME	Moderate holds	Short holds	Long holds with repetitions
BREATH	Smooth, even breath	Even smooth breath	Normal
FOCUS	Holding strong and the breath	Stillness and breath	Strengthening and commitment
MOVE	Maintain strong arms, legs, and lift torso	Hold strong and lift to open up	Strong arms, legs, and torso, extend up

MOVING INTO THE POSE

1 Sit in Dandasana, pg156. Inhale and place the palms down close to the hips fingertips facing the feet. Bend the knees until the soles of the feet are on the floor hip distance apart and your shins are vertical (beginners can work with the feet and knees 6-10" apart).

2 Exhale, lift up the torso and thighs until they are parallel with the floor. Keep the head back, as you lengthen and lift the entire spine.

3 After you have established this position, move to the next level by straightening the legs.

IMPORTANT POINTS

- Fingers are spread wide
- Lift up out of arms and shoulders
- Spine moves up into the body
- Chest opens to the ceiling
- Legs strong and extended

HOLDING THE POSE

Inhale. Exhale, extend through the legs and lift the spine up toward the ceiling. Hold the tailbone up and keep the low back in Neutral. Lengthen the neck. Hold this position for 10-20 seconds to begin.

COMPLETING THE POSE

Exhale. Bend the knees and return to Dandasana. Re-establish Dandasana and see how you feel.

GENERAL PRECAUTIONS

Proceed slowly with shoulder injuries and weak wrists.

Yoga Mudrasana

YOGA SEAL

	VATA ↓↓↓	PITTA ↓↓↓	KAPHA ↓
TIME	Long holds and repetitions	Long holds and repetitions	Short holds
BREATH	Even, smooth, long breath	Smooth, easy breath	Even, smooth breath
FOCUS	Being still and grounded	Release and breathe	Releasing and extending
MOVE	Lengthen inner torso, move heels deep into low abdomen	Soften the neck, open chest forward, move heels deep into low abdomen	Extend spine, open chest, move heels deep into low abdomen

MOVING INTO THE POSE

1 From Dandaṣana, inhale as you bend your left knee. Hold the outside of your left ankle. Exhale as you lift and place your left ankle on top of your right thigh (heel close to your right hipbone and toes hanging over outside of the thigh) in Half Lotus position. Inhale. Exhale as you lift your right ankle and place it over your left leg on top of your left thigh. Your knees are close to the floor.

2 Exhale and draw the spine up. Beginning from your lower back, pivot at your hips and bend forward over your legs bringing your forehead down to the floor.

3 Bring your arms behind you and clasp the left wrist with the right hand.

HOLDING THE POSE

With each inhalation, imagine the breath flowing down the back into the buttocks and floor. With every exhalation, feel gravity relaxing you forward and down. Hold for 20–40 seconds to begin.

COMPLETING THE POSE

Return to sitting in full lotus and release the arms and legs.

IMPORTANT POINTS

- Even weight on sitting bones
- Shoulders relaxed down
- Heels press into lower abdomen
- Belly relaxes forward
- Spine and neck are lengthened

LEARNING AT HOME: MODIFICATIONS

Sit on your heels in Basic Virasana and follow the instructions from step #2.

ꟸ SITTING FORWARD BENDS ꟹ

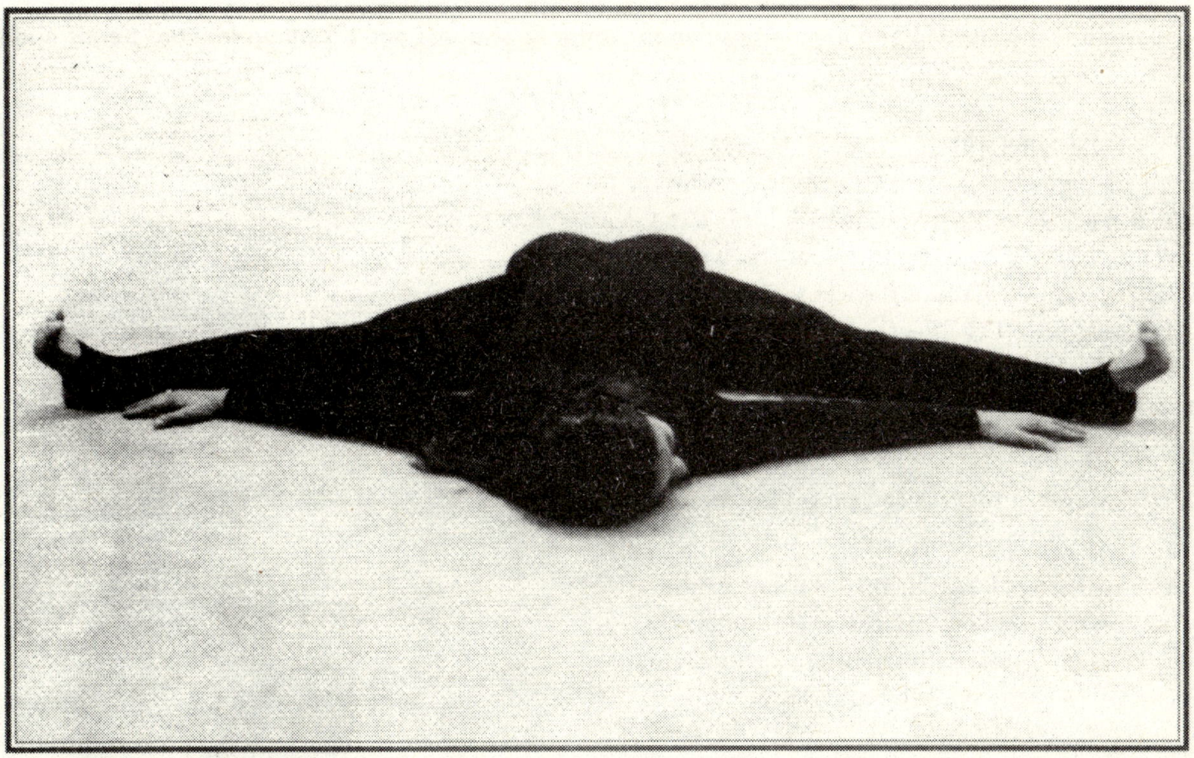

JUDITH LASATER IN UPAVISTHA KONASANA

Dandasana

STAFF POSE

	VATA ↓↓↓	PITTA	KAPHA ↓
TIME	Long holds and repetitions	Moderate holds	Long holds and repetitions
BREATH	Smooth and even or light Ujjayi	Smooth and easy or light Ujjayi	Normal or Ujjayi
FOCUS	Centering, breath	Breath and Neutral back	Strengthening, lifting
MOVE	Extend legs and lift spine	Energize legs and inner torso	Extend legs, lift torso, open chest

Dandasana is the starting and ending position for some floor poses and all sitting forward bends and twists.

MOVING INTO THE POSE

Sit with the legs stretched out straight in front of you. Pull the flesh of the buttocks back behind and away from each sitting bone. Press out through the heels as you pull the balls of the feet toward you (it's ok if the heels lift off the floor). Keep the torso extending upward, straight and tall.

HOLDING THE POSE

1 Inhale, lengthen the legs and press the knees to the floor. Review the foundation points.

2 With each exhalation, hold the tailbone down as you draw the spine up (all the way through the top of the head). Work with Important Actions. Hold the pose for 15–30 seconds to begin.

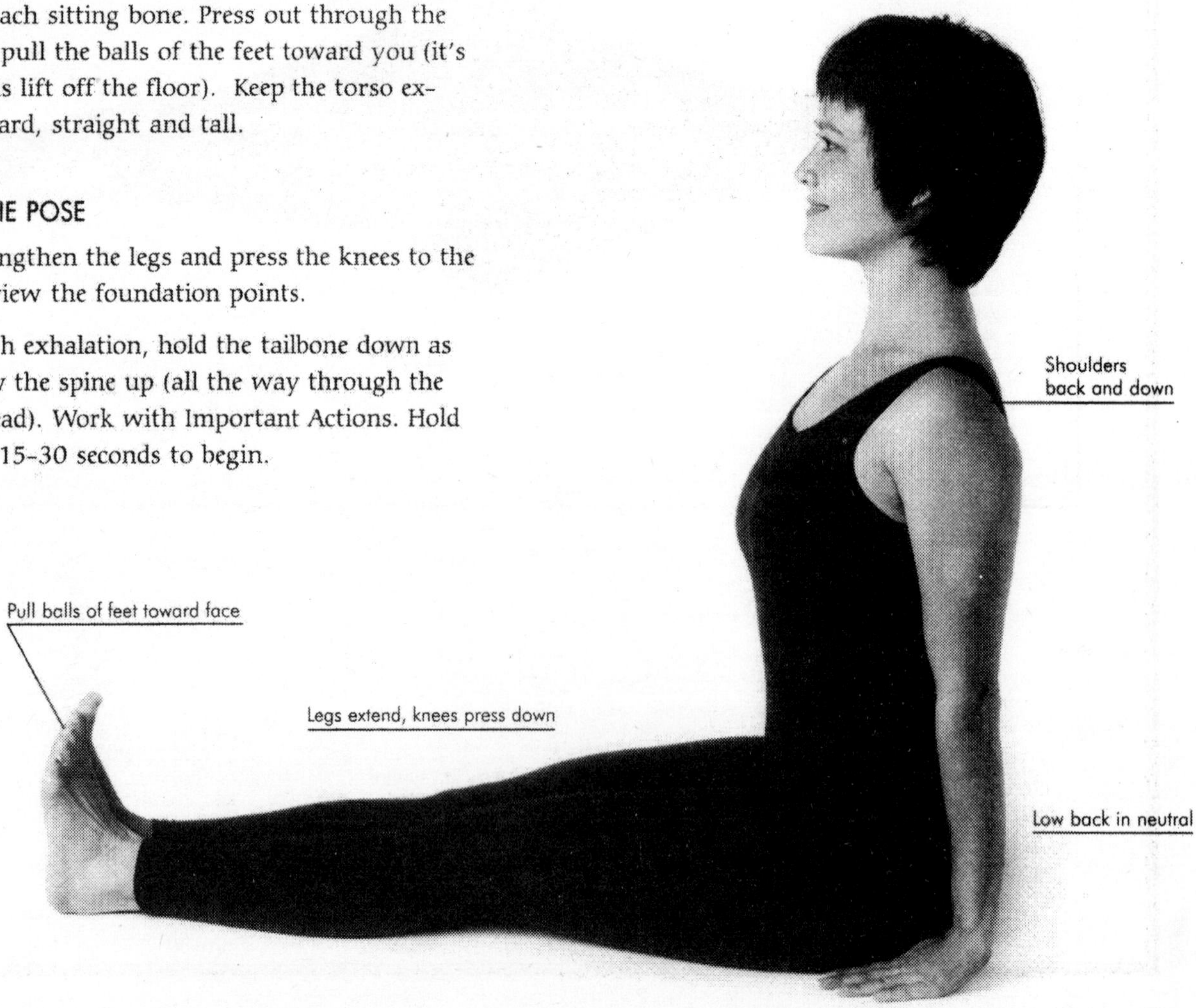

LEARNING AT HOME: MODIFICATIONS

• Sit with the entire back on the wall to learn the spine's position.

• Practice Wall Push, pg 63 to learn movement and technique. The movements of the legs and back are the same as the Wall Push.

* If your back is rounded, sit on blankets or a small cushion to straighten your spine.

IMPORTANT ACTIONS

- Sit directly on sitting bones
- Lift the spine (inner torso) upward
- Extend through lower legs and heels
- Lengthen back of the neck
- Shoulders roll back and down

GENERAL PRECAUTIONS

If the hamstring muscles are tight, sit on a blanket to lift the buttocks and support the knees. In that case do not press the knees down.

Janu Sirsasana

HEAD TO KNEE POSE

	VATA ↓↓↓	PITTA ↓↓↓	KAPHA ↑↑
TIME	Long holds and repetitions	Long holds and repetitions	Short holds
BREATH	Long and smooth or light Ujjayi	Smooth and easy or light Ujjayi	Normal or Ujjayi
FOCUS	Being still, breath	Easy extension, breath	Strengthening and lengthening
MOVE	Strong legs, extend inner torso	Energize legs, soften neck, open chest	Strong legs, extend spine, open chest

MOVING INTO THE POSE

1 From Dandasána, inhale and bend the left knee pulling the left foot near the perineum. Pull back on the right hip so that you face the right leg.

2 Exhale, lengthen the right leg, extending out through the heel. Simultaneously strengthen and press the right knee to the floor. Inhale. Exhale, and draw the spine up and forward to move the low abdomen toward the center of the right thigh. Do not round the back. Move the whole torso by moving the lower back into the body.

IMPORTANT ACTIONS

- Chin is in
- Move from the lower back
- Extend the front body and spine
- Lengthen the back of the neck
- Chest stays open
- Sit evenly on sitting bones
- Extend through heels

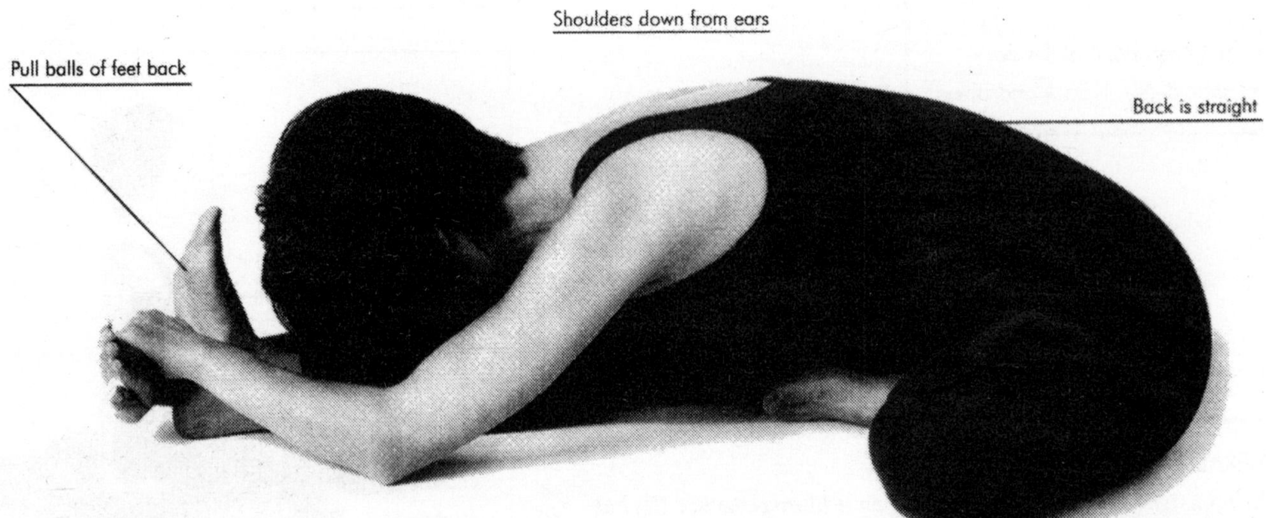

HOLDING THE POSE

With each inhalation, focus on foundation points. With each exhalation focus on Important Actions. Hold for 20-60 seconds to begin.

COMPLETING THE POSE

Exhale, return to Dandasana. See how you feel before repeating other side.

LEARNING AT HOME: MODIFICATIONS

- Use a belt or towel around the extended leg, holding the corners so that the back may remain straight as you work the hamstrings.
- If the hamstring muscles are tight, you may want to sit on a blanket that lifts the buttocks and supports the knees. In that case do not press your knee down.

GENERAL PRECAUTIONS

With sciatica the back must remain straight.

Supta Padangusthasana

ONE LEG STRETCHED UP LYING DOWN

	VATA ↓↓	PITTA ↓↓↓	KAPHA ↑
TIME	Long holds and repetitions	Long holds and repetitions	Short holds
BREATH	Long smooth breath or Ujjayi	Smooth, easy breath or light Ujjayi	Normal or Ujjayi
FOCUS	Lengthening on the breath	Lengthening on the breath	Lengthening on the breath
MOVE	Lengthen inner torso, extend leg from sitting bone, chest open	Lengthen inner torso, extend leg from sitting bone, chest open	Lengthen torso, shoulders back, open chest. Extend legs

MOVING INTO THE POSE

Lying on your back, strengthen and straighten your legs. Inhale, bend the right knee and take hold of the right foot with the right hand (first two fingers of the right hand around the big toe). As you exhale, straighten the right knee pushing the right heel up toward the ceiling. The right arm remains straight.

IMPORTANT ACTIONS

- Lengthen through the heels and strengthen both legs
- Keep the chest open
- Stretch upward leg with each exhalation
- Neck is relaxed with chin in
- Pull the right hip down and away from your waist to level the hips

HOLDING THE POSE

1 With each inhalation establish the Foundation Points marked on photo. With each exhalation strengthen both legs and extend out through the heels. Bring the lifted leg closer to the face. Hold for 20-60 seconds.

2 Keeping your hips facing the ceiling (level), open the straight left leg out to the left side. Hold 20-60 seconds.

COMPLETING THE POSE

On an exhalation bring the left leg straight back up to center. Hold your lower back in contact with the floor as you slowly lower the left leg. Repeat on the other side.

LEARNING AT HOME: MODIFICATIONS

If needed, use a belt around the foot of the extended leg so the back can remain straight. Shoulders are back and down with the chest open.

Upavistha Konasana

OPEN LEGS FORWARD BEND

VATA ↓↓ PITTA ↓↓↓ KAPHA ↑↑

	VATA ↓↓	PITTA ↓↓↓	KAPHA ↑↑
TIME	Long holds and repetitions	Long holds and repetitions	Short holds
BREATH	Slow, smooth or light Ujjayi	Smooth, even or light Ujjayi	Normal or Ujjayi
FOCUS	Stillness	Release	Extending
MOVE	Strong legs, extend inner torso	Soften neck, open chest	Strong legs, extend spine, open chest

MOVING INTO THE POSE

1 From Dandasana, pg156, exhale and spread the legs wide apart. Pull the flesh of the buttocks back, away from the sitting bones. Lengthen backs of the legs, extending out through the heels. Knees and toes face the ceiling – do not let the legs roll in or out. Press the fingertips on the floor behind you and draw the lower spine into the body and lift it up. Work with a straight spine.

2 Inhale and strengthen the legs extending out through the heels. Exhale and extend the torso forward, moving the low spine and abdomen toward the floor (between the legs). Repeat #2, working to keep the spine straight as you extend forward.

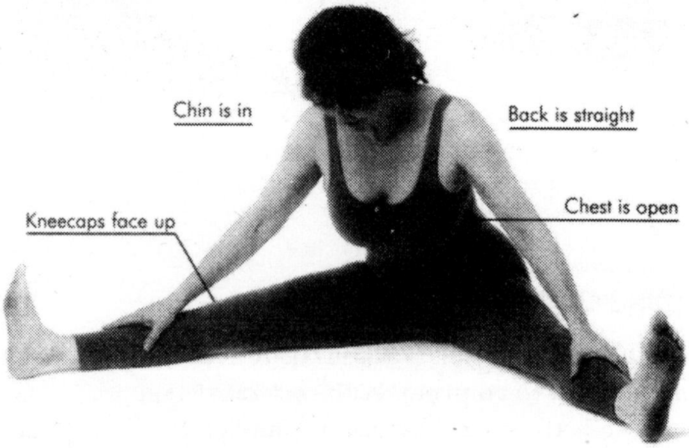

COMPLETING THE POSE

Exhale. Come up with a straight spine, pivoting from the hips. Re-establish Dandasana and see how you feel.

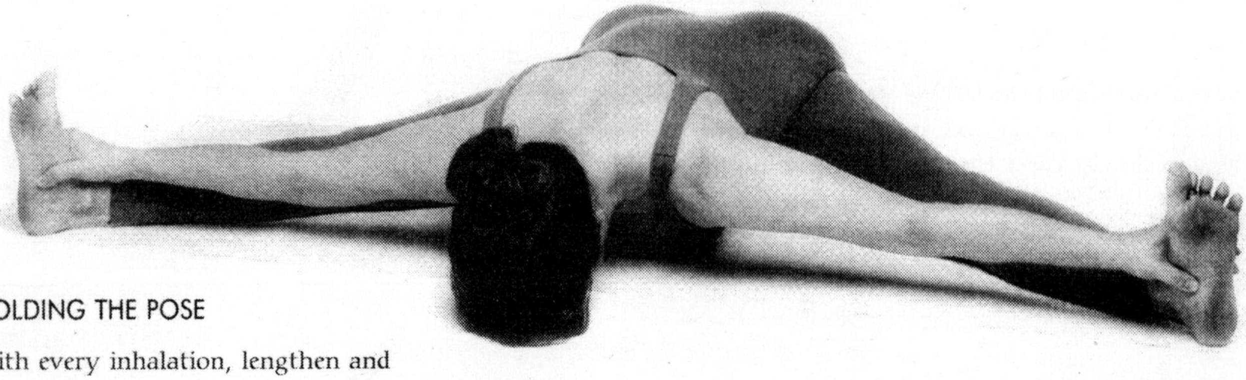

HOLDING THE POSE

With every inhalation, lengthen and strengthen the legs. With every exhalation extend the spine up toward your head and forward. Continue for 20-60 seconds to begin.

GENERAL PRECAUTIONS

Not for those with hip replacements or sciatica.

Parsva Upavistha Konasana

OVER ONE OPEN LEG FORWARD BEND

	VATA ↓↓	PITTA ↓↓↓	KAPHA ↑↑
TIME	Long holds and repetitions	Long holds and repetitions	Short holds
BREATH	Slow, smooth or light Ujjayi	Smooth, even or light Ujjayi	Normal or Ujjayi
FOCUS	Stillness	Release	Extending
MOVE	Strengthen legs, extend inner torso, lengthen back of neck	Soften neck, open chest, extend legs and spine	Strengthen legs, extend spine, open chest

MOVING INTO THE POSE

Establish Upavistha Konasana legs (Moving Into the Pose). Inhale as you turn the torso to face over the right leg. Exhale, move the (always straight) spine forward, reaching the front body over the right leg.

HOLDING THE POSE

With every inhalation, lengthen and strengthen the legs. Hold the right calf or foot with the hands or just lengthen the hands on the floor. Keep the chest open and arms relaxed (see foundation points on Upavistha Konasana photo). With every exhalation, extend the spine forward and use the Important Actions list. Continue to lengthen for 20-60 seconds to begin. Inhale and bring the straight torso up pivoting from the hip joints.

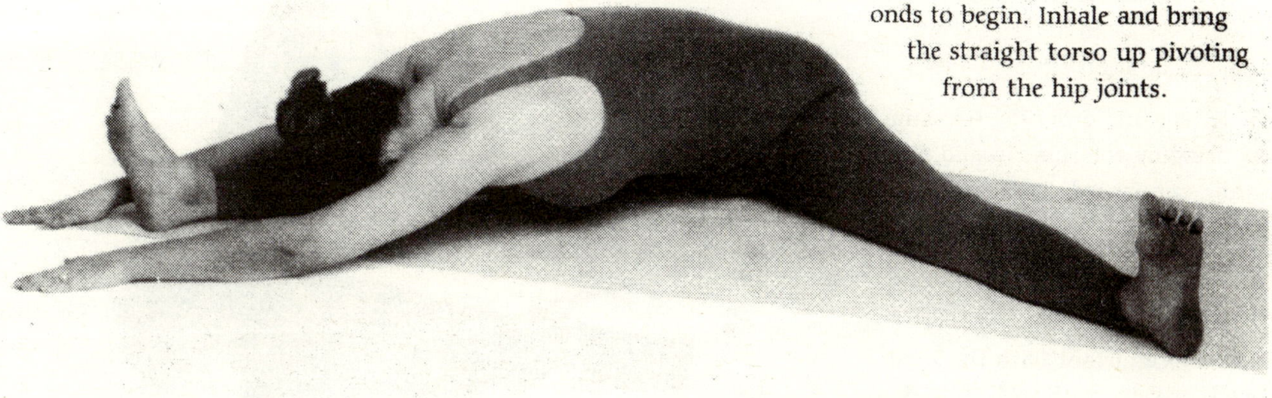

COMPLETING THE POSE

On an exhalation, return to sitting and repeat on other side.

LEARNING AT HOME: MODIFICATIONS

Use a belt or towel around the foot so that your back may remain straight as you stretch your legs.

IMPORTANT ACTIONS

Same for Upavistha Konasana

- Press the knees down
- Extend lower legs out through the heels
- Balls of feet move toward the face
- Shoulders move back and down
- Spine moves up to extend forward

GENERAL PRECAUTIONS

Not for those with hip replacements or sciatica.

Triang Mukhaikapada Paschimottanasana

THREE LIMBS FACING LEG FORWARD BEND

	VATA ↓↓↓	PITTA ↓↓	KAPHA ↑↑↑
TIME	Long holds and repetitions	Long holds and repetitions	Short holds
BREATH	Long smooth breath or light Ujjayi	Smooth, easy breath or light Ujjayi	Ujjayi
FOCUS	Stillness and breath	Release and breath	Strengthening and extending
MOVE	Extend inner torso, lengthen the neck	Soften the neck, open chest forward	Strong leg, extend spine, open chest

MOVING INTO THE POSE

1 From Dandasana, pg 156, inhale lengthen, and strengthen the right leg, press the knee to the floor, and extend out through the heel. Exhale, bend the left knee bringing the left foot back to side of the buttocks with the calf muscle rolled out away from the thigh. Extend toes straight back. Inhale, sit evenly balanced on both sitting bones.

2 Exhale and draw the spine up, bringing the spine in and the low abdomen forward. Do not round the back.

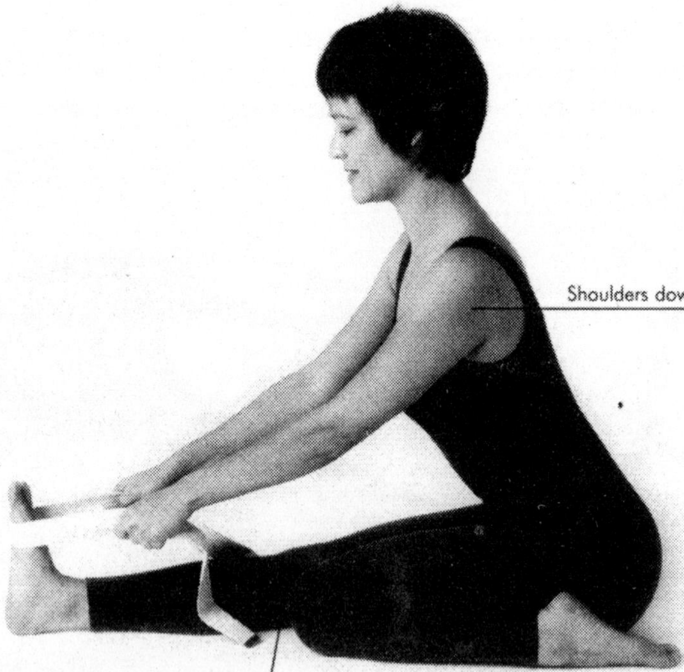

HOLDING THE POSE

Hold the right foot with the hands, towel, or belt. With each inhalation establish the foundation points (on the photo). With each exhalation, employ the Important Actions list. Lift the spine into the body and up as you move forward over the thigh while exhaling. Hold 20-60 seconds to begin.

COMPLETING THE POSE

Repeat on the other side. On an exhalation return to Dandasana and see how you feel.

GENERAL PRECAUTIONS

Not for those with sciatica or spinal disk problems.

IMPORTANT ACTIONS

- Press the straight knee down
- Extend out through leg and heel
- Pull ball of foot back
- Belly extends forward
- Chin is in
- Chest is open
- Straight spine moves into body

DOSHIC NOTES

As with most forward bends, it soothes Vata imbalance and reduces Pitta. Keep the chest open to help balance the increase in Kapha in this pose.

LEARNING AT HOME: MODIFICATIONS

- Use a belt or towel around the extended leg so that the back may remain straight as you work the hamstrings.
- Sit with the left hip on a folded blanket to level the hips.
- If the hamstring muscles are tight, you may want to sit on a blanket that lifts the buttocks and supports the knee of the straight leg.
- To relieve pressure in the knee: Kneeling, roll a small piece of tissue into a tight ball. Press the tissue ball into the back of the knee as you bend the leg and sit all the way down.

Ardha Baddha Padma Paschimottanasana

HALF LOTUS FORWARD BEND POSE

	VATA ↓↓↓	PITTA ↓↓↓	KAPHA ↑↑↑
TIME	Long holds and repetitions	Long holds and repetitions	Short holds
BREATH	Long, smooth or light Ujjayi	Smooth, easy or light Ujjayi	Ujjayi
FOCUS	Stillness	Release and breathe	Strengthening and extending
MOVE	Pivot the hips to extend inner torso, move heel deep into abdomen	Soften the neck, lengthen spine and open chest forward	Strong leg, pivot the hips, work to extend spine, open chest

MOVING INTO THE POSE

1 From Dandasana, pg 156, bend your right knee. Place the outside of the right ankle on the left thigh (close to the hipbone) in Half Lotus (bent knee close to the floor). Pull the left hip back and face over left leg.

2 Exhale and draw the spine up. Pivoting at the hips, lift the spine up and pull it into the body to move forward.

HOLDING THE POSE

As you inhale, ground and lengthen the straight leg. As you exhale, extend the spine up toward the head and lengthen the front torso forward. Hold for 20-60 seconds to begin.

COMPLETING THE POSE

Move back into Dandasana. Repeat to the other side.

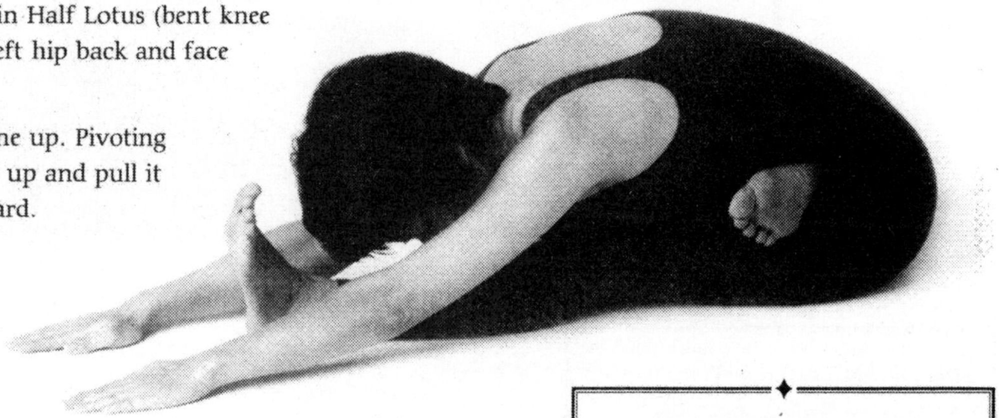

IMPORTANT ACTIONS

- Press the straight knee down
- Extend straight leg through heel
- Pull ball of foot back
- Shoulders down, arms relaxed
- Straight spine moves into body to lengthen forward
- Chin is in

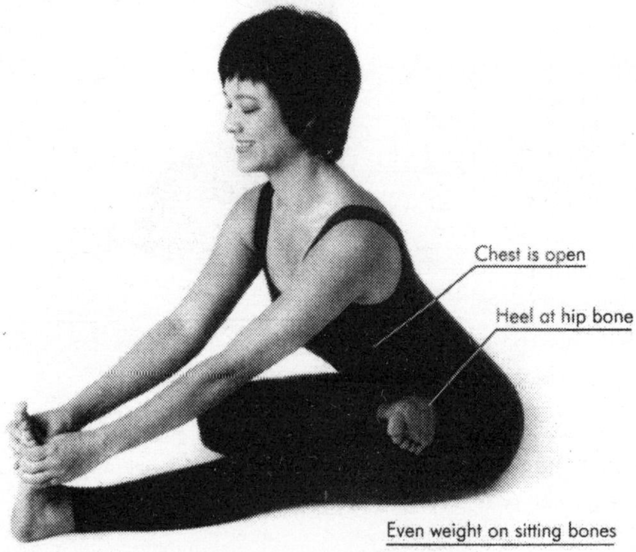

LEARNING AT HOME: MODIFICATIONS

Place belt around the straight leg foot and pull with the arms so that the back can remain straight. Keep the chest open as you stretch the leg.

GENERAL PRECAUTIONS

Not for hip replacements or knee problems. Consult a physician.

Parivrtta Janu Sirsasana

REVOLVED HEAD TO KNEE POSE

	VATA ↓↓	PITTA ↓↓	KAPHA ↑
TIME	Long holds	Long holds and repetitions	Short holds
BREATH	Long and smooth or light Ujjayi	Smooth and easy or light Ujjayi	Normal or Ujjayi
FOCUS	Stability, stillness	Opening, breath	Strengthening and extending
MOVE	Strengthen leg, extend side torso, open chest and shoulders	Lengthen straight leg, revolve and open chest	Strengthen leg, extend side torso, open chest and shoulders

MOVING INTO THE POSE

1 From Dandasana, pull the left foot into the perineum. Open hips to the left until the left hip is in line with the straight right leg. Press the right knee to the floor, extending out through the heel.

2 Inhale, slide the right hand and arm along the inside of the right leg reaching toward the foot. Exhale as you extend the right side of the torso down toward the right foot. Take hold of the foot (fingers on sole—thumb on top of foot) with the right hand. Extend left arm over the head to hold the right foot (thumb on top, fingers on sole).

HOLDING THE POSE

With each inhalation establish the position of the straight leg. With each exhalation extend the left ribs along the thigh and rotate the chest toward the ceiling. Hold for 15-30 seconds to begin.

COMPLETING THE POSE

Return to Dandasana and repeat other side.

LEARNING AT HOME: MODIFICATIONS

Use a belt or towel to hold the foot of the extended leg so you can lengthen the straight spine.

IMPORTANT ACTIONS

- Draw the straight leg into the hip joint to lengthen torso
- Bring in the right side of the spine to revolve the chest
- Keep neck relaxed, head between the arms
- Extend on the exhalations
- Pull ball of extended foot back
- Shoulders stay down
- Hold in the chin

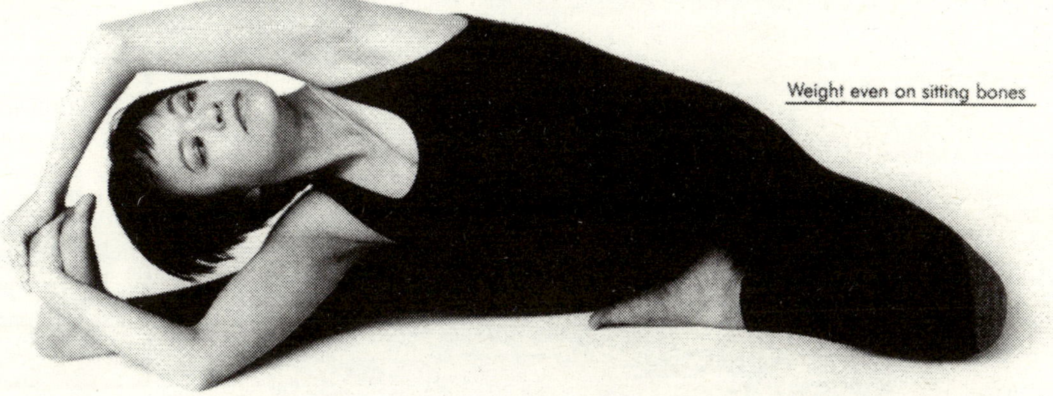

GENERAL PRECAUTIONS

This posture is contraindicated for spinal disk problems and hip replacements.

Urdhva Mukha Paschimottanasana

UPWARD FACING FORWARD BEND

	VATA ↓↓↓	PITTA ↓↓↓	KAPHA ↑↑
TIME	Long holds and repetitions	Long holds and repetitions	Short holds
BREATH	Long, smooth or light Ujjayi	Smooth, easy or light Ujjayi	Ujjayi
FOCUS	Stillness	Release and breathe	Extending
MOVE	Lengthen torso, open chest, stretch legs	Soften the neck, lengthen torso, stretch legs	Stretch legs, lengthen torso, open chest

MOVING INTO THE POSE

1 Lying on the back, stretch the arms over the head and lengthen the body.

2 Inhale and bend the knees to the chest. Hold the heels with interlocked hands (or use a towel or belt). Exhale and straighten the legs extending through the heels.

DOSHIC NOTES

As with most forward bends, it soothes Vata imbalance and reduces Pitta. Keep the chest open to help balance the increase in Kapha in this pose.

HOLDING THE POSE

With each exhalation focus on foundation points. With every exhalation focus on Important Actions. Hold for 20-30 seconds to begin.

LEARNING AT HOME: MODIFICATIONS

- Use a belt or towel around the feet so the back can remain straight as you stretch the legs.
- Use preparatory poses first: Dog pose; Supta Padangusthasana; Uttanasana; Paschimottanasana.

IMPORTANT ACTIONS

- Extend through the heels
- Keep shoulders on the floor
- Relax the neck and throat
- Keep the back straight
- Hips and tailbone on the floor

Extending through back of legs

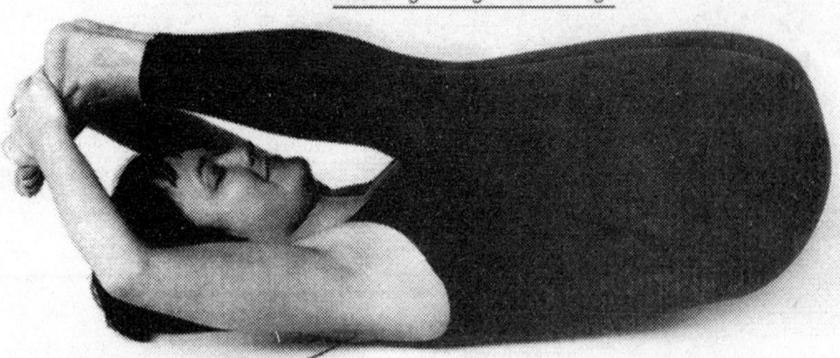

Shoulders down and back

Spine Straight

Kurmasana

TORTOISE POSE

	VATA ↓↓↓	PITTA ↓↓↓	KAPHA ↑↑↑
TIME	Long holds and repetitions	Long holds and repetitions	Short holds
BREATH	Long smooth breath or any breath	Smooth, easy breath or light Ujjayi	Ujjayi
FOCUS	Stillness and breath	Release and breath	Strengthening and extending
MOVE	Extend inner torso	Lengthen forward	Extend inner torso

MOVING INTO THE POSE

1 From Dandasâna, pg 156, spread the legs apart. Bend and draw the knees up (heels on the floor). Keep the knees and toes facing the ceiling at all times. Inhale and lengthen the torso forward. Exhale, dip the right shoulder toward the floor as you insert the right arm under the right bent knee. Repeat on the left side.

2 Inhale. Exhale, stretch the arms straight out to the sides as you bring the shoulders and head to the floor. Keep the knees in close to the armpits. Slowly straighten the legs bringing the knees down.

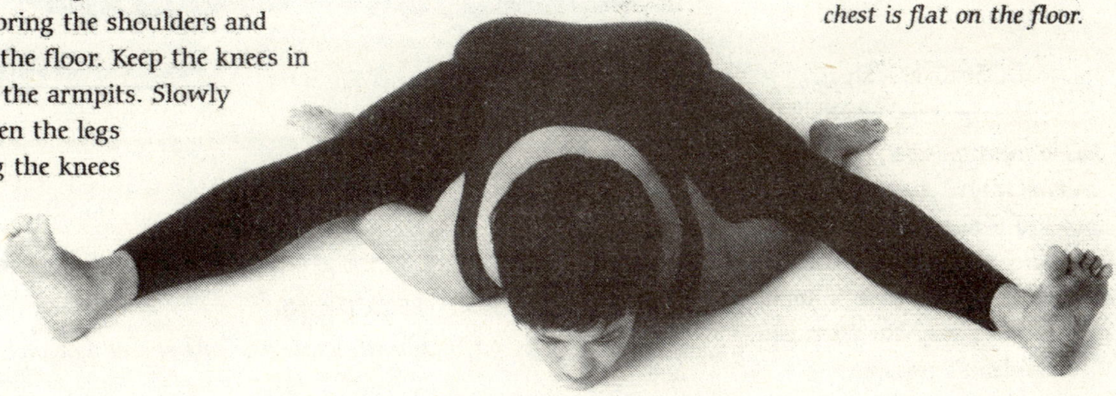

HOLDING THE POSE

Inhale and receive the breath. Exhale, lengthen the spine bringing the chest and abdomen toward the floor and extending the arms and legs along the floor. Hold for 30-60 seconds to begin.

COMPLETING THE POSE

Exhale, bend the knees and release the arms. Bring the torso up and return to Dandasana.

LEARNING AT HOME: MODIFICATIONS

The pose is easier with the legs a little closer together. Use gravity to lengthen forward.

IMPORTANT POINTS

- Knees always face the ceiling
- Move forward from the low back
- Lengthen the spine
- Bring abdomen toward the floor
- Extend arms and legs outward

GENERAL PRECAUTIONS

For hyperextended elbows, work with the elbows slightly bent until your chest is flat on the floor.

Paschimottanasana

FULL FORWARD BEND

	VATA ↓↓↓	PITTA ↓↓↓	KAPHA ↑↑↑
TIME	Long holds and repetitions	Long holds and repetitions	Short holds
BREATH	Long, smooth or light Ujjayi	Smooth, easy breath or light Ujjayi	Ujjayi
FOCUS	Stillness, breath	Release, breath	Strengthening and extending
MOVE	Extend inner torso, lengthen neck	Soften the neck, lengthen forward	Strong legs, extend spine, open chest

Paschimottanasana literally means extension of the west side of body.

MOVING INTO THE POSE

Sit in Dandasana, pg 156. Exhale as you press the knees down, lengthen the legs, and extend out through the heels (it is ok if heels lift up). Inhale, raise the arms up lengthening the spine. Exhale, pivoting from the hip joints, extend the arms and torso forward. Move from the lower back to bring the abdomen toward the thighs. Keep the spine straight and the chest open.

HOLDING THE POSE

With every inhalation, lengthen and strengthen the legs. With every exhalation, extend the straight spine up and forward bringing the abdomen to the thighs. Hold for 30-60 seconds to begin.

DOSHIC NOTES

Paschimottanasana regulates Apana Vayu. As with most forward bends it soothes Vata imbalance and reduces Pitta. To help balance the increase in Kapha in this pose, keep the chest as open as possible.

GENERAL PRECAUTIONS

Not for those with sciatica or any spinal disk problems.

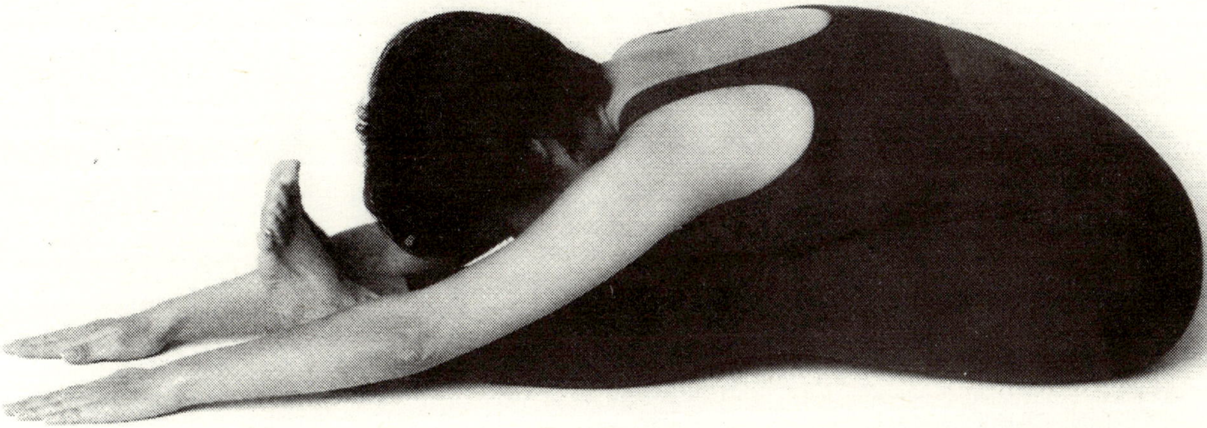

COMPLETING THE POSE

As you inhale, pivot at the hip joints, bringing the torso up to sitting. Re-establish Dandasana and see how you feel.

IMPORTANT ACTIONS

- Press the knees down
- Initiate movement from low spine
- Spine moves up toward head and forward toward the floor
- Belly lengthens forward
- Shoulders down from the ears
- Chin is in
- Neck is soft
- Shoulders and arms relaxed

LEARNING AT HOME: MODIFICATIONS

• Use a belt or towel around the legs so that the back may remain straight as you stretch the hamstrings.

• Brace your feet with a chair to keep the balls of the feet moving back and hold the back of the chair with the back straight.

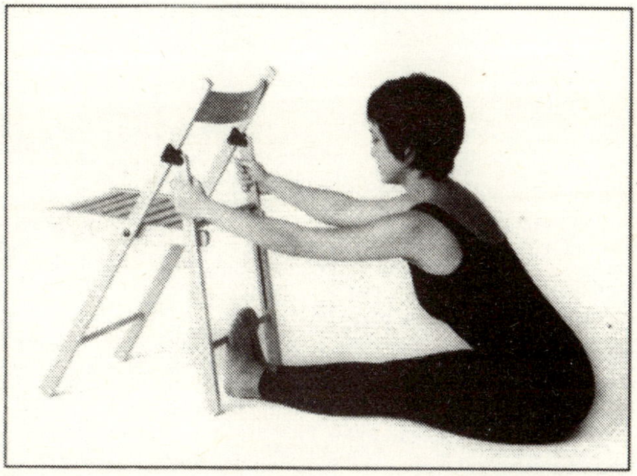

TWISTS

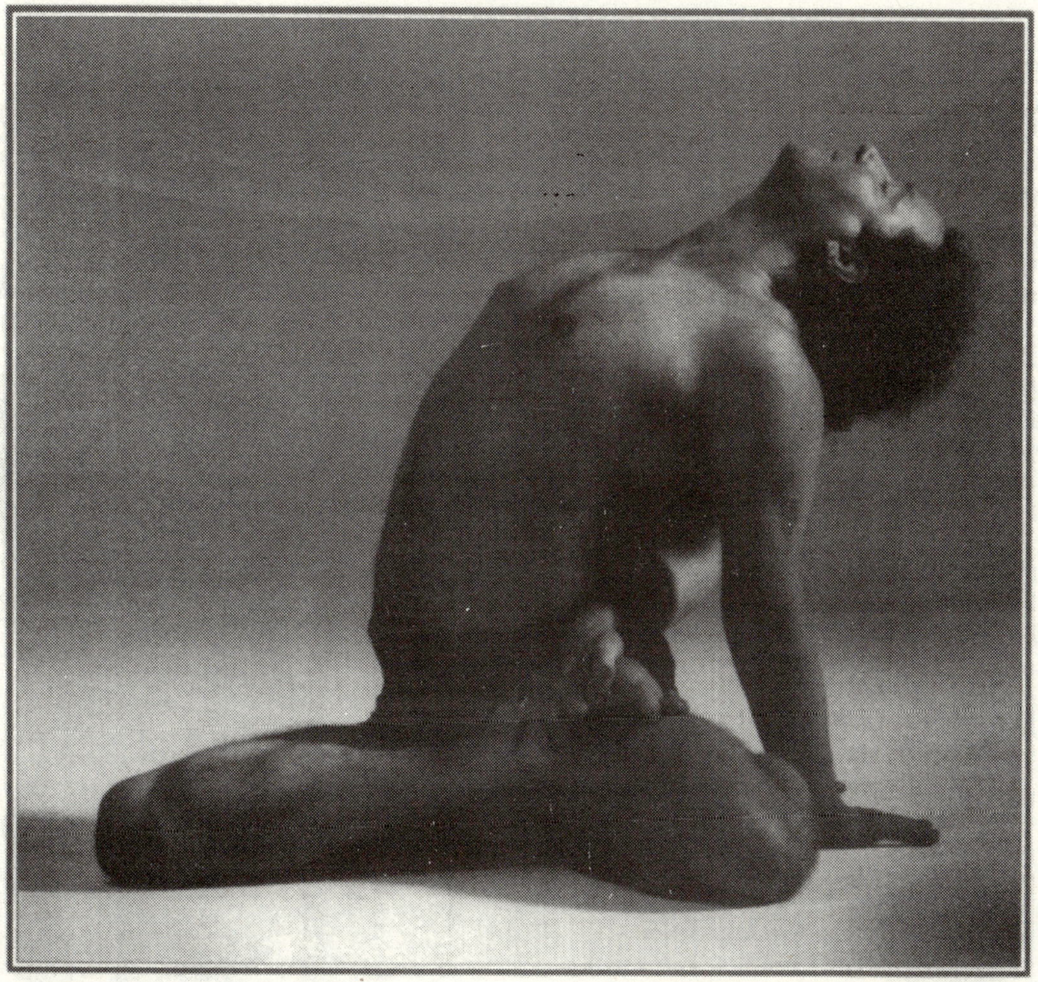

ERICH SCHIFFMANN IN BHARADVAJASANA II

Two Chair Twists

SITTING AND STANDING CHAIR TWISTS

	VATA ↓	PITTA ↓	KAPHA ↓
TIME	Moderate holds	Any holds – no strain	Moderate-Long holds
BREATH	Full, expanded breathing	Full, expanded breathing	Full, expanded breathing
FOCUS	Stillness, breath	Easy grounding, breath	Rotating around the spine
MOVE	Grounding, lifting, and rotating body around the spine	Lifting and rotating the body around the spine	Lift, rotation, opening the chest

MOVING INTO THE POSE

Sitting Chair Twist

1 Sit sideways on a chair (without arms). Sit with the spine pulled up (check: feel the spine, pull any protruding bones in by pulling the spine into the body). Keep the weight even on both sitting bones.

2 Inhale and take hold of both sides of the back of the chair as pictured. Exhale, lift and rotate the torso toward the right.

Standing Chair Twist

1 Place a chair sideways to the wall or a kitchen counter. Stand tall with the spine pulled up and into the body. Inhale and place the right foot on the chair and the hands (shoulder width apart) on the wall or kitchen counters.

2 Exhale and rotate the whole torso toward the wall on the right. Use the spine as the center of the rotation and turn the body around it.

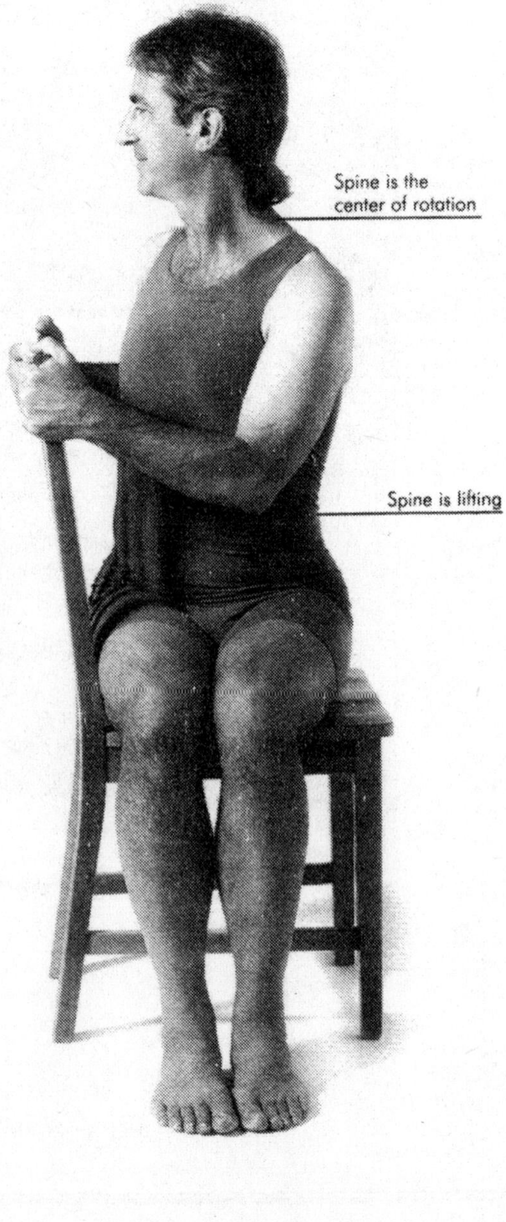

HOLDING THE POSE

1 On each inhalation establish the Foundation Points. On each exhalation, lift and turn focusing on the Important Actions.

2 Turning the head is optional. If it feels right for you, then turn the head toward the right, comfortably looking over the right shoulder. Hold for 20-40 seconds.

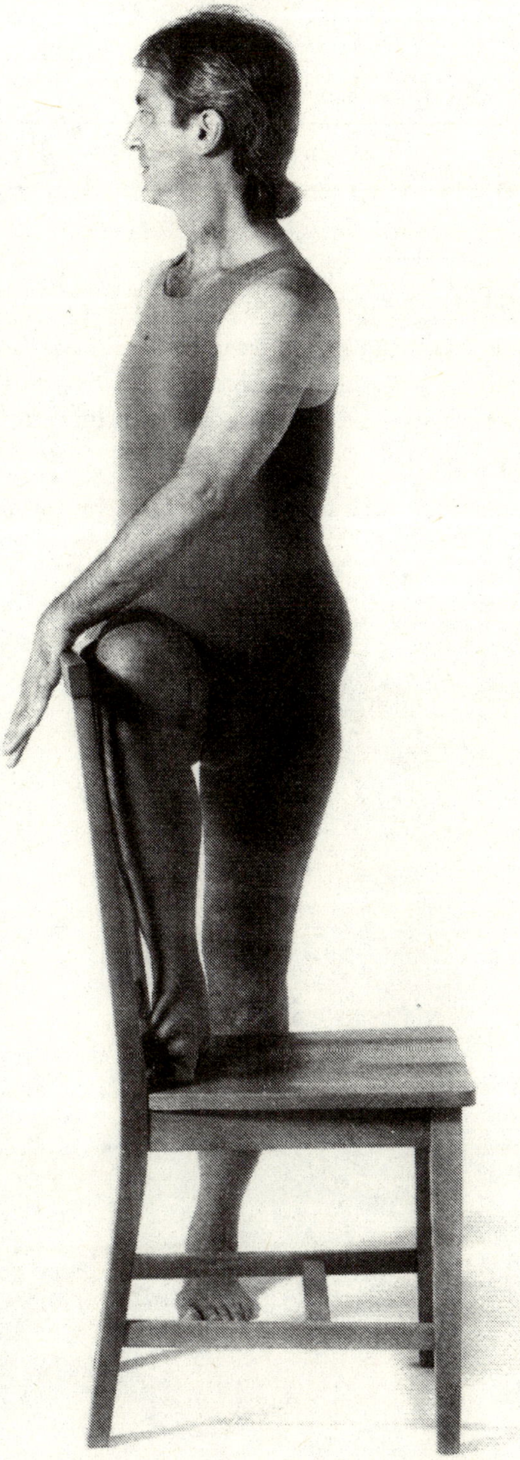

COMPLETING THE POSE

Return back to where you began. Repeat on the other side.

IMPORTANT ACTIONS

- Sit or stand evenly
- Turn the base of your spine first
- Spine lifts to turn
- Abdomen is turning
- Head is last to turn

DOSHIC NOTES

As with most twists, these positions reduce Vata, Pitta, and Kapha.

GENERAL PRECAUTIONS

- *It is most important to breathe fully in twists – feel free to breathe through your mouth.*
- *If there is back pain, stop practice and consult a physician.*

Bharadvajasana I

LEGS SIDE SITTING TWIST POSE

	VATA ↓	PITTA ↓	KAPHA ↓
TIME	Any holding	Any holding	Any holding
BREATH	Full easy breathing	Full easy breathing	Full easy breathing
FOCUS	Stillness and stability	Grounding and breathing	Lifting and breathing
MOVE	Hold hips down, lift and rotate	Lift, lengthen, and rotate	Lift, rotate, opening chest

MOVING INTO THE POSE

1 From Dandasana, pg 156, bend the knees and bring both of the feet to the left hip (right arch under left ankle). Keep both buttocks on the floor.

2 With the fingertips on the floor for support, turn the torso half way to the right. Then take hold of the outside of the right thigh with the left hand. Place the right hand on the floor behind you for support.

HOLDING THE POSE

With every inhalation, sit into the floor. Keep the feet close to the hip with the knees facing forward. With every exhalation lift the spine and turn (first from the base of the spine) to the right. Hold 15-30 seconds.

Optional: The head completes the twist by turning easily to the right.

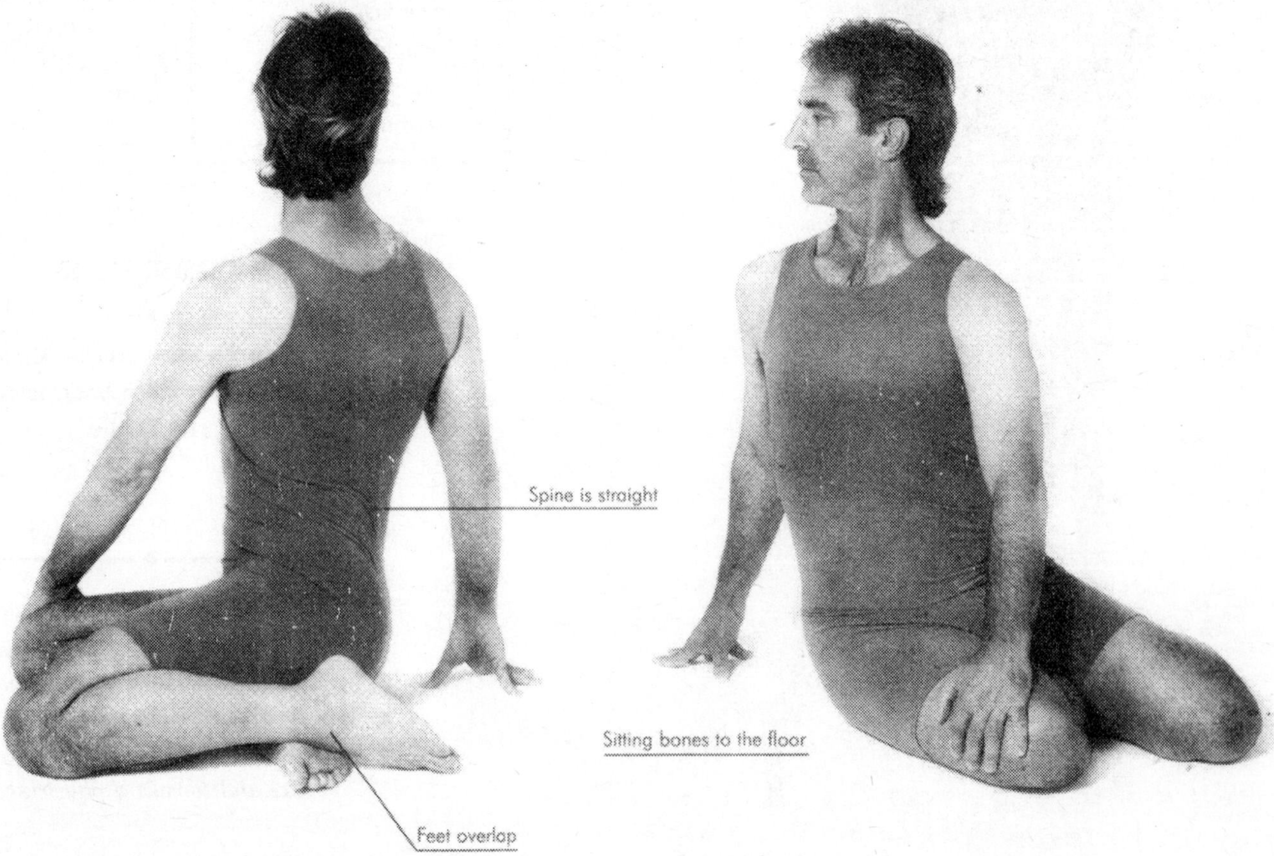

COMPLETING THE POSE

Inhale; straighten the legs and return back to Dandasana. Repeat on the other side.

LEARNING AT HOME: MODIFICATIONS

- More advanced arms: From Step 2, place the back of your left hand (with the palm facing out) on the outside of the right thigh. Slide the hand under the outer right thigh until the palm of the hand is flat on the floor. Turning to the right, reach around and take hold of your left arm above the elbow.
- If both sitting bones are not touching the floor, support the raised one with folded blankets.

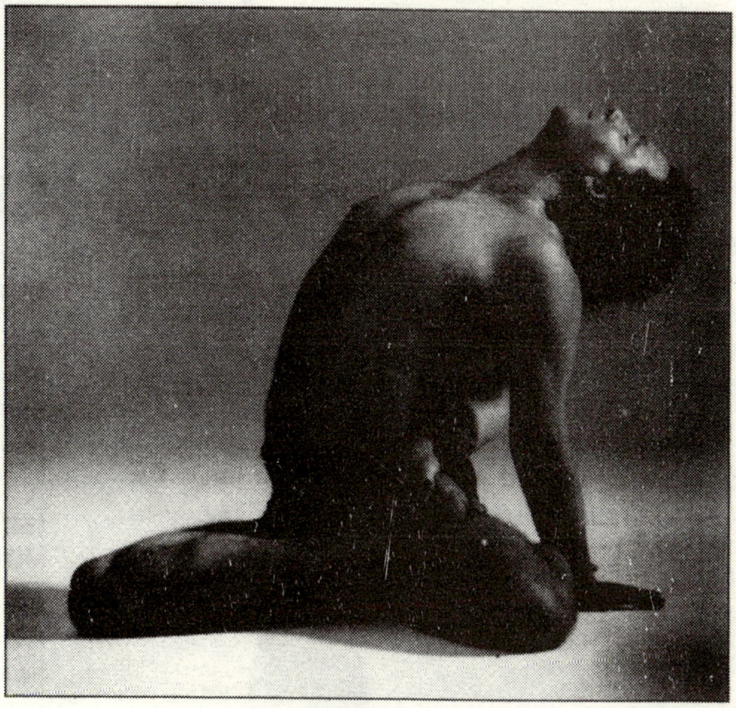

Bharadvajasana II Variation

IMPORTANT ACTIONS

- Lengthen the spine
- Keep the chest open
- Left shoulder and arm lengthen

GENERAL PRECAUTIONS

- *It is most important to breathe fully in twisting movements even if you need to breathe through the mouth.*
- *With existing back pain, do not practice twisting until you consult a physician.*

Marichyasana I

SAGE TWIST I

	VATA ↓	PITTA ↓	KAPHA ↓
TIME	Any holding time	Any holding time	Any holding time
BREATH	Full, expanded breathing	Full, expanded breathing	Full, expanded breathing
FOCUS	Stillness, stability	Grounding, breath	Lifting and breathing
MOVE	Ground, lift and rotate	Internal lift and rotation	Extension, rotation, open chest

MOVING INTO THE POSE

Position #1

1 Sit in Dandasana, pg 156. Bend the left leg and place the foot on the floor, heel close to the right sitting bone. Both knees face the ceiling. The ball of the left foot is turned inward (pigeon-toed) slightly.

2 Press the floor with the right fingertips and lift the spine. Turn to the right and reach the left arm forward, placing the back of the left upper arm on the inside front of the left knee. Wrap the left arm around the left knee and clasp the hands behind the back.

3 Sitting evenly on both sitting bones, lengthen the spine upward and turn to the right (begin the rotation from the base of spine). Keep the chest open and extend through the right leg.

Optional: Let the head turn right, comfortably looking over the right shoulder.

Position #2

Complete steps 1 and 2 of Position #1. Then bend the torso forward over the straight leg. Keep the lower back straight as you move forward. Chest open.

HOLDING THE POSE

Keep your breathing full and steady at all times. On inhalations, focus on foundation points. On exhalations, focus on Important Actions. Remain in each position for 10-30 seconds, breathing fully.

LEARNING AT HOME: MODIFICATIONS

Hold on to a belt or towel if the hands do not meet in back.

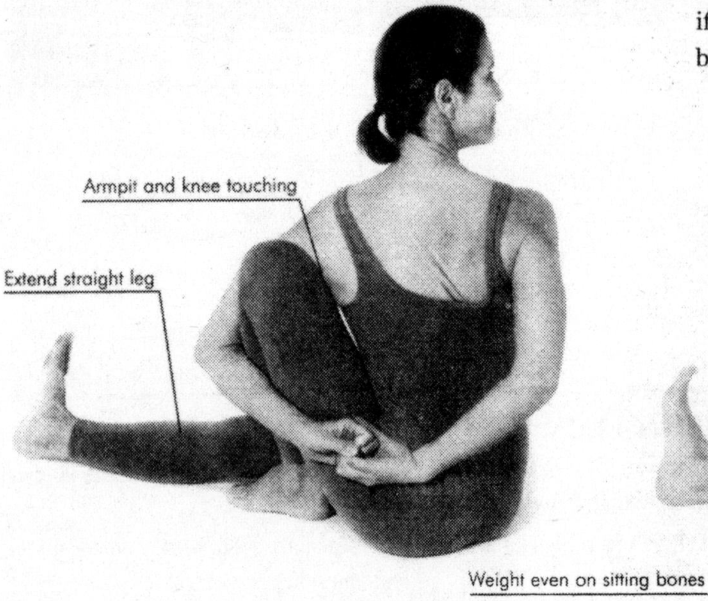

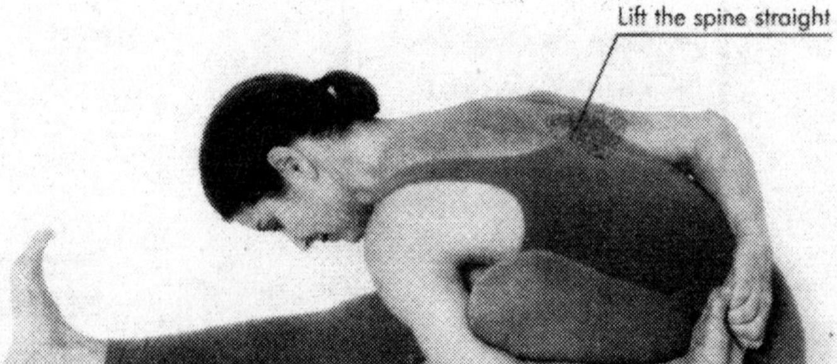

Marichyasana II

SAGE TWIST II

	VATA ↓	PITTA ↓	KAPHA ↓
TIME	Any holding time	Any holding time	Any holding time
BREATH	Full breathing	Full breathing	Full breathing
FOCUS	Stillness, breath	Breath, and lifting spine	Lifting, breathing
MOVE	Extend spine, open the chest	Extend spine, open the chest	Extend spine, open the chest

MOVING INTO THE POSE

Sit in Marichyasana I. Place the left foot high on top of the right thigh so you are in half lotus.

HOLDING THE POSE

1 Clasp the left wrist with the right hand. Exhale and bend forward to place the head on the left knee. If possible reach the chin beyond the knee bringing it to the floor.

2 Fully inhale as you come back up to sitting. Exhale as you bend forward again. Repeat, extending forward a little more with each breath. Repeat to other side.

COMPLETING THE POSE

Exhale, release the arms and legs returning to Dandasana. Repeat to other side.

GENERAL PRECAUTIONS

- *If there is back pain do not practice twists and consult a physician.*
- *Neck problems need not turn the head.*
- *Marichyasana II: Make sure the hips are well opened before practicing half lotus.*

DOSHIC NOTES

As with most twists this posture reduces Vata, Pitta, & Kapha. Be sure to breathe fully. These twists stabilize the spine.

IMPORTANT ACTIONS

- Breathe fully
- Extend the spine up and forward
- Keep the chest open
- Foot presses the floor
- Abdomen is turning
- Move from base of spine

Marichyasana III

SAGE TWIST III

	VATA ↓	PITTA ↓	KAPHA ↓
TIME	Moderate holding	Any holding	Any holding
BREATH	Full breathing	Full breathing	Full breathing
FOCUS	Stillness and breath	Easy grounding and breath	Lifting and breathing
MOVE	Grounding, internal lift and rotation	Grounding, internal lift and rotation	Lift, rotation, opening the chest

MOVING INTO THE POSE

1 Sit in Dandasana, pg 156. Bend the left leg and place the foot close to the left sit bone. Both knee-caps face the ceiling. Turn the ball of the left foot slightly inward (pigeon toe). Press the fingertips on the floor and elongate the spine upward. Sit evenly on both sitting bones

2 Inhale and place the right upper arm on the outside of the left knee and use one of the three arm positions shown on photos.

3 Exhale and slowly turn to the left, beginning the rotation from the base of the spine.

HOLDING THE POSE

1 With every exhalation, lift the spine and ribs as you continue to turn the abdomen. Extend through the right leg.

2 Inhale and let the head turn toward the left, comfortably looking over the left shoulder (optional). Hold 15-30 seconds breathing fully.

COMPLETING THE POSE

On an exhalation, return to Dandasana. Repeat other side.

LEARNING AT HOME: MODIFICATIONS

If the hands are too far apart in the pose, use a belt.

IMPORTANT ACTIONS

- Turn from base of spine
- Breathe fully at all times
- Extend the spine upward
- Lengthen the straight leg

GENERAL PRECAUTIONS

If there is existing back pain or it is created by the pose, do not practice twisting movements until consulting a physician.

Ardha Matsyendrasana I

HALF FISH I

	VATA ↓	PITTA ↓	KAPHA ↓
TIME	Moderate holding	Any holding	Any holding
BREATH	Full breathing	Full breathing	Full breathing
FOCUS	Stillness and breath	Easy grounding and breath	Lifting and breathing
MOVE	Grounding, internal lift and rotation	Grounding, internal lift and rotation	Lift, rotation, opening the chest

MOVING INTO THE POSE

Level I

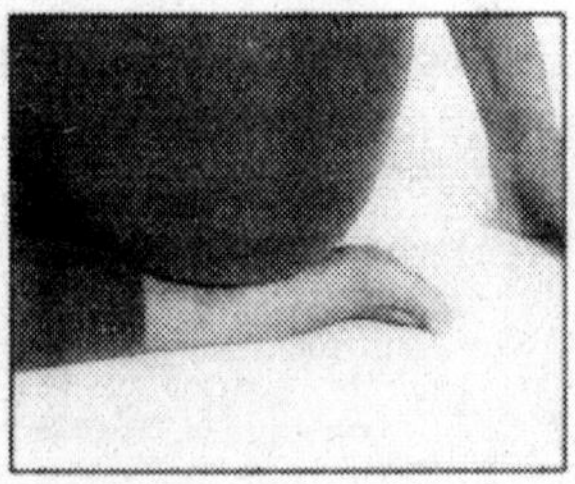

1 From Dandasana, pg 156, bend the right knee keeping the leg on the floor, sole of the foot facing up. Sit on the right heel so that the left sitting bone is directly on the arch of the foot (right knee faces forward). *Note:* sit bone pressing into the arch is reflexology for the spine.

2 Take the left foot over the right knee and onto the floor on the outside of the right leg.

3 Press the floor with the fingertips to elongate the spine upward. Slowly turn to the left beginning the rotation from the base of the spine. Place the right arm on the outside of the left knee with the hand and forearm vertical. Inhale, lifting the ribs; exhale and turn.

Level II

4 Bring the back of the right armpit in contact with the left knee. Move the back of the right arm around to encircle the left knee. Clasp the left hand as on page 183.

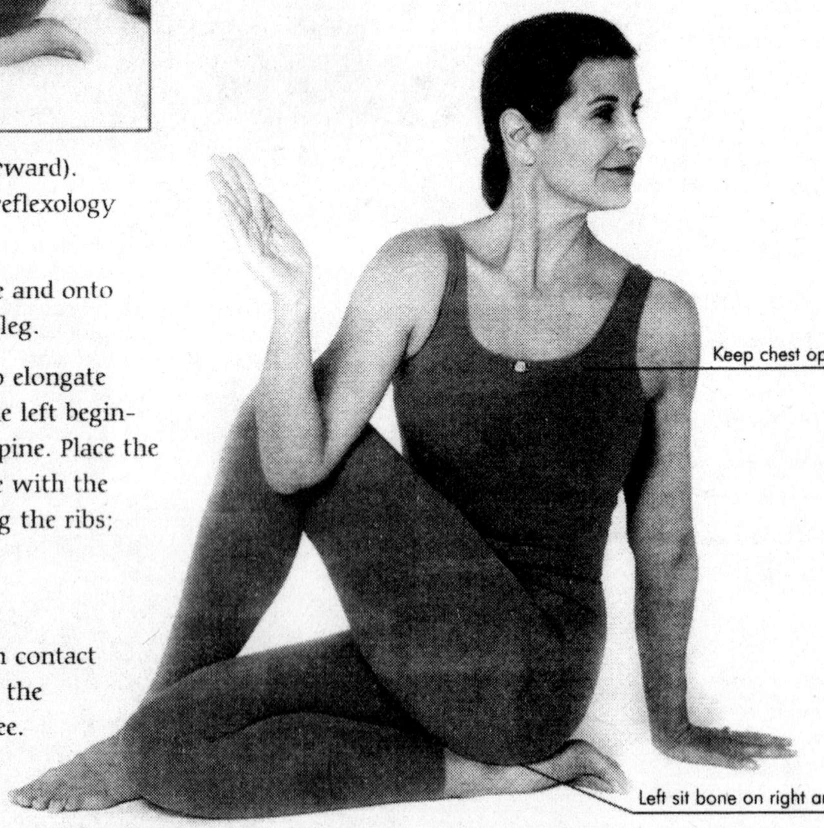

Level I

HOLDING THE POSE

It is most important that the breath remain full and steady at all times in all twisting poses. Each inhale, ground and balance. Each exhale, straighten, lift, and turn the spine. Hold 15-30 seconds to begin.

Level II

COMPLETING THE POSE

Return to Dandasana. Repeat to other side.

IMPORTANT ACTIONS

- Keep the torso lifting
- Turn from the base of the spine
- Bring the trunk closer to the leg

LEARNING AT HOME

• Alternate arm position: slide the arm under the bent knee as shown.

• Use a belt or towel if the hands are too far apart.

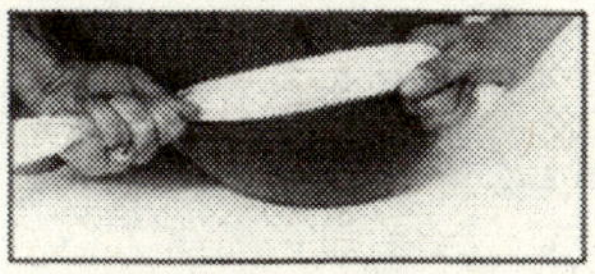

• If needed sit and lean on the wall to help with balance.

• You may place a folded blanket under the foot for comfort.

GENERAL PRECAUTIONS

If there is back pain or discomfort is created by this pose, stop twisting movements and consult a physician.

Alligator Twists Variations I–IV

	VATA ↓	PITTA ↓	KAPHA ↓
TIME	Moderate holding	Any holding	Any holding
BREATH	Full breathing	Full breathing	Full breathing
FOCUS	Moving slowly on the breath	Move slowly as you breathe	Move as you breath
MOVE	Lengthen and lift spine to twist	Lengthen and lift spine to twist	Lengthen and lift spine to twist

TECHNIQUE FOR THE POSES

There are four positions. The instructions are similar for each with the exception of the foot and leg placement. Begin lying on the back, legs straight and arms out to the sides (on the floor) in line with the shoulders—making a 'T' position of the body. We will call this 'center.' Breathe evenly and fully. Make the movements 'fit' the breathing, both taking the same length of time.

Position #1

1 Keep your legs together and feet as if you are standing on them. Inhale push through the heels and straighten the legs. Hold the legs strongthroughout.

2 As you exhale turn the hips and legs to the left. The legs and feet remain touching each other, not the floor. Shoulders, arms, and hands remain on the floor. Let the head turn toward the right. Hold for a few breaths.

3 As you inhale bring the body back to center.

4 As you exhale turn the body to the right. Hold for a few breaths. As you inhale move back to center.

Position #2

1 Inhale and place your right heel between the first two toes of your left foot. Turn your legs and feet toward the left as you exhale. Keep your legs strong and shoulders on the floor. Turn your head to the right if you like.

2 As you inhale move back to center. Exhale the right foot down. Inhale the left foot up.

3 Exhale and turn to the right. Hold for a few breaths and return to center on an inhalation.

Position #3

1 As you inhale bend your right knee placing your right foot on your left knee. Continue to maintain a strong straight left leg pushing through the heel.

2 As you exhale turn the lower body toward the left. Hold for a few breaths.

3 As you inhale move back to center. Exhale the right leg down. Inhale the left foot up onto the right knee.

4 Exhale and turn to the right. Hold for a few breaths and return to center on an inhalation.

Position #4

1 As you inhale bend both knees and bring them to your chest. As you exhale turn your hips and legs to the left bringing your knees up and under your left elbow. Always keep your shoulders flat on the floor. Head moves toward the right if comfortable. Hold for a few breaths.

2 Inhale and move the hips and legs back to center. Repeat other side.

COMPLETING THE POSE

Relax on your back into Savasana, pg 190.

DOSHIC NOTES

These spinal rotations are beneficial for Vata, Pitta, and Kapha. It reduces fat, tones the liver, spleen, and pancreas, and is good for digestive health.

GENERAL PRECAUTIONS

If there is existing back pain or discomfort is created by the pose, stop practicing twists and see your physician.

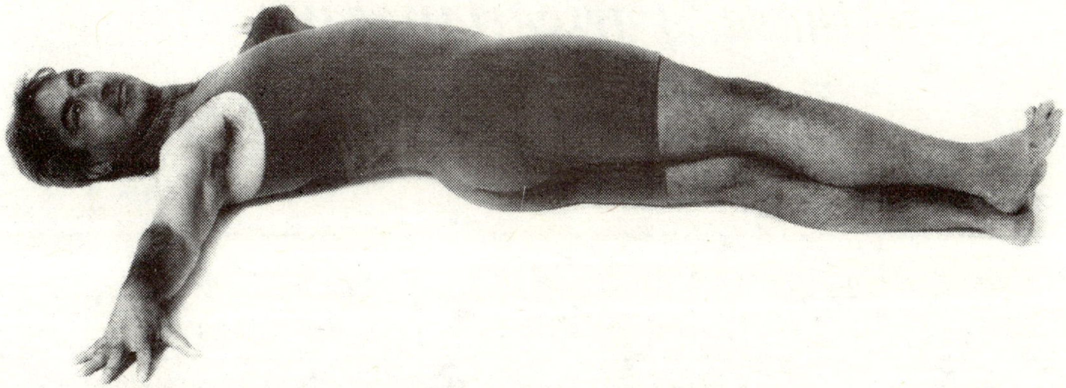

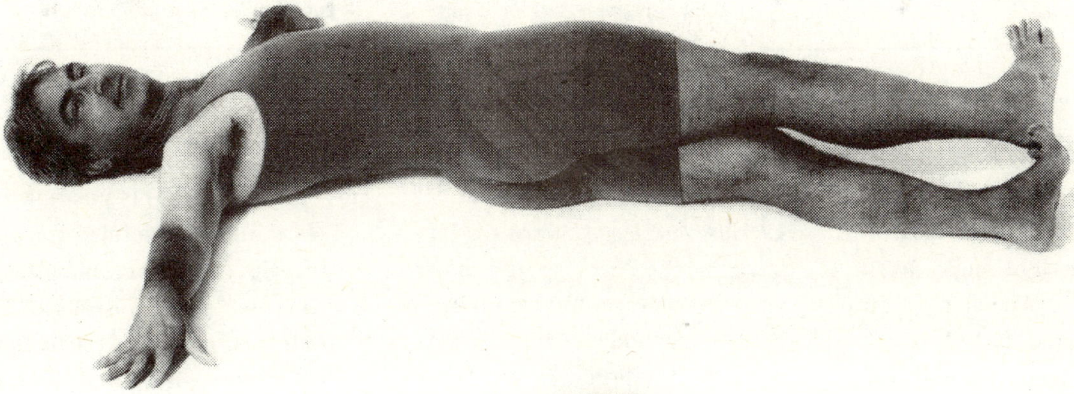

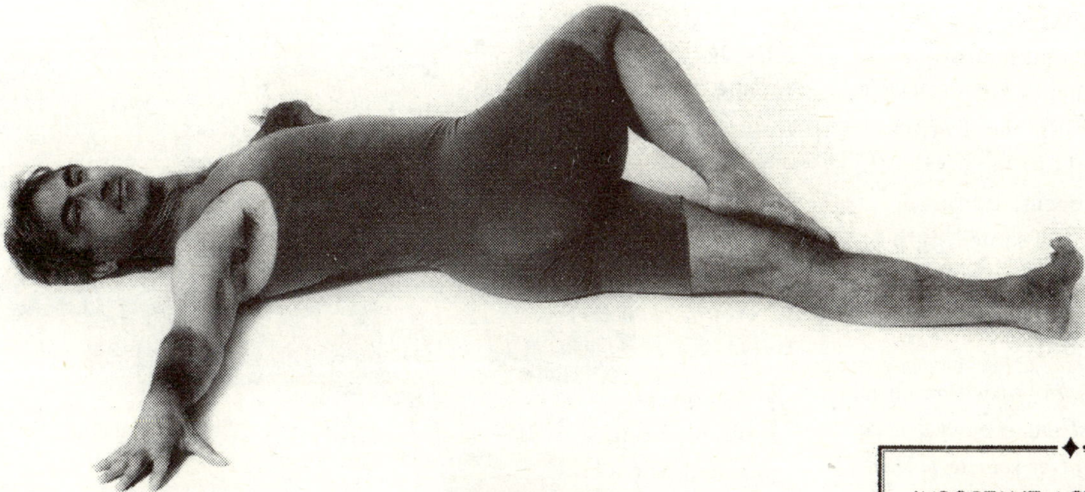

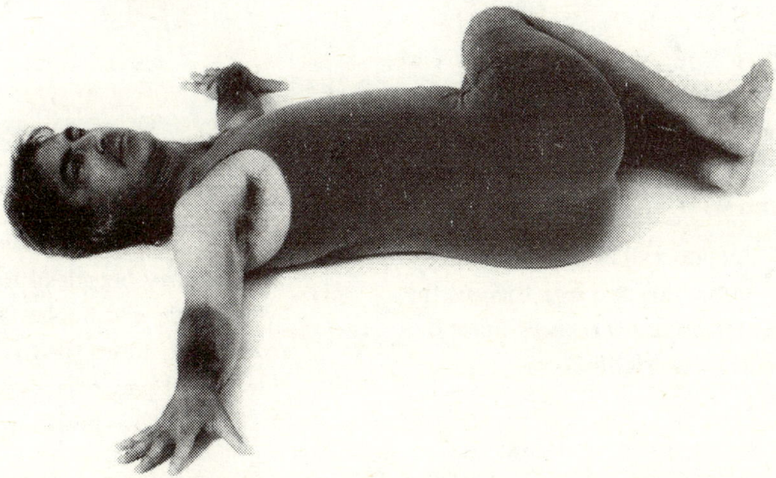

IMPORTANT ACTIONS

- Always full deep breathing
- Turn and change positions on the breath
- Make each movement the same length of time as each breath.
- Push through the heel of the straight leg
- Lift the spine inward and upward and then turn
- Shoulders, arms, and hands remain flat on the floor

Jathara Parivartanasana

REVOLVING STOMACH POSE

	VATA ↓	PITTA ↓	KAPHA ↓
TIME	Moderate holding	Any holding without strain	Any holding
BREATH	Full breathing	Full breathing	Full breathing
FOCUS	Straight spine and legs	Widened back, lengthened legs	Pushing through the feet
MOVE	Lengthen spine and lift to turn	Lengthen spine and lift to turn	Lengthen spine and lift to turn

PREPARATION FOR POSE

Begin lying on your back with your legs straight. Place your arms out to your sides (at right angles to the body) on the floor. The arms are in line with the shoulders and make a 'T' shape of the body. We will call this 'T' position center. Use the Ujjayi breathing and focus on making your movements 'fit' your breathing. Both the movements and breath should be long, smooth, and even. Both begin and finish together, taking the same length of time.

Beginning Position:

Practice this beginning position until the muscles are strong enough to support the weight of your legs, then move to Jathara Parivartanasana.

1 Inhale and bend your knees to your chest. Exhale as you straighten your legs, pushing the feet toward the ceiling. Extend through the heels and pull the balls of the feet down toward your face.

2 As you exhale, shift your hips a few inches over to the right. Inhale and again bend your knees and bring them down to your chest.

3 As you exhale, turn your hips and legs toward the left, bringing the knees up and under your left elbow. Draw your spine up into the body arching your upper back (shoulders and arms stay on the floor). Rotate your chest back toward your right. Inhale. With each exhalation lengthen the spine and open the chest. Remain in this position with the spine rotated for 10-20 seconds to begin breathing fully.

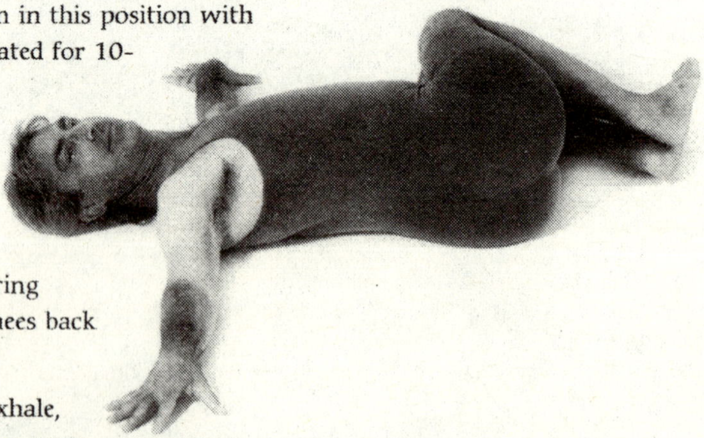

4 As you inhale, bring your bent knees back to center.

5 As you exhale, straighten your legs and shift your hips to center and then to the left. Inhale and bend your knees.

6 As you exhale, slowly turn your hips and legs toward the right bringing the knees up and under your right elbow.

7 Remain in this position with your spine rotated for a few breaths (10-20 seconds). Return to center on an inhalation. Exhale, bringing the feet to the floor before you straighten the legs. Relax in Savasana.

DOSHIC NOTES

This spinal rotation movement is very beneficial for Vata, Pitta, and Kapha. It reduces fat, tones the liver, spleen, and pancreas. Good for digestive health.

Jathara Parivartanasana:

1 Inhale and bend your knees to your chest. Exhale as you straighten your legs, pushing feet toward the ceiling. Extend through the heels and pull the balls of the feet down toward your face.

2 As you exhale, shift your hips a few inches over to the right. Inhale.

3 As you exhale, strengthen the legs and extend out through the heels. Slowly lower your straight legs to the left, bringing your feet toward your left hand. The left side of the left foot touches the floor (or your hand). Keep the feet and legs together.

4 Draw your spine up as if you are arching your back. Rotate your chest back toward your right as the legs extend to the left. As you inhale, strengthen and lengthen the legs extending out through the heels. With each exhalation lengthen the spine and open the chest. Remain in this position with the spine rotated for 10-20 seconds to begin breathing fully.

5 As you exhale, bring your legs back up to center. Remember to move and breathe with meditative awareness.

6 As you inhale, shift your hips to center and then to your left side.

7 As you exhale, slowly lower your straight legs to your right, bringing your feet toward your right hand. Repeat steps 3 and 4 on this side.

8 Remain in this position with your spine rotated for a few breaths (10-20 seconds). Return to center on an exhalation. Inhale. Bring the feet to the floor before you straighten the legs. Relax in Savasana.

IMPORTANT ACTIONS

- Full deep breathing
- Move with the breath
- Push through the heels
- Draw the spine into the body
- Shoulders, arms, and hands always remain on the floor
- Lengthen the top leg

LEARNING AT HOME: MODIFICATIONS

- In the beginning try using a block or bolster under your feet (or bent knees) to reduce the amount of rotation and increase your comfort.
- Try placing your buttocks against the wall with your legs extended up the wall. Slide your bent knees or straight legs down the wall into the pose on your right. Keep lengthening your hips (especially the top hip) and extending both sitting bones so they always touch the wall.

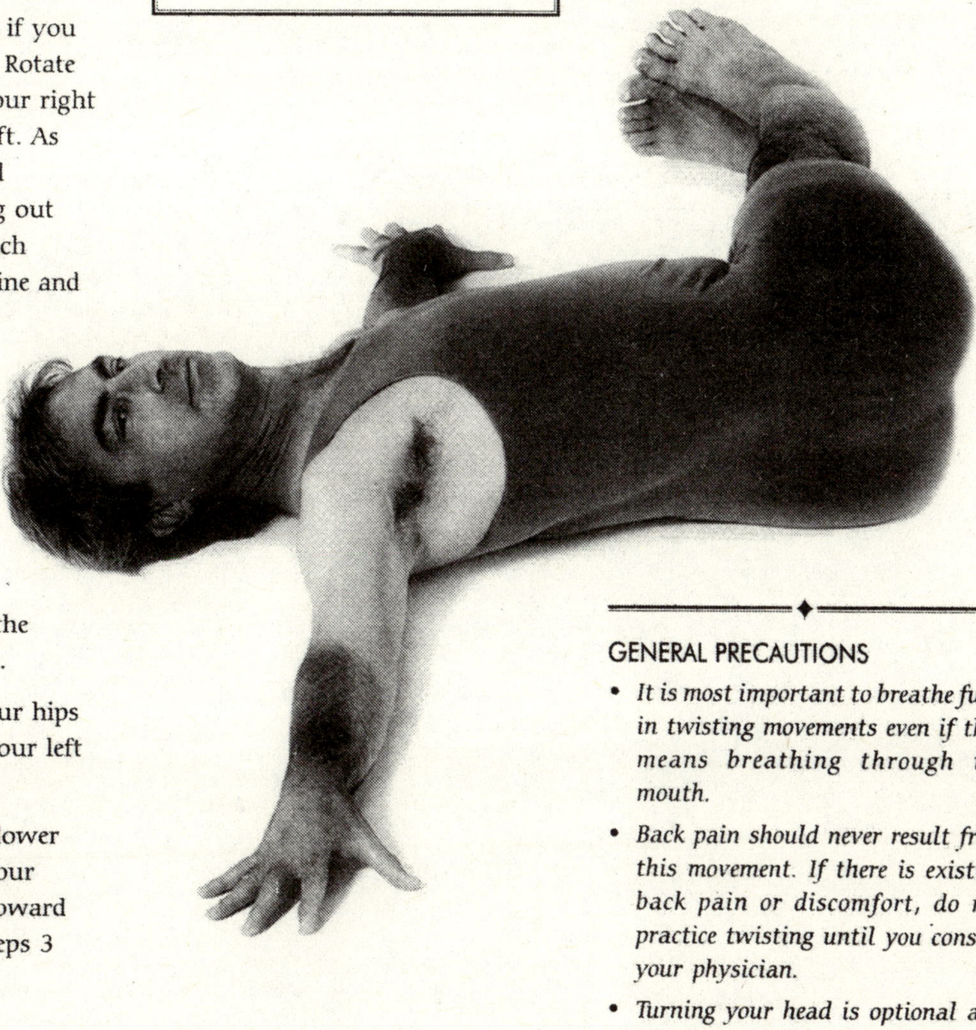

GENERAL PRECAUTIONS

- *It is most important to breathe fully in twisting movements even if that means breathing through the mouth.*
- *Back pain should never result from this movement. If there is existing back pain or discomfort, do not practice twisting until you consult your physician.*
- *Turning your head is optional and if it does not feel right for you, keep your face centered.*

ꙮ SAVASANA ꙮ

PATRICIA HANSEN IN YOGAMUDRASANA

Savasana

CORPSE POSE (RELAXATION POSE)

VATA ↓↓↓ PITTA ↓↓↓ KAPHA ↓

	VATA ↓↓↓	PITTA ↓↓↓	KAPHA ↓
TIME	Daily 20 - 30 minutes or more	Daily 15 - 25 minutes or more	Daily 5 -15 minutes
BREATH	Easy, relaxed breath	Soft, relaxed breath	Let the body breathe itself
FOCUS	Relax into stillness	Letting go into stillness	Release and relax

THE POSE

Lay comfortably on the back with the legs stretched long and slightly apart. Calf muscles are pulled to the inside of each leg. Make sure to keep the body warm. Pull the shoulders down and tuck them under you as you lengthen the arms along the floor at the sides, palms up. Lengthen the neck. Inhale deeply. Exhale and allow the whole body to let go and comfortably relax. Systematically release all tension held in each part of the body. Then release the mind by focusing on the movement of the breath through the body. Completely relax.

COMPLETING THE POSE

Slowly deepen the breath. Bring your attention into your body and gently move your fingers and toes. Inhale and bend your left knee. Keep the head in contact with the floor as you roll over onto your right side. Use the arms to push yourself up to sitting.

LEARNING AT HOME: MODIFICATIONS

Shown here are 3 Savasanas with different types of supports and coverings appropriate (and usually preferable) for each of the three doshas. Please practice Savasana in the way that feels right for you.

Here are some suggestions for a more comfortable practice:

- Place a small rolled towel under the neck for support.
- Cover the eyes with a cloth or eye bags.
- Place a small towel under the hands to keep the wrist straight and comfortable.
- Support the ankle with a rolled towel (about 3" thick).
- Cover yourself for warmth or comfort.

DOSHIC NOTES

Savasana is the most important asana as it helps relieve accumulated Vata, Pitta and stress. It should always complete your asana practice.

IMPORTANT POINTS

- Shoulders are pulled down and tucked under
- Neck is long and relaxed
- Face is parallel to floor
- Lower back is in Neutral

GENERAL PRECAUTIONS

For back problems, place a bolster or rolled blankets under the thighs and knees to lengthen the lower back. Place a roll under the neck to support its curve.

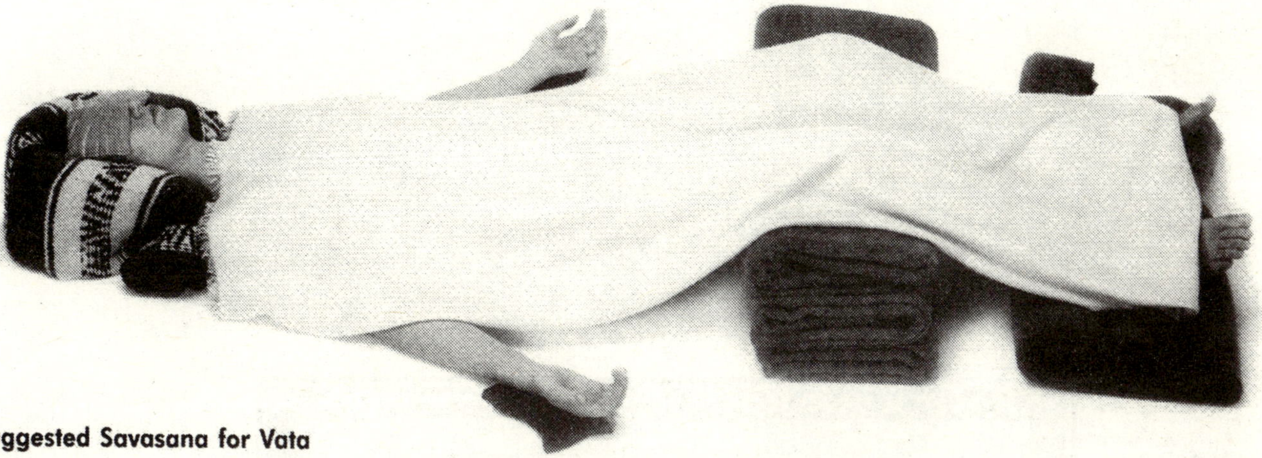

Suggested Savasana for Vata

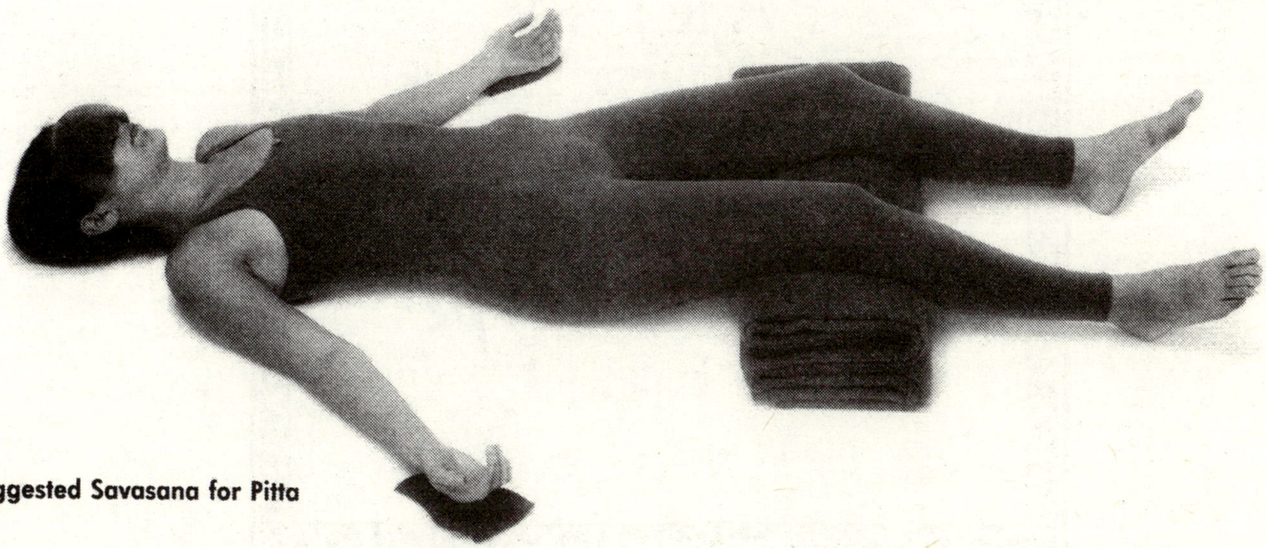

Suggested Savasana for Pitta

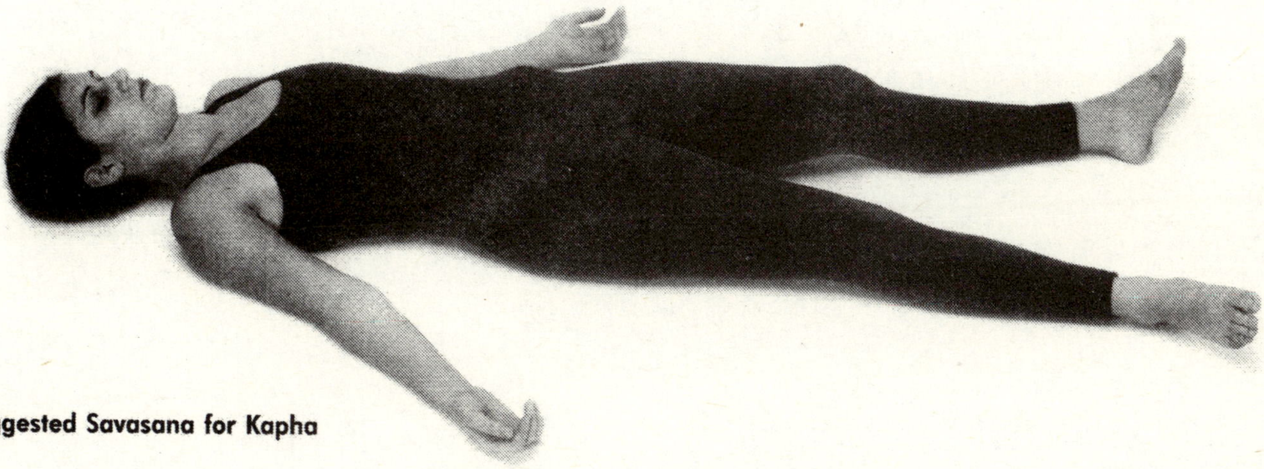

Suggested Savasana for Kapha

PART IV

Asana Sequences for Your Type

SANDRA SUMMERFIELD KOZAK IN PARIVRTTAIKA PADA SIRSASANA

IV. 10 ADAPTING YOUR PROGRAM

For a really effective Yoga practice, it is not enough to mechanically follow a series of set prescriptions. Our practice must have the same flexibility that we are trying to develop in our bodies. This chapter shows how to adapt your asana programs relative to age, health, life-style, and seasonal requirements.

ADAPTING TO YOUR CURRENT LIFE STAGE

AGE

Yoga follows the flow of nature. When we think of altering the practice of Yoga for different age groups we should remember the nature and energy of these particular groups. For example, children's programs will focus on holding their attention and having fun while giving them ways to learn about themselves and explore new experiences. According to Ayurveda, childhood is the Kapha phase of life, so postures and movements to reduce Kapha (mucus) are important. These should aim at clearing congestion from the head and sinuses, and preventing Kapha from increasing in the lungs and lymph glands. This way, children will suffer from fewer colds, flu, or allergies.

Teens and young adults have more energy and need to express it. So, in asana practice, a more intense, rajasic style of practice is appropriate, having a fair amount of movement and exertion. After adolescence begins the Pitta stage of life in which people want to be noticed and achieve things that give them recognition in the external world. Young men, in particular, easily become overheated and aggressive. This means that the practice, however vigorous, should end on a cooling and calming note, with proper relaxation, or Pitta will be aggravated.

As we grow older our energy level slowly lowers. We will want our Yoga practice to increase it rather than deplete it. An appropriate practice would focus on revitalizing body systems and maintaining flexibility and strength. Older, mature people are naturally quieter. A quieter practice that emphasizes the process of the practice, working consciously with the breath, is much more beneficial than a practice that uses large quantities of energy. Taking on strenuous postures is best done in a systematic way to avoid injuries.

The onset of old age marks the stage of Vata dosha. The aging process increases Vata, depleting our bodily fluids and restricting our movement. It sets in motion various degenerative diseases, particularly arthritis and other conditions that damage the bones. To counter this, we need an asana program that maintains a healthy range of motion for all the joints in the body, particularly the spine. Restorative poses become necessary both to sustain energy after difficult postures and to restore vitality when overly tired or stressed.

As asana is an ideal exercise to reduce Vata, it becomes more important to practice it as we get older, particularly if we are of Vata constitution. For those who want to live longer, asana is the ideal exercise. As the baby boomer generation becomes elderly in the coming years, they are going to want to emphasize asana practice even more. Through releasing Vata, it opens up the energy of Prana to renew us at a very deep level of body and mind.

Helpful Yoga practices for the elderly include: Eye exercises to maintain vision; modified or full inversions to counter the effects of gravity that age the body; Uddiyana and Mula Bandhas to give additional support; quadriceps and hamstring stretching to maintain mobility; upper body strengthening and opening to facilitate proper breathing; and general strengthening and stretching.

Older people naturally become more introverted and contemplative. Old age marks the period in life in which our outer or material development naturally gives way to an inner or spiritual quest. Developing the mind by practicing concentration (Dharana) techniques that sharpen the focus and meditation (Dhyana) to release the past are important at this time.

Of course, individuals in each group will have different energy levels and will want to tailor their programs accordingly. It is also important to remember that every age group will benefit from breathing practices and regular relaxation practices. Note the table of the stages of life below. The years given are only approximate. The shift from one stage to another is by degrees.

Stages of Life

Dosha	Age	Orientation
Kapha	0 – 18	Enjoyment
Pitta	18 – 55	Achievement
Vata	55+	Spiritual Development

SEX

Your yoga practice is an excellent tool to bring the active and passive energies of your body into balance, which makes it less prone to injury, overuse problems, and premature aging.

Male energy is aggressive and strong but can be inflexible and rigid. Men tend to be stiff and need more stretching to keep their energy flowing. Shoulders, legs, and hips should be made more open to create balance with the strength. Most men need to work at learning to maintain their stretches with even breathing for a period of at least forty to sixty seconds each.

Female energy is adaptable but not always energetic or determined. Women tend to be weaker than they are stiff, so to bring them to balance includes strengthening as well as stretching. In general, women need to strengthen their upper bodies, arms and pelvic stabilizer muscles. They benefit from strengthening and stretching the legs including the adductors and abductors.

MENSTRUATION

It is best not to practice asanas during your menstrual period. If the flow is excessive, you may find relief from practicing Virasana, Uttanasana, Baddha Konasana, Janu Sirsasana, Upavistha Konasana, and Paschimottanasana. If you feel it necessary to practice asana, do not do any strenuous postures like standing poses. Since the natural flow is downward during the monthly cycle, inverted poses, which reverse this downward flow, are not advised.

PREGNANCY

During the first trimester of pregnancy, you can practice any of the normal asanas. After the first trimester, do not practice any asanas that put pressure on the abdomen like cobra and bow poses. Students new to yoga should exercise caution in taking on a new yoga practice or any new or strenuous postures during the advanced stages of pregnancy. The most benefit for the mother-to-be for the delivery of the baby comes from the practice of pelvic and hip-opening poses, both standing and sitting.

Baddha Konasana and Upavista Konasana are both very good and can be practiced during the entire course of pregnancy. Also, postures that bring strength and flexibility to the spine are valuable for supporting the extra weight of the baby. Pregnant women should practice inverted poses, if they feel a desire to, and if they have had regular prior experience practicing them. But even with prior experience, it is wise to stop all inverted postures in the third trimester or at the advice of your doctor.

After childbirth do not practice asanas for at least one month. When you do restart your practice, begin slowly and gently. Keep your yoga practice mild until at least three months after delivery, allowing the body its natural and needed restoration period.

ENVIRONMENT: REGIONAL WEATHER, SEASONAL CHANGES

The doshas reflect seasonal and environmental influences. We must adjust for these in order to create the most effective practice.

The desert, where the air is dry, warm and clear is a Kapha-reducing environment. Kapha types are so well balanced by the desert environment that they can practice a more generalized yoga practice in that climate. But Vata and Pitta types do not do well in a desert environment and should avoid the excess heat and dryness. All the poses that increase Kapha will be beneficial to Vata and Pitta to stabilize and ground the desert's big sky heat and dry energy.

Vata is best reduced by a moist tropical environment where the temperature does not fluctuate greatly, like Hawaii. The tropics are a perfect Vata reducing climate and a balancing, enjoyable environment for them. Vatas will not need to focus so much on Vata reducing poses since the weather itself is constantly reducing excess Vata. But Pittas and Kaphas will need to work harder on their dosha-reducing programs to balance the effects of the heat and moisture.

Cool and wet weather is generally Pitta reducing. In Seattle, Washington, a Pitta type is happily cooled and moistened. However, a Vata type who lives in such cold damp climates benefit from creating warmth in their Yoga practice. Kaphas prefer a dry and warm environment, so they also benefit from practicing strenuous, heating postures in cool damp climates since that is the most Kapha provoking type of weather.

In a dry and cold environment like the high desert or the northern plains, Vata is very challenged. This climate is the opposite of what soothes them, so they will want to create heat and moisture in their lives. Pittas do well with the coolness but have problems with the intense sunlight. Kaphas do well with the dryness but find the cold difficult, so they too will benefit from practicing heating postures.

The East Coast and Midwest climate, with hot and damp summers, is Pitta aggravating in the summer. The cold and damp winters are Kapha aggravating, though as a whole these climates promote Kapha with their constant moisture. In such four season climates seasonal adjustments are very important.

Climate Factors that Reduce the Doshas

Vata	Warm & Moist
Pitta	Cool & a Little Dry
Kapha	Warm & Dry

Note that Pitta has a damp quality that makes Pittas suffer in hot damp conditions, but they do well in cool damp conditions. Heat or cold is the main factor for them. Dryness or dampness is secondary.

Seasonal Changes

As the seasons change, the environmental effects on the doshas changes. Your Yoga practice can be selected to help balance the effects of these changes in the weather.

Summer brings warmth, usually with some humidity, which means that Vata types will be soothed by the heat and moisture. But the heat increases Pitta, so Pitta types will want to practice Pitta reducing postures for balance. Vata and Kapha are pacified by the heat of the summer sun and can reduce their focus on any doshic reducing practice.

Fall has a cooling and drying effect, as the leaves begin to turn, with more moderate temperatures, so Vata will be increasing. Pitta will be decreasing with the cooling temperatures. The dryness will also keep Kapha from increasing. The focus should be on reducing Vata and increasing moisture in the bodily tissues.

Winter brings very cold and often dry weather that disturbs Vata, particularly in early winter. Kapha is increased by the cold of winter, and by the dampness that is part of many winter climates, particularly in late winter. Pittas do better in winter than the other types. However, extreme cold causes more health complaints in all types because the body requires a significant amount of warmth. Therefore, winter is the main season for colds, flu and other infectious diseases. Maintaining a more active asana program in the winter helps maintain our bodily warmth and power of circulation in order to prevent such diseases.

Spring is a season typically of wet and cool weather that is Kapha in nature and good for reducing Pitta. While Vata benefits from the moisture and rising temperatures of spring, it is increased by stormy and windy weather. While this is more common in the fall, it can happen in any season and varies by climate. In many areas, like the Southwest, spring is also windy.

We must remember the nature of our home environment as well because we spend more time indoors. In winter, many people, even in wet climates, use dry heat that has Vata aggravating properties. In the summer, cool and dry air conditioning can also aggravate Vata. Make sure to have the appropriate temperature and humidity in your house, particularly in the room in which you sleep.

Seasonal Effects on the Doshas

Summer *(hot with some humidity)*	Vata -	Pitta ++	Kapha -
Fall *(cool and dry)*	Vata +	Pitta -	Kapha -
Winter *(cold and damp)*	Vata +	Pitta -	Kapha +
Spring *(warm and wet)*	Vata -	Pitta +	Kapha +

BEHAVIORAL AND LIFE-STYLE CONSIDERATIONS

Each doshic type tends to a behavior and lifestyle that increases its own energy. Vata types are prone to excessive activity because that is the normal expression of Vata. On a physical level, this manifests as restless moving, exercising and traveling. On a social level, there is much busyness with unstable and changeable work and relationship situations. Vatas have hectic lives, ever engaged in new projects, constantly talking and not taking proper care of themselves through adequate food or rest. Asana practice should aim at calming Vata by strengthening their focus and stilling their activity.

Pitta types are disturbed by excess heat, drive and passion, pursuing high levels of achievement in life. Their positive focus often becomes excessive or obsessive, preventing them from being calm and relaxed. They are typically driven, intense and unyielding. Asana practice should aim at releasing this drive, soothing their irritation, and allowing them to be receptive and open.

Kaphas tend toward a sedentary life, pursuing ease and comfort, with reduced activity or expression, which is the opposite of what they need. They love to sleep but do better with much less sleep than they think they need. It is the challenge of Kapha to fight this sedentary lifestyle and stay active, alert and motivated. Making their Yoga practice dynamic and strenuous helps balance this Kapha tendency.

NUTRITIONAL INTAKE

Ayurveda recommends specific diets for each doshic type. You can examine these in various books on Ayurvedic diet and cooking. Food is what goes into the body and exercise is what comes out of it. For proper asana, which is right exercise, proper nutrition is necessary. For this, an Ayurvedic diet is the best place to start.

Vata types need a rich and nutritive diet, balanced by the proper amount of spices to insure good digestion of heavier food articles. This can be achieved by a diet based on whole grains, beans, seeds and nuts, dairy products and root vegetables, along with mild spices like ginger, cinnamon, turmeric, and cardamom. Many Vata types feel better if they take dairy, eggs or even animal products (though Ayurveda does not like to prescribe meat based upon karmic considerations). Vatas suffer quickly from dietary indiscretions, lack of proper nutrition and irregular eating habits.

Pitta types need a cooling and nutritive diet avoiding hot spices, oily food, sour articles, salt and alcohol. They generally have a strong appetite and good thirst. They can digest food easily and tolerate a number of different food types, which often makes them undiscriminating about what they eat. They do well with cooling food like rice and mung beans, light oils (like sunflower or ghee), and reduced spices (except for coriander, cloves, cinnamon, cumin, and turmeric). They benefit from more salads and raw food, particularly in the late spring and summer.

Kapha types need light and hot food and a generally reducing diet. They do well with more spices, including cayenne, black pepper and mustard, while avoiding dairy, sugar, oily food, and anything heavy, greasy or sticky. They do best with light meals, plenty of cooked vegetables, and occasional fasting. They should avoid eating after sunset or in the early morning. Their tendency is to get addicted to Kapha food, sweet, oily or heavy food articles.

HOW TO PRACTICE TO PACIFY THE DOSHAS

MOVING OR STILL

Vatas do best with predominantly still poses, but in severe Vata excess this may be too difficult to maintain. Then Vatas benefit from slow controlled movement with conscious breathing.

Kaphas benefit from increased movement because it energizes them. But Kaphas can also benefit from holding still in an intense or strenuous position like the headstand or some standing poses, particularly if accompanied by deep breathing.

Pittas benefit from slow easy movement or from remaining still, if there is not a lot of strain. They need to relax their intense focus in life with postures that allow them to let go.

HOW LONG TO HOLD STATIC POSES

Each asana has a suggested time for holding it. However, in general, Vatas should hold a pose, but without stress, in order to develop stability and to reduce excess Vata. Pittas should hold a pose only as long as there is no strain or heat created. Kaphas benefit from remaining in the poses to the point of work, holding them beyond what feels comfortable.

ASANA AND PRANAYAMA: USING THE BREATH TO MODIFY THE EFFECTS OF ASANA

Vata is best served by using a slow, steady, conscious deep breathing. Ujjayi, the sound made by closing the throat, can be used by Vatas for holding focus (but lightly applied so as to avoid strain).

Pittas benefit from closing the glottis as well. They can breathe out through their mouths to reduce heat. When Pittas push themselves in a pose the breath will change. The Ujjayi sound can be used throughout their practice to let them hear if they begin to push themselves.

Kaphas need to breathe deeply in the poses. Rapid breathing like Bhastrika (breath of fire) is also good for them.

Ayurveda applies alternate nostril breathing for balancing the doshas. Breathing in through the right (solar) nostril and out through the left (lunar) nostril increases heat and reduces Kapha. Breathing in through the left (lunar) nostril and out through the right (solar) nostril decreases heat and reduces Pitta. Vatas benefit by doing both types of alternate nostril breathing, particularly right nostril breathing in the morning and left nostril breathing in the evening.

DEGREE OF CHALLENGE AND EXERTION

Vata types are best served by the challenge of remaining still and holding the pose consciously aware of the body in that position. Pittas must not overexert themselves as creates more Pitta energy. Pittas benefit from the challenge of being gentle with themselves, which can be their greatest challenge. Sedentary Kapha is challenged by activity and so they can overcome their challenge by continuing the practice long past the time when they want to stop.

Vatas tend toward Vata energy and love active and fast movements that produce more Vata. Pittas want to exert themselves pushing toward their goal. Kaphas would rather not exert themselves at all. The challenge for all of the doshas is to work against their natural tendencies.

IV. 11 TWO TYPES OF ASANA PROGRAMS FOR YOUR TYPE

GENERAL NOTES FOR ALL PROGRAMS

In this section, you are given two different types of Vata, Pitta or Kapha reducing programs. The first is an Instant Change Program consisting of classes that immediately relieve the discomfort associated with high Vata, high Pitta, or high Kapha. The second is the Long Term Program that outlines six to nine months of classes for each of the doshas. These classes are well rounded in their design and over time permanently reduce any excess of the doshas. Both programs are offered in four degrees of difficulty: Levels I, II, III and IV.

- Level I is designed for those who want to build a strong foundation for starting their practice, for those who attend an occasional class but do not have a regular practice of their own, or for those who are new to Yoga.
- Level II is for students who have been studying Yoga for a minimum of one to two years, who attend at least one asana class weekly, who have created some awareness in their bodies, and are knowledgeable about a number of asanas.
- Level III is for students who have an asana teacher and a strong daily practice. They should be advanced in their use of focused movement, have the ability to hold their foundation as they grow the poses, and use the breath as a vehicle for extension and development.
- Level IV addresses the needs of advanced students and teachers. Sample classes, suggestions and ideas for program development are offered.

GROWING IN YOUR PRACTICE

As the student progresses, their alignment and technique advance as well. They learn to form and hold strong foundations as they practice each asana. They are able to remain in poses for longer periods of time with a mastery over their breath. Their practice is done for learning about themselves, being present in each moment, and maintaining a strong attention within the energy field of each asana.

AT WHAT LEVEL ARE YOU?

If you are not sure about what level you should begin a program, choose the easier practices. The exception is if you are feeling that your Kapha is too high (if you are feeling heavy, dull, congested or inert). Then you might want to work harder to get your energy moving. While it is important that the student remains injury free, we suggest that Kaphas work themselves harder than they like. Pushing themselves beyond their ordinary limits will feel better and become easier within a short time.

Vata and Pitta types usually push themselves too much already, which works against effective energy management. If you are Vata or Pitta, it is better to work slowly and consistently to develop strength and flexibility, rather than try to force anything quickly.

RESTORING BALANCE

A good rule to remember is that once our dosha is out of balance, we gravitate toward those things that imbalance it further, not toward those that bring it back into balance. For example, agitated Vata types tend to pursue things that stimulate and agitate them further, like excess or abrupt movements. This means that the poses which are attractive to a person whose dosha is too high are likely to be those that increase it further. Many Vata types like to do strong backbends because these poses feel good to them. But strong backbends can provoke Vata derangements, like feelings of anxiety and fear. Each doshic type should remember that doing what feels good in the moment won't necessarily be balancing in the long run. They should focus on poses that leave them feeling centered and comfortable both at the end of their practice and for the rest of the day.

REVERSING EFFECTS

Some asanas may increase a dosha, but you may still need to practice them for various reasons. Use the following five ideas to help counteract the provoking effects of Yoga postures:

1. Breathe fully and consciously when moving into the poses and holding them.
2. Shorten the length of time that you hold the pose that increases the dosha.
3. Lengthen the time and amount of counteracting poses that reduce the dosha.
4. Limit the number of days in the week that you practice dosha-increasing poses.
5. Make the length of your Savasana appropriate for your doshic type.

You will find the classes from both short and long term programs are valuable for your daily experience and overall health. Remember, as your 'Yoga for Your Type' classes eliminate doshic excesses, your disease potential will be reduced, insuring comfort and good health.

IV. 12 INSTANT CHANGE PROGRAMS FOR EACH DOSHIC TYPE

Instant Change Programs are offered in two lengths: as short twenty to thirty-minute practices or as longer fifty to sixty-minute classes. While we advocate longer practices, we know this isn't always possible.

- SHORTER PRACTICES: For a 20 - 30 minute session, do only the postures pictured in the shaded areas.
- LONGER PRACTICES: For a 40 - 50 minute session, practice all of the postures listed in the Instant Change Programs.
- LEVEL IV POSES: The photographs in Levels I, II, and III are intended to assist the student with easy identification of the postures. Because the Level IV postures are intended for more advanced Yoga practitioners, they are only listed. The Level IV poses for a shorter practice are marked with an asterisk.

Working with all the poses listed in a prescribed class lengthens the practice significantly. For a longer ninety-minute or more practice, use the entire list, extend the holding times, and repeat some or all of the postures.

Surya Namaskar, the Sun Salutation, should be done easily and slowly for Vata and Pitta and more strenuously for Kapha.

VATA REDUCING INSTANT CHANGE PROGRAMS

To reduce excess Vata, practice in a quiet, grounded and systematic way. Vatas should think of building core strength in the body while maintaining flexibility. The balance between strength and flexibility is critical for a positive experience of the Vata dosha.

Remember that it is best for Vatas to work the poses with the breath and hold the standing, sitting, all forward bends, and twists longer than they are inclined to do. Remaining still will be the Vata challenge as well as the reward.

LEVEL I INSTANT VATA REDUCING

Surya Namaskar, Position 4, pg 66

Wall Push, pg 63 or Adho Mukha Svanasana, pg 100

Tadasana, pg 70

Utkatasana, pg 82

Trikonasana, pg 74

Virabhadrasana I, pg 86

Parsvottanasana, pg 84

Padangusthasana, pg 92

Navasana, pg 145

Preparation for Sirsasana, pg 112

Child's Pose, pg 61

Viparita Karani, pg 121 or Sarvangasana II, pg 103

Back Vinyasa, pg 124

LEVEL I INSTANT VATA REDUCING (continued)

Dandasana, pg 156

2 Janu Sirsasana, pg 158

Paschimottanasana, pg 170

Basic Virasana, pg 142

Sitting Chair Twist, pg 174

Marichyasana III, pg 180

Alligator Twists I-III, pg 184

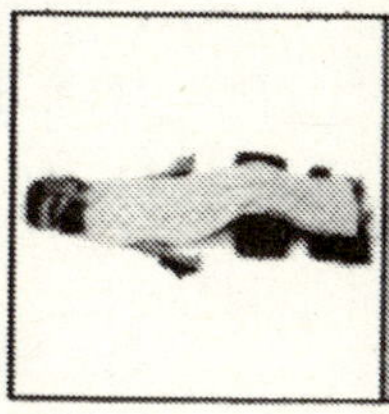
Savasana for 20-30 minutes, pg 190

LEVEL II INSTANT VATA REDUCING

Parsvakonasana, pg 80

Virabhadrasana I, pg 86

Virabhadrasana III, pg 88

Uttanasana, pg 97

Urdhva Prasarita Eka Padasana, pg 94

Preparation for Sirsasana, pg 112

Sarvangasana II or III, pg 103

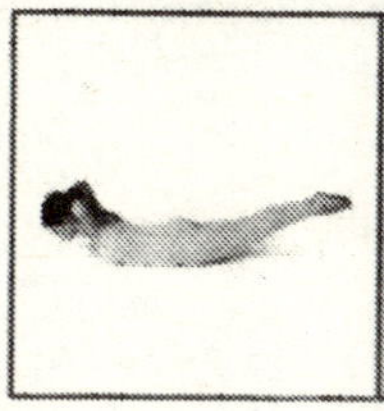
Makarasana, pg 128

Supta Virasana, pg 144

Purvottanasana, pg 152

Child's Pose, pg 61

Siddhasana, pg 141

Dandasana, pg 156

Baddha Konasana, pg 140

Upavistha Konasana, pg 162

Parsva Upavistha Konasana, pg 163

Janu Sirsasana, pg 158

Paschimottanasana, pg 170

Marichyasana III, pg 180

Alligator Twists III & IV, pg 184

Savasana for 20-30 minutes, pg 190

LEVEL III INSTANT VATA REDUCING

Parivrtta Trikonasana, pg 76

Parsvakonasana, pg 80

Urdhva Prasarita Ekapadasana, pg 94

Padahastasana, pg 96

Sirsasana, pg 118

Sarvangasana III, pg 104

Halasana, pg 108

Makarasana, pg 128

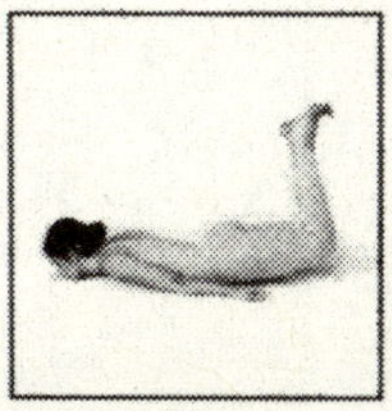

Salabhasana III, pg 127

Child's pose, pg 61

Urdhva Prasarita Padasana, pg 148

Navasana, pg 145

Janu Sirsasana, pg 158

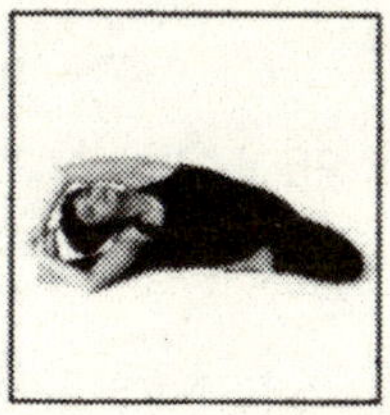

Parivrtta Janu Sirsasana, pg 167

Triang Mukhaikapada Paschimottanasana, pg 164

Ardha Baddha Padma Paschimottanasana, pg 166

Paschimottanasana, pg 170

Siddhasana, pg 141

LEVEL III INSTANT VATA REDUCING (continued)

Ardha Matsyendrasana I or II, pg 182

Jathara Parivartanasana, pg 186

Savasana for 20-30 minutes, pg 190

LEVEL IV INSTANT VATA REDUCING

Sirsasana *

Any Sirsasana Variation

Bakasana

Niralamba Sarvangasana

Pindasana in Sarvangasana *

Eka Pada Rajakapotasana *

Hanumanasana

Yoga Mudrasana *

Kurmasana *

Malasana *

Ardha Baddha Padma Paschimottanasana *

Parsva Upavistha Konasana *

Urdhva Mukha Paschimottanasana

Parivrtta Paschimottanasana

Pasasana or Marichyasana II *

Savasana for 20-30 minutes *

PITTA REDUCING INSTANT CHANGE PROGRAMS

Remember the Pitta energy presses forward in an impulsive manner. Excess Pitta is reduced by practicing in an effortless, non-goal oriented way, working at about seventy five percent of our capacity. Rest assured that when a Pitta person practices effortlessly they will still be working harder than everyone else. Use the breath to monitor the level of work intensity. Forward bends and twists are very effective in both reducing excess Pitta and in bringing up low Pitta. Hold these postures for longer periods to reduce Pitta.

LEVEL I INSTANT PITTA REDUCING

Cat Stretch, pg 60

Back Vinyasa, pg 124

Adho Mukha Svanasana, pg 100

Surya Namaskar Position #4, pg 66

Padottanasana, pg 83 or Wall Hang, pg 64

LEVEL I INSTANT PITTA REDUCING (continued)

Standing Chair Twist, pg 175

Viparita Karani, pg 121

Child's Pose, pg 61

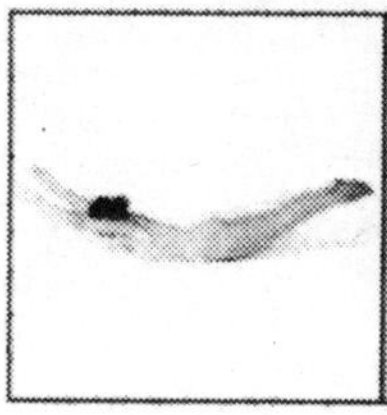

Back Vinyasa, pg 124

Salabhasana II, pg 127

Child's pose, pg 61

Siddhasana, pg 141

Supta Padangusthasana, pg 160

Janu Sirsasana, pg 158

Upavistha Konasana, pg 162

Paschimottanasana, pg 170

Sitting Chair Twist, pg 174

Alligator Twists II & III, pg 184

Savasana for 15-25 minutes, pg 190

LEVEL II INSTANT PITTA REDUCING

2 Surya Namaskar, pg 66

Padottanasana, pg 83

Sarvangasana II, pg 103

Dipada Pidam, pg 110

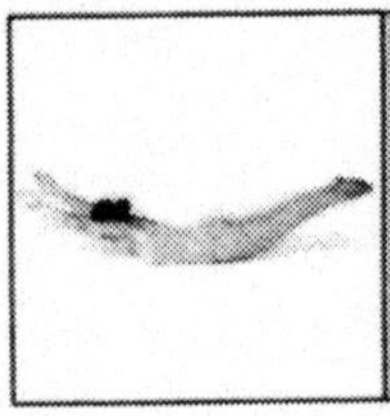
Back Vinyasa, pg 124

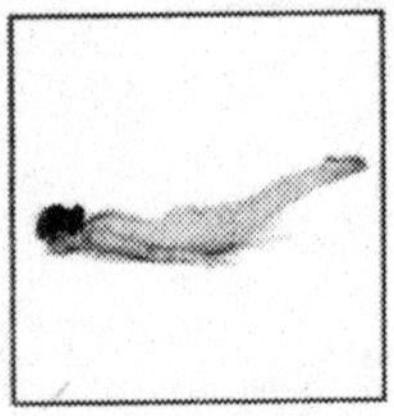
Salabhasana II, pg 127

Child's Pose, pg 61

Supta Padangusthasana, pg 160

Janu Sirsasana, pg 158

Parivrtta Janu Sirsasana, pg 167

Anantasana, pg 147

Upavistha Konasana, pg 162

Parsva Upavistha Konasana, pg 163

Viparita Karani, pg 121

Marichyasana III, pg 180

Bharadvajasana I, pg 176

Alligator Twists I-IV, pg 184

Jathara Parivartanasana, pg 186

Savasana for 15-25 minutes, pg 190

LEVEL III INSTANT PITTA REDUCING

Adho Mukha Svanasana, pg 100

Adho Mukha Vrksasana, pg 114

Sarvangasana III, pg 104

Setu Bandha Sarvangasana Variation, pg 107

Makarasana, pg 128

Niralamba Bhujangasana I, pg 126

Supta Virasana, pg 144

Supta Padangusthasana, pg 160

Akarna Dhanurasana

Parivrtta Janu Sirsasana, pg 167

Viparita Karani, pg 121

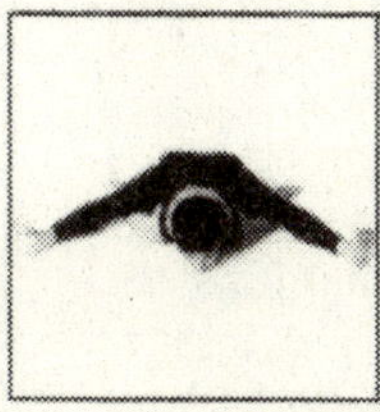
Kurmasana, pg 169

Paschimottanasana, pg 170

Jathara Parivartanasana, pg 186

Marichyasana I, pg 178

Savasana for 15-25 minutes, pg 190

LEVEL IV INSTANT PITTA REDUCING

Pincha Mayurasana

Adho Mukha Vrksasana

Sarvangasana & Variations

Niralamba Sarvangasana *

Eka Pada Sirsasana *

Urdhva Dhanurasana *

Eka Pada Urdhva Dhanurasana *

Yoganidrasana

Hanumanasana

Urdhva Mukha Paschimottanasana *

Parivrtta Paschimottanasana

Any Ardha Matsyendrasana *

Jathara Parivartanasana *

Savasana for 20-25 minutes *

KAPHA REDUCING INSTANT CHANGE PROGRAMS

Kaphas should always remember to practice in an energetic way. The challenge for Kapha is to keep up the level of effort needed to reduce their dosha. When a Kapha practices energetically they are usually not exceeding their capacity. Kaphas benefit from standing poses, headstands, all inverted poses, and backbends. Headstands and handstands are especially good for reducing Kapha. When there is excess body weight, first strengthen the shoulders, arms and legs, then master the armstands and shoulderstands. Avoid putting excess weight on the head in headstands until the upper body has been strengthened. Since forward bends increase Kapha, hold these positions for a shorter time.

LEVEL I INSTANT KAPHA REDUCING

2 Surya Namaskar, pg 66

Adho Mukha Svanasana, pg 100

Tadasana, pg 70

Vrksasana, pg 72

Trikonasana, pg 74

Virabhadrasana I, pg 86

Virabhadrasana II, pg 78

Preparation for Sirsasana, pg 112

Sarvangasana I, pg 102

Niralamba Bhujangasana I, pg 126

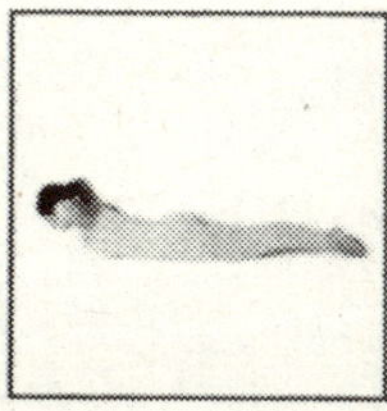
Niralamba Bhujangasana II, pg 126

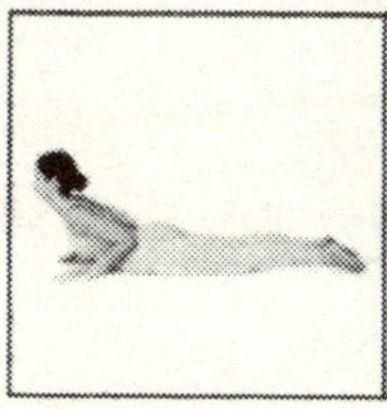
Niralamba Bhujangasana III, pg 126

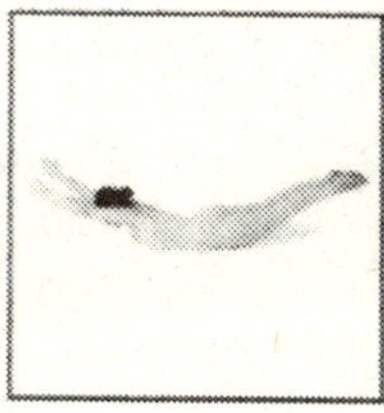
Salabhasana I, pg 127

Salabhasana II, pg 127

Salabhasana III, pg 127

Navasana, pg 145

Upavistha Konasana, pg 162

Alligator Twists I-III, pg 184

Savasana for 5-15 minutes, pg 190

LEVEL II INSTANT KAPHA REDUCING

4-6 Surya Namaskar, pg 66

Trikonasana, pg 74

Parivrtta Trikonasana, pg 76

Ardha Chandrasana, pg 90

Virabhadrasana I, pg 86

Virabhadrasana III, pg 88

Chest Opening at Wall, pg 62

Urdhva Prasarita Ekapadasana, pg 94

Urdhva Prasarita Padasana, pg 148

Sirsasana, pg 118

Sarvangasana I or II, pg 102

Dipada Pidam, pg 110

Purvottanasana, pg 152

Navasana, pg 145

Marichyasana III, pg 180

Alligator Twists III & IV, pg 184

Savasana for 5-15 minutes, pg 190

LEVEL III INSTANT KAPHA REDUCING

4-8 Surya Namaskar (Jumping), pg 66

2-4 Adho Mukha Vrksasana, pg 114

2-4 Pincha Mayurasana, pg 116

Sirsasana, pg 118

Sarvangasana II or III, pg 103, 104

Setu Bandha Sarvangasana, pg 107

Dhanurasana, pg 129

Niralamba Bhujangasana II, pg 126

Urdhva Dhanurasana, pg 132

Eka Pada Rajakapotasana Stretch, pg 134

Parivrttaika Pada Sirsasana, pg 120

Navasana, pg 145

Purvottanasana, pg 152

Vasisthasana, pg 151

LEVEL III INSTANT KAPHA REDUCING (continued)

Akarna Dhanurasana

Supta Padangusthasana, pg 160

Parivrtta Janu Sirsasana, pg 167

Savasana for 5-15 minutes, pg 190

LEVEL IV INSTANT KAPHA REDUCING

Surya Namaskar (Jumpings)

Any Sirsasana & Variations *

Sarvangasana & Variations *

Niralamba Sarvangasana

Uttana Padasana

Eka Pada Urdhva Dhanurasana *

Eka Pada Viparita Dandasana *

Eka Pada Rajakapotasana I

Vasisthasana

Visvamitrasana *

Supta Padangusthasana

Urdhva Mukha Paschimottanasana *

Marichyasana I *

Any Ardha Matsyendrasana

Savasana for 5 - 15 minutes *

IV. 13 LONG TERM DOSHA REDUCING PROGRAMS FOR EACH DOSHIC TYPE

The Long Term programs provide six to nine months of classes. Each doshic program is designed to reduce the buildup of doshic excess at their primary sites of accumulation (stomach for Kapha, small intestine for Pitta and large intestine for Vata). The Long Term programs have been given in detail for Levels I & II for each of the doshas. Most students will fall into one of these two categories if they are growing their practices in a well-rounded way.

Each class should be used for seven to nine days before moving on to the next class. When taking on a new practice within your doshic program, use the first few days to learn the poses, the technique and the sequence of the program. Days four through seven can be used to improve your technique and to begin focusing on the breath. In the last few days concentrate on the breath as the vehicle for the natural extension of the pose.

It is assumed that Levels III and IV students have more experience with technique, sequencing, and energy balancing of the poses. So for these levels, sample classes, ideas, and suggestions are given for creating the blend of asanas suitable for balancing their doshas. More specific details are not needed since these students will be able to design their own long term practices using the information in this book.

Two sample classes (practices) are outlined for Levels III and IV. For a longer experience of the energy changes produced by these programs, Level III or IV students may want to follow the Level II series for a longer period.

LONG TERM VATA REDUCING PROGRAM

GENERAL NOTES

Generally, asanas that are grounding, stabilizing, and strengthening will reduce excess Vata. These qualities are found in standing poses, especially the standing hip closing poses like Warrior I and III and standing forward bends like Padangusthasana. Also floor poses and all sitting forward bends are Vata pacifying. On the other hand, backbends increase Vata dosha if done excessively or unconsciously. Backbending is essential for the long-term maintenance of the Vata spine but should be done gently. Like twisting poses, they keep the spine supple by not allowing excess Vata to accumulate in the bones of the back. Savasana is the best pose for pacifying Vata and should be practiced daily for twenty to thirty minutes as a conclusion to the asana practice.

Using the breath for control and focus will effectively reduce Vata. By concentrating on the quality, quantity, and movement of the breath, the practitioner can easily remain quiet, holding the pose for an extended period of time. Excess Vata creates fidgeting and the need to constantly move. This fidgeting movement stimulates more Vata. Discipline is required because the practice must be done in a controlled, attentive manner. The longer the practitioner is able to hold these calming, quieting poses the more effective the poses will be.

Think of creating 'core' strength, stability, and stamina by using small controlled movements to strengthen and maintain the integrity of the spinal muscles, the trunk erector muscles, the pelvic stabilizing muscles, and the abdominal muscles. It is very important for Vata types to remain aware of the strength needed to maintain core integrity as they develop the flexibility needed in the spine and joints. Vata types want to flex to their maximum and flex often. In time, this can create too much flexibility. Balance should remain foremost in Vata's thinking and movement practice.

Each dosha tends to seek its own energy rather than moving toward balance. Vata types love to move. In fact, the more Vata a person is the more movement you will observe in them. When the practitioner is severely Vata provoked, it may not even be possible for them to be still. In this case, beginning with a very slow vinyasa (movement series), like an easy sun salutation, help initiates the pacifying process. As Vata becomes pacified, the practice of stillness gets easier.

LEVEL III AND IV STUDENTS

The advanced practitioner should be familiar with the poses that are listed in their programs. For this reason, many of these poses are not detailed in this book. Advanced practitioners will know their bodies and honor their limitations, selecting the appropriate poses accordingly. If you do have questions about the advanced positions, please talk with your asana teacher or refer to *Light On Yoga* by B.K.S. Iyengar.

For the advanced student, samples of dosha-reducing practices are given. From these guides they can easily construct their own programs.

To continue advancing your practice, slowly increase the time that you hold each pose. More advanced students hold their postures longer with quiet smooth breathing throughout the entire practice. Whenever practicing poses that provoke Vata energy, consider using the breath as a constant reference for stillness.

The Level III student should already have a working knowledge of posture selection and sequencing as well as how to progress and change their practice over time. At this point they should understand how to balance their bodies through their practice. If after using the Level III sample practice sessions the Level III student wants to gain more insight into the energetic qualities of the poses and program progression, we suggest that they use the Level II practice sessions. Of course, they can make Level II practice more challenging by holding the poses longer and remaining focused while sustaining a grounded quiet place within themselves.

Grounding and focusing on the quiet, nourishing breath is a good perspective for a Vata type's practice at any level. Remember to always choose balance and self-support, strength and stability.

LONG TERM VATA REDUCING PROGRAMS

LEVEL I VATA

Level I VATA Practice #1, Week 1

Pelvic Tilt pg 59; Neck Stretch pg 57; Cat Stretch pg 60; Tadasana pg 70; Vrksasana pg 72; Wall Push pg 63; Wall Hang pg 64; Adho Mukha Svanasana pg 100; Viparita Karani pg 121; Back Vinyasa pg 124; Child's Pose pg 61; Baddha Konasana pg 140; Dandasana pg 156; Janu Sirsasana pg 158; Sitting Chair Twist pg 174; 20-30 minute Savasana pg 190.

Level I VATA Practice #2, Week 2

Cat Stretch pg 60; Runner's Lunge pg 66; Tadasana pg 70; Utkatasana pg 82; Trikonasana pg 74; Virabhadrasana I pg 86; Wall Hang pg 64; Standing Chair Twist pg 175; Sarvangasana I pg 102; Niralamba Bhujangasana I pg 126; Salabhasana I pg 127; Dandasana pg 156; Janu Sirsasana pg 158; Alligator Twists I-IV pg 184; 20-30 minute Savasana pg 190.

Level I VATA Practice #3, Week 3

2 Surya Namaskar pg 66; Adho Mukha Svanasana pg 100; Sarvangasana I or II pg 102; Depada Pidam pg 110; 2 Back Vinyasa pg 124; Purvottanasana pg 152; Child's Pose pg 61; Baddha Konasana pg 140; Siddhasana pg 141; Upavistha Konasana pg 162; Paschimottanasana pg 170; Alligator Twists I-III pg 184; 20-30 minute Savasana pg 190.

Level I VATA Practice #4, Week 4

Utkatasana pg 82; Trikonasana pg 74; Virabhadrasana II pg 78; Parsvakonasana pg 80; Virbhadrasana I pg 86; Padangusthasana pg 92; Sarvangasana II pg 103; Niralamba Bhujangasana III pg 126; Salabhasana II pg 127; Child's Pose pg 61; Supta Padangusthasana pg 160; Janu Sirsasana pg 158; Triang Mukhaikapada Paschimottanasana pg 164; Alligator Twists III-IV pg 184; 20-30 minute Savasana pg 190.

Level I VATA Practice #5, Week 5 & 6

Alternate Practices #1, 2, 3, & 4 daily.

Level I VATA Practice #6, Week 7

2 Surya Namaskar pg 66; Virabhadrasana II pg 78; Parsvakonasana pg 80; Parsvottanasana pg 84; Urdhva Prasarita Ekapadasana pg 94; Uttanasana pg 97; Sarvangasana II or III pg 102-4; Niralamba Bhujangasana I pg 126; Salabhasana I pg 127; Child's Pose pg 61; Janu Sirsasana pg 158; Parivrtta Janu Sirsasana pg 167; Paschimottanasana pg 170; Marichyasana I pg 178; 20-30 minute Savasana pg 190.

Level I VATA Practice #7, Week 8

Tadasana pg 70; Parsvakonasana pg 80; Padottanansna pg 83; Padangusthasana pg 92; Adho Mukha Svanasana pg 100; Sarvangasana II or III pg 102-4; Depada Pidam pg 110; Back Vinyasa pg 124; Salabhasana II or I pg 127; Urdhva Prasarita Padasana pg 148; Navasana pg 145; Purvottanasana pg 152; Upavistha Konasana pg 162; Janu Sirsasana pg 158; Marichyasana III pg 180; 20-30 minute Savasana pg 190.

Level I VATA Practice #8, Week 9

Trikonasana pg 74; Parivrtta Trikonasana pg 76; Virabhadrasana I & III pg 86-8; Urdhva Prasarita Ekapadasana pg 94; Uttanasana pg 97; Preparation for Sirsasana pg 112 pg; Sarvangasana II or III pg 102-4; Niralamba Bhujangasana II pg 126; Salabhasana I pg 127; Dhanurasana pg 129; Child's Pose pg 61; Triang Mukhaikapada Paschimottanasana pg 164; Paschimottanasana pg

170; Bharadvajasana I pg 176; Marichyasana I pg 178; 20-30 minute Savasana pg 190.

Level I VATA Practice #9, Weeks 10 & 11

Alternate various combinations of Practices #6, 7, and 8 daily for two or more weeks. Focus on maintaining a smooth even breath throughout the entire practice. Slowly increase the number of times that you do each pose or lengthen the time each pose is held in order to advance the practice.

Level I VATA Practice #10, Weeks 12 & 13

Alternate Practices #1 through #9.

To continue progressing in this beginner program, add two or three new poses (using the sequencing given in this book) and eliminate two or three postures that you have mastered. Examine the progression in Level I Practice Programs #1 through #4 to see how the practice is extended and changed.

Level I VATA Practice #11, Weeks 14 - 16

Create your own combinations by mixing and matching various combinations from Practices #1 through #9.

LEVEL II VATA

Level II VATA Practice #1, Week 1

2 Surya Namaskar pg 66; Adho Mukha Svanasana pg 100; Preparation for Sirsasana pg 112; Sarvangasana II or III pg 102-4; Halasana pg 108; Depada Pidam pg 110; Makarasana pg 128; Dhanurasana pg 129; Child's Pose pg 61; Vasisthasana pg 151; Supta Padangusthasana pg 160; Triang Mukhaikapada Paschimottanasana pg 164; Paschimottanasana pg 170; Marichyasana III pg 180; Alligator Twists I-IV pg 184; 20-30 minute Savasana pg 190.

Level II VATA Practice #2, Week 2

Adho Mukha Svanasana pg 100; Trikonasana pg 74; Parivrtta Trikonasana pg 76; Ardha Chandrasana pg 90; Virabhadrasana I & III pg 86-88; Padangusthasana pg 92; Niralamba Bhujangasana I pg 126; Salabhasana III pg 127; Purvottanasana pg 152; Virasana pg 143; Supta Virasana pg 144; Janu Sirsasana pg 158; Parivrtta Janu Sirsasana pg 167; Ardha Matsyendrasana I pg 182; Bharadvajasana I pg 176; 20-30 minute Savasana pg 190.

Level II VATA Practice #3, Week 3

2 Surya Namaskar pg 66; Pincha Mayurasana pg 116; Preparation for Sirsasana pg 112; Sarvangasana II or III pg 102-4; Depada Pidam pg 110; Makarasana pg 128; Dhanurasana pg 129; Purvottanasana pg 152; Child's Pose pg 61; Urdhva Prasarita Padasana pg 148; Upavistha Konasana pg 162; Parsva Upavistha Konasana pg 163; Ardha Baddha Padma Paschimottanasana pg 166; Ardha Matsyendrasana I pg 182; Alligator Twists I-IV pg 184; 20-30 minute Savasana pg 190.

Level II VATA Practice #4, Week 4

Padottanasana pg 83; Virabhadrasana III pg 88; Urdhva Prasarita Ekapadasana pg 94; Padangusthasana pg 92 or Padahastasana pg 96; Salamba Sarvangasana II or III pg 102-4; Halasana pg 108 or Depada Pidam pg 110; Salabhasana II pg 127; Dhanurasana pg 129; Urdhva Dhanurasana pg 132; Child's Pose pg 61; Supta Virasana pg 144; Supta Padangusthasana pg 160; Paschimottanasana pg 170; Bharadvajasana I pg 176; Marichyasana I pg 178; 20-30 minute Savasana pg 190.

Level II VATA Practice #5, Weeks 5 & 6

Alternate Practices #1, 2, 3, and 4 daily.

Level II VATA Practice #6, Week 7

Parsvakonasana pg 80; Parsvottanasana pg 84; Urdhva Prasarita Ekapadasana pg 94; Padahastasana pg 96 or Padangusthasana pg 92; Uttanasana pg 97; Sirsasana pg 118; Sarvangasana III pg 104; 2 Makarasana pg 128; Dhanurasana pg 129 or Urdhva Dhanurasana pg 132; Purvottanasana pg 152; Dwi Pada Viparita Dandasana pg 136; Urdhva Prasarita Padasana pg 148; Ardha Baddha Padma Paschimottanasana pg 166; Janu Sirsasana pg 158; Jathara Parivartanasana pg 186; 20-30 minute Savasana pg 190.

Level II VATA Practice #7, Week 8

2-6 Surya Namaskar pg 66; Sirsasana pg 118; Sarvangasana II or III with Variations pg 102-104; Halasana pg 108; Niralamba Bhujangasana III pg 126; Salabhasana III pg 127; Eka Pada Rajakapotasana I or Stretch pg 135; Child's Pose pg 61; Anantasana pg 147; Upavistha Konasana pg 162 or Kurmasana pg 169; Triang Mukhaikapada Paschimottanasana pg 164; Ardha Matsyendrasana I pg 182; Marichyasana II or III pg 179-180; 20-30 minute Savasana pg 190.

Level II VATA Practice #8, Week 9 & 10

Virabhadrasana I pg 86; Virabhadrasana III pg 88; Padottanasana pg 83; Uttanasana pg 97; Adho Mukha Vrksasana pg 114; Pincha Mayurasana pg 116; Sarvangasana II or III pg 102-4; Makarasana pg 128; Chaturanga Dandasana pg 150; Vasisthasana pg 151; Supta Padangusthasana pg 160; Urdhva Mukha Paschimottanasana pg 168; Ubhya Padangusthasana pg 146; Janu Sirsasana pg 158; Jathara Parivartanasana pg 186; 20-30 minute Savasana pg 190.

Level II VATA Practice #9, Weeks 10 & 11

Alternate between Level II Practices #5, 6, and 7, changing daily.

Level II VATA Practice #10, Weeks 12 - 20

Alternate between all Practices from Level I and II choosing a different Practice daily. Substitute similar poses within like categories to increase the difficulty level or mix and match categories of several practices for added variety.

LEVEL III & IV VATA

The Level III and IV Yoga practitioner will want to remember that Vata is lowered by positions that require constant muscular holding. The more holding, the more Vata reduces. Vata is also lowered by poses that grow from the pelvis and stimulate the large intestine and colon. Poses that are grounding, forward bends and well-rooted inversions are also good for them. Keep your spine flexible but maintain strength on each of its four sides. Vatas should always maintain strength in their muscles. With their smaller bone structure they need to use their muscles, not their bones, for support in their poses.

It is best for Vata to balance or limit the time spent moving in jumping style practices. These more dynamic practices tend to aggravate Vata and Pitta energies and are best suited for Kapha types.

The practices for Levels III and IV are intentionally long lists of appropriately measured categories to pacify this dosha. We recommend that you cut each practice down to the size you like but maintain the same relative proportions of each category.

The English names are supplied here for anyone unfamiliar with the Sanskrit terminology. Many of the asanas for Levels III and IV are not described in this book so please refer to *Light On Yoga* by B.K.S. Iyengar for further descriptions.

LEVEL III VATA

Two examples of Level III Long Term Vata Pacifying Practices follow.

LEVEL III VATA EXAMPLE PRACTICE #1

Standing Poses	
Utkatasana	Power Chair Pose
Trikonasana	Triangle Pose
Parivrtta Trikonasana	Revolving Triangle Pose
Virabhadrasana I	Warrior Pose I
Virabhadrasana III	Warrior Pose III
Parsvakonasana	Extended Side Angle
Parivrtta Parsvakonasana	Revolving Extended Side Angle Pose
Uttihita Hasta Padangusthasana	Extended Hand & Foot Pose
Uttanasana	Intense Stretch Forward Bend
Inverted Poses	
Sirsasana	Headstand
Sarvangasana	Shoulderstand
Setu Bandha Sarvangasana	Shoulderstand drops down into Bridge Pose
Backbends	
Bhekasana or Dhanurasana	Frog Pose or Bow Pose
Urdhva Dhanurasana	Upward Bow
Dwi Pada Viparita Dandasana	Inverted Arch
Floor Poses	
Vasisthasana	Side Plank Pose
Virasana IV	Bowing Hero Pose
Sitting Forward Bends	
Ardha Baddha Padma Paschimottanasana	Half Lotus Forward Bend Pose
Triang Mukhaikapada Paschimottanasana	TMP
Paschimottanasana	Full Forward Bend
Twists	
Bharadvajasana I	Legs Sideways Sitting Twist
Jathara Parivartanasana	Revolving Stomach Twist
Savasana	20-30 Minutes

LEVEL III VATA

Long Term Pacifying Practices (continued)

LEVEL III VATA EXAMPLE PRACTICE #2

Inverted Poses	
Adho Mukha Vrksasana	Hand Stand
Sirsasana	Headstand
Eka Pada Sirsasana	Revolving Legs in Sirsasana
Urdhva Konasana in Sirsasana	Upward Open Angle in Headstand
Sarvangasana	Shoulderstand
Eka Pada Sarvangasana	One Leg Extended Shoulderstand
Setu Bandha Sarvangasana	Shoulderstand drops down into Bridge Pose
Backbends	
Dhanurasana	Bow Pose
Urdhva Dhanurasana	Upward Bow Pose
Eka Pada Urdhva Dhanurasana	One Leg Upward Bow Pose
Floor Poses	
Purvottanasana	Intense Front Extension
Virasana IV	Bowing Hero Pose
Ardha Navasana	Half Boat Pose
Forward Bends	
Upavistha Konasana	Open Legs Forward Bend
Parsva Upavistha Konasana	Over One Open Leg Forward Bend
Parvritta Janu Sirsasana	Revolving Head to Knee Pose
Triang Mukhaikapada Paschimottanasana	Three Limbs Facing Forward Bend (TMP)
Paschimottanasana	Full Forward Bend
Twists	
Marichyasana III	Sage Twist III
Ardha Matsyendrasana I or II	Half Fish Twist I or II
Bharadvajasana II	Legs Side Sitting Twist
Savasana	20-30 Minutes

LEVEL IV VATA

Two examples of Level IV Long Term Vata Pacifying Practices follow.

LEVEL IV VATA EXAMPLE PRACTICE #1

Inverted Poses	
Pincha Mayurasana	Arm Stand (peacock feather)
Sirsasana	Headstand
Parsva Urdhva Padmasana	Upward Lotus in Headstand
Parivrittaikapada Sirsasana	Revolving Legs in Headstand
Eka Pada Sirsasana	One Leg Down in Headstand
Bakasana	Crane Pose
Sarvangasana	Shoulderstand
Eka Pada Sarvangasana	One Leg Extended Shoulderstand
Parsva Sarvangasana	Sideways Shoulderstand
Parsva Urdhva Padmasana Sarvangasana	Sideways Lifted Lotus in Shoulderstand
Parsva Halasana	Sideways Plow Pose
Setu Bandha Sarvangasana	Shoulderstand into Bridge Pose
Backbends	
Bhujangasana or Bhekasana	Cobra Pose or Frog Pose
Uttana Padasana	Stretched Back Legs Up
Urdhva Dhanurasana	Upward Bow (Push Up From Floor)
Floor Poses	
Yoga Mudrasana	Yoga Seal Pose
Yoganidrasana	Yoga Sleep Pose
Forward Bends	
Janu Sirsasana	Head to Knee Pose
Upavistha Konasana	Open Legs Forward Bend
Kurmasana	Tortoise Pose
Supta Kurmasana	Lying Tortoise Pose
Urdhva Mukha Paschimottanasana	Upward Facing Forward Bend
Paschimottanasana	Full Forward Bend
Twists	
Parvritta Paschimottanasana	Full Forward Bend
Pasasana	Noose Twist
Jathara Parivartanasana	Revolving Stomach Twist
Savasana	20 Minutes

LEVEL IV VATA

Long Term Pacifying Practices (continued)

LEVEL IV VATA EXAMPLE PRACTICE #2

Standing Poses	
Parivrtta Trikonasana	Revolving Triangle Pose
Parsvakonasana	Extended Side Angle
Parivrtta Parsvakonasana	Revolving Extended Side Angle Pose
Parsvottanasana	Intense Sideways Stretch Pose
Parivrtta Ardha Chandrasana	Revolving Half Moon Pose
Virabhadrasana III	Warrior Pose III
Uttanasana II	Intense Stretch Forward Bend
Padahastasana	Feet on Hands Forward Bend
Backbends	
Urdhva Mukha Svanasana	Upward Facing Dog Pose
Urdhva Dhanurasana from Standing	Upward Bow (Drop back)
Dwi Pada Viparita Dandasana	Inverted Arch Pose
Eka Pada Viparita Dandasana	Inverted Arch Leg Up Pose
Eka Pada Rajakapotasana I	One Leg Pigeon Pose
Floor Poses	
Malasana I	Garland Pose
Tolasana	Scales Balance Pose (in Lotus)
Padma Mayurasana	Lotus Peacock Pose
Kandasana or Yoga Mudrasana	Knot Pose or Yoga Seal Pose
Forward Bends	
Ardha Baddha Padma Paschimottanasana	Bound Angle forward bend
Yoganidrasana	Yoga Sleep
Paschimottanasana VIII	Full Forward Bend
Twists	
Pasasana	Noose Twist
Ardha Matsyendrasana II	Half Fish III
Savasana	20 Minutes

LONG TERM PITTA REDUCING PROGRAMS

GENERAL NOTES

Pitta types like to strive, but the focus and strain inherent in their drive to achieve increases Pitta dosha. Diffusing this focus and reducing the amount of effort are two behaviors that keep Pittas in balance. At times when Pittas are severely provoked and softening their focus is difficult, it is easier to begin the practice with slow and easy Sun Salutations. Pitta types need to remain flexible and soft throughout their lives because if excess Pitta is not softened, it can become stiff, hot, and too tight. It may help Pittas to realize that they can use their powerful will to maintain a soft and gentle approach. This will be their greatest challenge and also yield their greatest reward.

Easy closing postures, gentle backward bending with breath awareness, and all forward bending and twisting positions are the most effective for reducing excess Pitta. Hip-opening poses tend to be less Pitta provoking than hip-closing poses. Standing forward bends are good but sitting forward bends are even better for pacifying Pitta dosha. It will be wise for Pitta to limit the time in headstand and armstand positions. Shoulderstands are good for Pitta, especially when practiced with support. It is important for Pitta to practice holding backbending poses in a gentle way. To begin, practice small cobra poses that are unsupported by the hands and arms so that the focus is on gaining strength in the extension of the spine rather than striving for full backbending.

Calming, centering, relaxing, sitting floor poses stimulate a parasympathetic response in the body and mind. Sitting forward bends are the best, reducing excess Pitta both short and long term. Twists create flexibility and balance of body and mind. Practicing Savasana for twenty to thirty minutes can pacify Pitta but it is important that Pitta does not experience irritation in the pose. If irritation occurs, shorten the Savasana to begin with and then gradually lengthen it over time.

LEVEL I PITTA

Level I PITTA Practice #1, Week 1

Neutral Spine pg 58; Pelvic Tilt pg 59; Neck Stretch pg 57; Cat Stretch pg 60; Vrksasana pg 72; Wall Hang pg 64; 2 Back Vinyasa pg 124; Child's Pose pg 61; Baddha Konasana pg 140; Janu Sirsasana pg 158; Upavistha Konasana pg 162; Alligator Twists II & III pg 184; 20+ minutes Savasana pg 190.

Level I PITTA Practice #2, Week 2

Cat Stretch pg 60; Trikonasana pg 74; Wall Hang pg 64; Padangusthasana pg 92; Standing Chair Twist pg 175; Viparita Karani pg 121; Salabhasana II pg 127; Niralamba Bhujangasana III pg 126; Child's Pose pg 61; Virasana pg 143; Janu Sirsasana pg 158; Paschimottanasana pg 170; Alligator Twists I-IV pg 184; 20+ minutes Savasana pg 190.

Level I PITTA Practice #3, Week 3

2 Surya Namaskar pg 66; Chest Opening at Wall pg 62; Neck Stretch pg 57; Sarvangasana I or II pg 102; Depada Pidam pg 110; Niralamba Bhujangasana II pg 126; Salabhasana I pg 127; Child's Pose pg 61; Siddhasana pg 141; Upavistha Konasana pg 162; Parsva Upavistha Konasana pg 163; Marichyasana III pg 180; 20+ minutes Savasana pg 190.

Level I PITTA Practice #4, Weeks 4 & 5

Alternate Practices #1, 2, and 3.

Level I PITTA Practice #5, Week 6

2 Surya Namaskar pg 66; Neck Stretch pg 57; Sarvangasana II pg 103; Depada Pidam pg 110; Makarasana pg 128; Niralamba Bhujangasana II pg 126; Eka Pada Rajakapotasana I pg 135 or Stretch pg 134; Child's Pose pg 61; Urdhva Prasarita Padasana pg 148; Janu Sirsasana pg 158; Triang Mukhaikapada Paschimottanasana pg 164; Sitting Chair Twist pg 174; Bharadvajasana I pg 176; 20+ minutes Savasana pg 190.

Level I PITTA Practice #6, Week 7

Cat Stretch pg 60; Adho Mukha Svanasana pg 100; Virabhadrasana II pg 78; Trikonasana pg 74; Ardha Chandrasana pg 90; Padangusthasana pg 92; Viparita Karani pg 121; Niralamba Bhujangasana I pg 126; Child's Pose pg 61; Supta Padangusthasana pg 160; Upavistha Konasana pg 162; Paschimottanasana pg 170; Marichyasana I pg 178; Alligator Twists III & IV pg 184; 20+ minutes Savasana pg 190.

Level I PITTA Practice #7, Week 8

2 Surya Namaskar pg 66; Standing Chair Twist pg 175; 2 Dhanurasana pg 129; Child's Pose pg 61; Urdhva Prasarita Padasana pg 148; Navasana pg 145; Siddhasana pg 141; Janu Sirsasana pg 158; Parivrtta Janu Sirsasana pg 167; Ardha Baddha Padma Paschimottanasana pg 166; Ardha Matsyendrasana I pg 182; Marichyasana III pg 180; 20+ minutes Savasana pg 190.

Level I PITTA Practice #8, Week 9

Parsvakonasana pg 80; Padottanasana pg 83; Uttanasana pg 97; Neck Stretch pg 57; Sarvangasana II or III pg 102-4; Makarasana pg 128; Dhanurasana pg 129 or Niralamba Bhujangasana III pg 126; Child's Pose pg 61; Virasana pg 143; Supta Virasana pg 144; Supta Padangusthasana pg 160; Triang Mukhaikapada Paschimottanasana pg 164; Parsva Upavistha Konasana pg 163; Bharadvajasana I pg 176; Alligator Twists I-IV pg 184; 20+ minutes Savasana pg 190.

Level I PITTA Practice #9, Weeks 10 & 11

Alternate Practices #5, 6 ,7, and 8, changing daily. Focus on maintaining a smooth even breath throughout each practice. Gradually increase the number of times you do each pose.

Level I PITTA Practice #10, Weeks 12 & 13

Alternate Practices #1 through #9.

Level I PITTA Practice #11, Weeks 14 - 16

Continue alternating Practices #1 through #9. Create your own combinations by mixing and matching various combinations from different Practices.

LEVEL II PITTA

Level II PITTA Practice #1, Week 1

Trikonasana pg 74; Parivrtta Trikonasana pg 76; Ardha Chandrasana pg 90; Uttanasana pg 97; Bhujangasana pg 130; Eka Pada Rajakapotasana Stretch pg 134; Dhanurasana pg 129; Urdhva Prasarita Padasana pg 148; Janu Sirsasana pg 158; Upavistha Konasana pg 162; Paschimottanasana pg 170; Ardha Matsyendrasana I pg 182; Alligator Twists I-IV pg 184; 20+ minutes Savasana pg 190.

Level II PITTA Practice #2, Week 2

2 Surya Namaskar pg 66; Adho Mukha Vrksasana pg 114; Viparita Karani pg 121; Salabhasana I pg 127; Purvottanasana pg 152; Supta Virasana pg 144; Child's Pose pg 61; Baddha Konasana pg 140; Janu Sirsasana pg 158; Parivrtta Janu Sirsasana pg 167; Ardha Baddha Padma Paschimottanasana pg 166; Marichyasana III pg 180; Jathara Parivartanasana pg 186; 20+ minutes Savasana pg 190.

Level II PITTA Practice #3, Week 3

2-4 Surya Namaskar pg 66; Pincha Mayurasana pg 116; Neck Stretch pg 57; Sarvangasana II or III pg 102-4; Halasana pg 108; Depada Pidam pg 110; 2 Makarasana pg 128; Child's Pose pg 61; Supta Padangusthasana pg 160; Triang Mukhaikapada Paschimottanasana pg 164; Paschimottanasana pg 170; Marichyasana I pg 178; Bharadvajasana I pg 176; 20+ minutes Savasana pg 190.

Level II PITTA Practice #4, Weeks 4 & 5

Alternate Practices #1, 2, 3, daily.

Level II PITTA Practice #5, Week 6

Parsvakonasana pg 80; Parsvottanasana pg 84; Uttanasana pg 97; Preparation for Sirsasana pg 112; Neck Stretch pg 57; Viparita Karani pg 121 or Sarvangasana III pg 104; Back Vinyasa pg 124; Dhanurasana pg 129 or Urdhva Dhanurasana pg 132; Child's Pose pg 61; Anantasana pg 147; 2 Upavistha Konasana pg 162; Ardha Baddha Padma Paschimottanasana pg 166; Jathara Parivartanasana pg 186; 20+ minutes Savasana pg 190.

Level II PITTA Practice #6, Week 7

2-4 Surya Namaskar pg 66; Preparation for Sirsasana pg 112; Neck Stretch pg 57; Sarvangasana II or III pg 102-4; Makarasana pg 128; Bhujangasana pg 130; Urdhva Prasarita Padasana pg 148; Vasisthasana pg 151; Janu Sirsasana pg 158; Parivrtta Janu Sirsasana pg 167; Urdhva Mukha Paschimottanasana pg 168; Ardha Matsyendrasana I pg 182; Marichyasana III pg 180; 20+ minutes Savasana pg 190.

Level II PITTA Practice #7, Week 8

Vrksasana pg 72; Virabhadrasana II pg 78; Urdhva Prasarita Ekapadasana pg 94; Padangusthasana pg 92; Adho Mukha Vrksasana pg 114; Pincha Mayurasana pg 116; Viparita Karani pg 121; Dhanurasana pg 129 or Urdhva Dhanurasana pg 132; Supta Virasana pg 144; Navasana pg 145; Yoga Mudrasana pg 153; Anantasana pg 147; Upavistha Konasana pg 162 or Kurmasana pg 169; Janu Sirsasana pg 158; Paschimottanasana pg 170; Alligator Twists I-IV pg 184; Jathara Parivartanasana pg 186; 20+ minutes Savasana pg 190.

Level II PITTA Practice #8, Weeks 9 & 10

Alternate between Level II Practices #5, 6, and 7, changing daily.

Level II PITTA Practice #9, Weeks 11 - 20

Choose a different Practice from Levels I and II alternating daily. Focus on smooth, even breathing throughout each Yoga class or practice.

LEVEL III & IV PITTA

A Level III or IV student or teacher should already have a working knowledge of how to sequence, select and progressively change their practice. We recommend that they begin practicing Level II until they gain any needed experience. The practice can be made challenging by holding the poses longer or with multiple repetitions.

The more advanced Yogini or Yogi will want to remember that Pitta is raised by inversions, most especially by headstand and its variations. For Pitta, the shoulderstand must always follow their headstand. Practicing the shoulderstand immediately following the headstand and for a longer period will soften the headstand's Pitta energy. Whenever practicing a Pitta provoking pose, move slowly and keep the experience comfortable. 'Easy does it' is a good motto for Pitta types, along with a focus on a soft, nourishing breath. This focus will serve Pitta types in all parts of their life.

The Practices for Levels III and IV are intentionally long lists of appropriately measured categories to pacify this dosha. We recommend you cut each practice down to the size you like but maintain the same relative proportions of each category.

The English names are supplied here for anyone unfamiliar with the Sanskrit terminology. Many asanas for Levels III and IV are not described in this book so please refer to *Light On Yoga* by B.K.S. Iyengar for further descriptions.

LEVEL III PITTA

Two examples of Level III Long Term Pitta Pacifying Practices follow.

LEVEL III PITTA EXAMPLE PRACTICE #1

Inverted Poses	
Sirsasana	Headstand
Parivrittaikapada Sirsasana	Revolving Legs in Headstand
Sarvangasana III	Full Shoulderstand
Eka Pada Sarvangasana	One Leg Extended Shoulderstand
Supta Konasana Sarvangasana	Open Angle Shoulderstand Variation
Parsvaika Pada Sarvangasana	Foot Sideways Shoulderstand Variation
Setu Bandha Sarvangasana	Shoulderstand into Bridge Pose
Backbends	
Makarasana	Locust Variation
Urdhva Dhanurasana	Upward Bow Pose
Floor Poses	
Virasana IV	Bowing Hero Pose
Anantasana	Serpent Pose
Hanumanasana	Prayer Splits Pose
Siddhasana	Perfect Sitting Pose
Forward Bends	
Triang Mukhaikapada Paschimottanasana	TMP
Ardha Baddha Padma Paschimottanasana	Half Lotus Forward Ben
Urdhva Mukha Paschimottanasana	Legs On Top Forward Bend
Paschimottanasana	Full Forward Bend Pose
Twists	
Jathara Parivartanasana	Revolving Stomach Twist
Savasana	20+ minutes

LEVEL III PITTA EXAMPLE PRACTICE #2

Inverted Poses	
Adho Mukha Vrksasana	Hand Stand (wall)
Sarvangasana III	Full Shoulderstand
Backbends	
Bhujangasana	Cobra Pose
Salabhasana III	Locust Pose III
Urdhva Dhanurasana	Upward Bow Pose
Eka Pada Urdhva Dhanurasana	Upward Bow One Leg Extended Pose
Floor Poses	
Yoga Mudrasana	Yoga Seal
Baddha Konasana	Bound Angle Pose
Forward Bends	
Janu Sirsasana	Head to Knee Pose
Parsva Upavistha Konasana	Over One Open Leg Forward Bend Pose
Kurmasana	Tortoise Pose
Paschimottanasana	Full Forward Bend
Twists	
Marichyasana III	Sage Twist III
Marichyasana II	Sage Twist II
Savasana	20+ minutes

LEVEL IV PITTA

Two examples of Advanced Level IV Long Term Pitta Pacifying Practices follow.

LEVEL IV PITTA EXAMPLE PRACTICE #1

Inverted Poses	
Sirsasana	Headstand
Parivrittaikapada Sirsasana	Revolving legs Headstand Variation
Parsva Eka Pada Sirsasana	One Leg Side Headstand Variation
Sarvangasana III	Full Shoulderstand
Pindasana Sarvangasana	Lotus Fetal in Shoulderstand
Parsva Halasana	Sideways Plow Pose
Karnapidasana	Knees to Ears Pose
Backbends	
Urdhva Dhanurasana	Upward Bow Pose
Eka Pada Urdhva Dhanurasana	Upward Bow One Leg Extended Pose
Floor Poses	
Supta Virasana	Reclining Hero Pose
Parvatasana	Lotus-Arms Stretched Up Pose
Yoga Mudrasana	Yogic Scal Pose
Yoganidrasana	Yoga Sleeping Pose
Forward Bends	
Janu Sirsasana	Head to Knee Pose
Triang Mukhaikapada Paschimottanasana	TMP
Krounchasana	Heron Pose
Ardha Baddha Padma Paschimottanasana	Bound Angle Forward Bend
Paschimottanasana VIII	Full Forward Bend
Twists	
Parvritta Paschimottanasana	Revolving Full Forward Bend Pose
Ardha Matsyendrasana II	Half Fish II
Ardha Matsyendrasana III	Half Fish III
Savasana	20+ minutes

LEVEL IV PITTA EXAMPLE PRACTICE #2

Warm Ups	
2-4 Surya Namaskar	Sun Salutations
Inverted Poses	
Adho Mukha Vrksasana	Handstand (Downward Facing Tree Pose)
Pincha Mayurasana	Arm Stand (Peacock Feather)
Backbends	
Urdhva Dhanurasana	Upward Bow Pose
Eka Pada Urdhva Dhanurasana	Upward Bow Leg Extended
Dwi Pada Viparita Dandasana	Inverted Arch Pose
Eka Pada Viparita Dandasana	Inverted Arch Pose Leg Extended
Eka Pada Rajakapotasana I, II, or III	One Leg Bow Pose I, II, or III
Floor Poses	
Yoga Mudrasana	Yoga Seal Pose
Kandasana	Knot Pose
Kurmasana	Tortoise Pose
Yoga Nidrasana	Yoga Sleep Pose
Forward Bends	
Ubhya Padangusthasana III	Balancing Foot Big Toe Pose III
Parvritta Janu Sirsasana	Revolving Head to Knee Pose
Urdhva Mukha Paschimottanasana I or II	Upward Facing Forward Bend Pose I or II
Paschimottanasana	Full Forward Bend Pose
Twists	
Pasasana or Any Bharadvajasana	Noose Twist or Legs Side Sitting Twist
Marichyasana II	Sage Twist II
Jathara Parivartanasana	Revolving Stomach Twist
Savasana	20+ minutes

LONG TERM KAPHA REDUCING PROGRAMS

GENERAL NOTES

Kaphas are most challenged by getting started, but with perseverance they can establish a disciplined practice that will transform their life experience. When Kapha is severely provoked, and it is difficult to even think of beginning a practice, start with movements done in a chair or poses on the floor. These small movements can generate enough energy for a fuller upright practice. As Kaphas take on an asana practice, they will benefit from first building strength. Along with gaining body strength, they will also be increasing their determination.

To reduce Kapha, stimulate and work the body. Vigorous activity, hard work, movement, inversion, standing poses, heat producing postures, and all backbending reduce Kapha energy. Begin backbends with small-unsupported cobra poses (no weight on the hands and arms), until you gain the strength needed for more advanced backbending. Kaphas will enjoy the feelings of exhilaration generated by these poses. Both flexing and strengthening will lighten and refresh the Kapha experience of life.

Most sitting poses are centering and relaxing, stimulating parasympathetic response in the body. Sitting poses that are more intense are better suited for pacifying Kapha dosha. Limit the time you spend in forward bends since they increase Kapha. When practicing forward bends keep them dynamic by moving into the positions with a straight spine. Maintaining the position of a strong back will create more hamstring stretch while strengthening the spine.

If there is excess weight associated with high Kapha, then proceed carefully with the inverted postures. Make sure to systematically build the strength you need for support. Guidance from an experienced teacher is very helpful to insure your safety.

Kaphas easily relax and do not need long Savasanas. Students at levels I and II will usually do better with ten minute Savasanas.

LEVEL I KAPHA

Level I KAPHA Practice #1, Week 1

Neck Stretch pg 57; Cat Stretch pg 60; Adho Mukha Svanasana pg 100; Chest Opening at Wall pg 62; Vrksasana pg 72; Trikonasana pg 74; Virabhadrasana I pg 86; Padottanasana pg 83; Standing Chair Twist pg 175; Preparation for Sirsasana pg 112; Sarvangasana I pg 102; 3 Back Vinyasa pg 124; Niralamba Bhujangasana I pg 126; Dandasana pg 156; Janu Sirsasana pg 158; Sitting Chair Twist pg 174; 10-15 minute Savasana pg 190.

Level I KAPHA Practice #2, Week 2

2 Surya Namaskar pg 66; Tadasana pg 70; Virabhadrasana II pg 78; Parsvakonasana pg 80; Wall Push pg 63; Sitting Chair Twist pg 174; Preparation for Sirsasana pg 112; Sarvangasana I pg 102; Depada Pidam pg 110; Back Vinyasa pg 124; Makarasana pg 128; Niralamba Bhujangasana II pg 126; Urdhva Prasarita Padasana pg 148; Upavistha Konasana pg 162; Alligator Twists I & II pg 184; 10-15 minute Savasana pg 190.

Level I KAPHA Practice #3, Week 3

4 Surya Namaskar pg 66; Adho Mukha Svanasana pg 100; Sarvangasana I or II pg 102; Niralamba Bhujangasana I pg 126; Niralamba Bhujangasana II pg 126; Salabhasana I and II pg 127; Purvottanasana pg 152; Vasisthasana pg 151; Urdhva Prasarita Padasana pg 148; Parsva Upavistha Konasana pg 163; Alligator Twists I-IV pg 184; 10-15 minute Savasana pg 190.

Level I KAPHA Practice #4, Weeks 4 & 5

Alternate practices #1, 2, 3, for 2 weeks

Level I KAPHA Practice #5, Week 6

4 Surya Namaskar pg 66; Chest Opening at Wall pg 62; Virabhadrasana I pg 86; Virabhadrasana III pg 88; Parsvottanasana pg 84; Preparation for Sirsasana pg 112; Sarvangasana II pg 103; Depada Pidam pg 110; Back Vinyasa pg 124; Salabhasana II pg 127; Eka Pada Rajakapotasana Stretch pg 135; Dhanurasana pg 129; Virasana pg 143; Supta Virasana pg 144; Janu Sirsasana pg 158; Alligator Twists I-IV pg 184; 10-15 minute Savasana pg 190.

Level I KAPHA Practice #6, Week 7

Trikonasana pg 74; Parivrtta Trikonasana pg 76; Ardha Chandrasana pg 90; Padangusthasana pg 92; Adho Mukha Svanasana pg 100; Adho Mukha Vrksasana pg 114; Preparation for Sirsasana pg 112; Sarvangasana II pg 103; Depada Pidam pg 110; Salabhasana I pg 127; Makarasana pg 128; Niralamba Bhujangasana III pg 126; Urdhva Prasarita Padasana pg 148; Janu Sirsasana pg 158; Parivrtta Janu Sirsasana pg 167; Alternate Marichyasana III pg 180 and Bharadvajasana I pg 176; 10-15 minute Savasana pg 190.

Level I KAPHA Practice #7, Week 8

4 Surya Namaskar (Jumpings) pg 66; Preparation for Sirsasana pg 112 or Sirsasana pg 118; Sarvangasana II or III pg 102-4; Makarasana pg 128; Dhanurasana pg 129; 2 Urdhva Dhanurasana pg 132; Purvottanasana pg 152; Chaturanga Dandasana pg 150; Navasana pg 145; Child's Pose pg 61; Baddha Konasana pg 140; Supta Padangusthasana pg 160; Paschimottanasana pg 170; Alligator Twists I-IV pg 184; 10-15 minute Savasana pg 190.

Level I KAPHA Practice #8, Weeks 9 & 10

Alternate Practices #4, 5, 6.

Level I KAPHA Practice #9, Weeks 11, 12 & 13

Alternate Practices #1 through #9.

Level I KAPHA Practice #10, Weeks 14 - 16

Continue alternating Practices #1 through #9. Create you own yoga practice by mixing and matching various combinations from the many Practices outlined.

LEVEL II KAPHA

Level II KAPHA Practice #1, Week 1

Parsvakonasana pg 80; Parivrtta Trikonasana pg 76; Parsvottanasana pg 84; Padottanasana pg 83; Sirsasana pg 118; Sarvangasana II or III pg 102-4; Depada Pidam pg 110; Eka Pada Rajakapotasana Stretch pg 134; Dhanurasana pg 129; Urdhva Dhanurasana pg 132; Child's Pose pg 61; Chaturanga Dandasana pg 150; Navasana pg 145; Triang Mukhaikapada Paschimottanasana pg 164; Upavistha Konasana pg 162; Bharadvajasana I pg 176; 10-15 minute Savasana pg 190.

Level II KAPHA Practice #2, Week 2

4-6 Surya Namaskar (Jumpings) pg 66; Adho Mukha Svanasana pg 100; Adho Mukha Vrksasana pg 114; Pincha Mayurasana pg 116; Sirsasana pg 118; Any Sarvangasana pg 102-4; Eka Pada Sarvangasana pg 106; 2 Makarasana pg 128; Salabhasana II pg 127; Bhujangasana pg 130; Upavistha Konasana pg 162; Parsva Upavistha Konasana pg 163; Jathara Parivartanasana pg 186; 10-15 minute Savasana pg 190.

Level II KAPHA Practice #3, Week 3

Trikonasana pg 74; Parivrtta Trikonasana pg 76; Ardha Chandrasana pg 90; Virabhadrasana I pg 86; Virabhadrasana III pg 88; Urdhva Prasarita Ekapadasana pg 94; Supta Virasana pg 144; 2 Bhujangasana pg 130; Dhanurasana pg 129; Urdhva Dhanurasana pg 132; Eka Pada Urdhva Dhanurasana pg 132; Janu Sirsasana pg 158; Parivrtta Janu Sirsasana pg 167; Ardha Matsyendrasana I pg 182; 10-15 minute Savasana pg 190.

Level II KAPHA Practice #4, Weeks 4 & 5

Alternate practices #1, 2, 3.

Level II KAPHA Practice #5, Week 6

2-4 Namaskar (Jumpings) pg 66; Sirsasana pg 118; Parsva Sirsasana pg 120; Any Sarvangasana pg 102-4; Eka Pada Sarvangasana pg 106; Setu Bandha Sarvangasana pg 107; Dhanurasana pg 129; Supta Virasana pg 144; Urdhva Dhanurasana pg 132; Child's Pose pg 61; Chaturanga Dandasana pg 150; Vasisthasana pg 151; Ardha Baddha Padma Paschimottanasana pg 166; Jathara Parivartanasana pg 186; 10-15 minute Savasana pg 190.

Level II KAPHA Practice #6, Week 7

6 Surya Namaskar (Jumpings) pg 66; Dhanurasana pg 129; Urdhva (or Eka Pada Urdhva) Dhanurasana pg 132; Dwi Pada Viparita Dandasana pg 136; Anantasana pg 147; Ubhya Padangusthasana pg 146; Parivrtta Janu Sirsasana pg 167; Urdhva Mukha Paschimottanasana pg 168; Marichyasana III pg 180; Marichyasana II pg 179; Ardha Matsyendrasana I pg 182; 10-15 minute Savasana pg 190.

Level II KAPHA Practice #7, Week 8

Parsvakonasana pg 80; Ardha Chandrasana pg 90; Virabhadrasana III pg 88; Urdhva Prasarita Ekapadasana pg 94; Adho Mukha Vrksasana pg 114; Pincha Mayurasana pg 116; Sirsasana Variations pg 118-20; Sarvangasana III pg 104; Setu Bandha Sarvangasana pg 107; Depada Pidam pg 110; Bhujangasana pg 130; Urdhva Dhanurasana pg 132; Eka Pada Rajakapotasana I pg 135 or Stretch pg 134; Anantasana pg 147 or Vasisthasana pg 151; Paschimottanasana pg 170; Jathara Parivar-tanasana pg 186; 10-15 minute Savasana pg 190.

Level II KAPHA Practice #8, Weeks 9 - 11

Alternate Practices #4, 5, 6.

Level II KAPHA Practice #9, Weeks 12 - 20

Alternate between all Practices from Level I and II choosing a different Practice daily

LEVEL III & IV

A Level III or IV student or teacher should already have a working knowledge of how to sequence, select and progressively change their practice. We recommend that they begin practicing Level II until they gain any needed experience.

The more advanced Level III and IV Yogi or Yogini needs to remember that Kapha is reduced by vigorous movement, backbends and inversions (most especially headstand and its variations). A practice that chooses stimulating postures over passive ones and focuses on working each pose is best for Kapha. Even though Kaphas may not prefer it, a shorter Savasana is better for them. More work and less rest is a focus that is good for Kaphas. Unlike Vatas, Kaphas can gain more energy from sleeping fewer hours each night.

The Practices for Levels III and IV are intentionally long lists of appropriately measured categories to pacify each dosha. We recommend you cut each practice down to the size you like but maintain the same relative proportions of each category.

The English names are supplied here for those unfamiliar with the Sanskrit terminology. Many asanas for Levels III and IV are not described in this book so please refer to *Light On Yoga* by B.K.S. Iyengar for further descriptions.

LEVEL III KAPHA

Two examples of Level III Long Term Kapha Pacifying Practices follow.

LEVEL III KAPHA EXAMPLE PRACTICE #1

Standing Poses	
Virabhadrasana II	Warrior Pose II
Parsvakonasana	Extended Side Angle Pose
Parivrtta Parsvakonasana	Revolving Extended Side Angle Pose
Ardha Chandrasana	Half Moon Pose
Virabhadrasana I	Warrior Pose I
Virabhadrasana III	Warrior Pose III
Parsvottanasana	Intense Sideways Stretch Pose
Hasta Padangusthasana	Extended Hand & Foot Pose
Urdhva Prasarita Ekapadasana	Upward Lifted Leg Forward Bend
Uttanasana	Intense Stretch Forward Bend
Inverted Poses	
Sirsasana	Headstand
Sarvangasana	Shoulderstand
Eka Pada Sarvangasana	One Foot Extended Shoulderstand
Backbends	
Salabhasana I	Locust Pose I
Salabhasana III	Locust Pose III
Dhanurasana	Bow Pose
Dwi Pada Viparita Dandasana	Two Legs Inverted Arch Pose
Eka Pada Viparita Dandasana	One Leg Inverted Arch Pose
Floor Poses	
Child's Pose	
Urdhva Prasarita Padasana	Upward Extended Feet Pose
Vasisthasana	Side Plank Pose
Siddhasana	Perfect Sitting Pose 3–5 minutes
Twists	
Bharadvajasana I	Sitting Twist
Jathara Parivartanasana	Revolving Stomach Twist
Savasana	10–15 minutes

LEVEL III KAPHA

Long Term Pacifying Practices (continued)

LEVEL III KAPHA EXAMPLE PRACTICE #2

Warm Ups	
Surya Namaskars	(Jumpings will work best)
Inverted Poses	
Adho Mukha Vrksasana	Hand Stand
Sirsasana	Headstand
Parivrittaikapada Sirsasana	Revolving Legs in Sirsasana
Urdhva Konasana in Sirsasana	Upward Open Angle in Headstand
Salamba Sarvangasana	Shoulderstand
Supta Konasana Sarvangasana	Open Angle Shoulderstand
Setu Bandha Sarvangasana	Bridge Pose from Shoulderstand
Backbends	
Makarasana	Locust Variation
Urdhva Mukha Svanasana	Upward Facing Dog Pose
Dhanurasana	Bow Pose
Urdhva Dhanurasana	Upward Bow Pose
Floor Poses	
Purvottanasana	Intense Front Extension
Navasana	Boat Pose
Yoga Mudrasana	Yoga Seal
Simhasana	Lion Pose
Forward Bends	
Parsva Upavistha Konasana	Over One Open Leg Forward Bend
Parvritta Janu Sirsasana	Revolving Head to Knee Pose
Triang Mukhaikapada Paschimottanasana	TMP
Twists	
Marichyasana I	Sage Twist I
Ardha Matsyendrasana II	Half Fish Twist II
Savasana	10-15 minutes

LEVEL IV KAPHA

Two examples of Level IV Long Term Kapha Pacifying Practices follow.

LEVEL IV KAPHA EXAMPLE PRACTICE #1

Inverted Poses	
Pincha Mayurasana	Arm Stand (Peacock Feather)
Vrschikasana I	Scorpion Pose
Sirsasana	Headstand
Parivrittaikapada Sirsasana	Revolving Legs in Sirsasana
Eka Pada Sirsasana	One Leg down in Sirsasana
Parsva Eka Pada Sirsasana	One leg side in Sirsasana
Parsva Urdhva Padmasana	Upward Lotus in Sirsasana
Bakasana	Crane Pose
Sarvangasana	Shoulderstand
Parsva Sarvangasana	Legs Sideways Shoulderstand
Setu Bandha Sarvangasana	Shoulderstand drops down into Bridge
Karnapidasana	Knees to Ears Pose
Backbends	
Urdhva Dhanurasana	Upward Bow (Push Up From Floor)
Urdhva Dhanurasana (from Standing)	Drop Back into Bow pose
Natarajasana	Dancer's Pose
Floor Poses	
Yoga Mudrasana	Yoga Seal Pose
Parvatasana	Lotus With Arms Stretched Up Pose
Ubhya Padangusthasana III	Holding Both Toes Pose
Forward Bends	
Parvritta Janu Sirsasana	Revolving Head to Knee Pose
Krounchasana	Heron Pose
Urdhva Mukha Paschimottanasana	Upward Facing Forward Bend
Parvritta Paschimottanasana	Revolving Full Forward Bend
Twists	
Pasasana	Noose Twist
Paripurna Ardha Matsyendrasana	Complete Twist
Jathara Parivartanasana	Revolving Stomach Twist Pose
Savasana	10-15 minutes

LEVEL IV KAPHA EXAMPLE PRACTICE #1

Inverted Poses	
Sirsasana	Headstand with Variation
Salamba Sarvangasana	Supported Shoulderstand with Variations
Parsva Halasana	Sideways Plow Pose
Standing Poses	
Parivrtta Trikonasana	Revolving Triangle Pose
Ardha Chandrasana	Half Moon Pose
Parsvakonasana	Extended Side Angle Pose
Parivrtta Parsvakonasana	Revolving Extended Side Angle Pose
Parsvottanasana	Intense Sideways Stretch Pose
Parivrtta Ardha Chandrasana	Revolving Half Moon Pose
Virabhadrasana I	Warrior Pose I
Virabhadrasana III	Warrior Pose III
Urdhva Prasarita Ekapadasana	Upward Lifted back Leg Forward Bend
Uttanasana II	Intense Stretch Pose
Backbends	
Uttana Padasana	Legs Up Lying Back
Supta Virasana	Reclining Hero
Eka Pada Rajakapotasana II	One Leg Bow II Pose
Floor Poses	
Mandalasana	Ring Pose
Tolasana	Scales Balance Pose
Ubhya Padangusthasana III	Holding Both Toes Pose
Hanumanasana	Prayer Splits Pose
Yoga Mudrasana	Yoga Seal Pose
Forward Bends	
Ardha Baddha Padma Paschimottanasana	Bound Angle Forward Bend
Parivrtta Paschimottanasana	Revolving Full Forward Bend
Paschimottanasana VI	Full Forward Bend
Twists	
Marichyasana II	Sage Twist II
Any Bharadvajasana	Legs Side Sitting Twist
Ardha Matsyendrasana II	Half Fish Pose II
Savasana	10-15 minutes

DAVID FRAWLEY IN SIDDHASANA

PART V

Appendices

V. 14 ENERGETICS OF ASANA PRACTICE ADVANCED MATERIAL

The energetics of asana can be looked at from many different angles. Besides regular doshic considerations, other energetic factors exist for determining the effects of asana practice. These additional considerations are mainly for Yoga teachers and advanced practitioners and are especially helpful in Yoga therapy. We have included them in the appendices for Yoga students who want a more complete view. They expand the range of asana considerations to the levels of Agni, Prana and the tissues (dhatus) of the body. Four main pairs of factors are significant, making eight in all:

Eight Main Factors of Asana Practice		
1. Expanding/Contracting	Pranic Movement	Vata, Air
2. Ascending/Descending	Pranic Movement	Vata, Air
3. Heating/Cooling	Effect on Agni	Pitta, Fire
4. Tonifying/Reducing	Effect on the Tissues	Kapha, Water

Asanas may be expanding or contracting and ascending or descending in their energy depending upon how they stimulate the flow of Prana (a Vata factor). They can be heating or cooling, depending upon whether they increase or decrease the digestive fire (a Pitta factor). They can be tonifying (Brimhana) or reducing (Langhana), depending upon whether they increase or decrease the bodily tissues (a Kapha factor). Generally, the four pairs come in two groups:

1. **Agni (Fiery)**	2. **Soma (Watery)**
Heating	Cooling
Expanding	Contracting
Ascending	Descending
Reducing	Tonifying

The most powerful energies in our natural environment are the forces of heating and cooling. These have the strongest effect upon our physical structure and movement. In Ayurveda they are most responsible for disturbing the doshas and causing disease. Most diseases begin either with a cold or with a fever. Heat is expanding, ascending and reducing (burning up its fuel). Conversely, cold is contracting, descending and tonifying (building up tissues). But sometimes these factors combine in other ways.

1. PRANIC MOVEMENT: ENERGETICS OF THE FIVE PRANAS

Understanding Prana requires understanding its subtypes and their effects. According to its direction of movement, Prana has five subtypes called *Vayus* or winds, which are also the five forms of Vata dosha. The five pranas possess specific actions on our physical structure and bodily functions. Each triggers certain emotions and holds certain mental states. The pranas work everywhere in body and mind as the primary powers.

TABLE OF THE FIVE PRANAS

1. PRANA VAYU—Energizing Prana
Inward movement of food, breath, impressions and thoughts.
Main propulsive energy governing the intake of nutrition on all levels. Functions include eating, inhalation, and reception of sensory impressions, emotions and ideas.
2. UDANA VAYU—Ascending Prana
Upward movement of food, breath, impressions and thoughts.
Governs output of energy and motivation. Functions include eructation, exhalation, speech and will. Represents the positive energy expression from our intake of nutritive substances.
3. VYANA VAYU—Expanding Prana
Outward movement of food, breath, impressions and thoughts.
Allows our energy to move outward, expand and release itself. Functions include circulation of nutrients, oxygen, and mental circulation as well as our exercise capacity.
4. SAMANA VAYU—Contracting and Consolidating Prana
Contraction or absorption of food, breath, impressions and thoughts.
Centers our energy and allows for the digestive process through which we are able to absorb new nutrients. Functions include digestion on all levels, as well as contraction and maintenance of equilibrium and homeostasis.
5. APANA VAYU — Descending and Stabilizing Prana
Downward movement of food, breath, impressions and thoughts.
Takes our energy downward and grounds it. Governs all forms of elimination from food and water (excretion and urination) to ideas. Also responsible for reproduction and supports the immune system.

Each prana has its energy center in the body, though it works to some degree everywhere.

Locations of the Five Pranas		
1. Prana	Head	Where we take in food, breath and impressions.
2. Udana	Neck	Upholds the head and body in general and is the site of speech.
3. Vyana	Chest	Allows us to expand our energy through respiration, circulation and movement of the arms.
4. Samana	Navel	Where we are centered and hold our equilibrium. It is also the site of digestion through the small intestine.
5. Apana	Lower Abdomen	Where we are grounded and have elimination through the urinary and excretory systems.

As energetic formations, asanas relate to Prana and its five subtypes. The five pranas govern the different types of postures and their muscular movements. Each prana has its special relevance in asana practice.

- The master Prana is behind all forms of movement, particularly of a forward moving or propulsive nature.
- Udana governs upward movement and extension of the spine, including holding an erect position. It also governs speech.
- Vyana governs outward extension, particularly of the arms and legs.
- Samana governs contraction of the arms and legs and holding a sitting posture.
- Apana governs downward movement, support and grounding, including standing on the feet.

Each prana relates to various practices relative to its location in the body.

Yoga Practices for the Five Pranas		
1. Prana	Head (upper two chakras)	Pranayama, sensory therapies and meditation
2. Udana	Throat	Mantra, chanting, upward directed poses
3. Vyana	Heart, chest and arms	Poses for extending arms and increasing circulation
4. Samana	Navel	Sitting poses, stabilization
5. Apana	Lower abdomen (lower two chakras to feet)	Prone (lying down) poses, inverted poses

Each asana contains a signature of Prana and its expression. Each prana relates to the asanas that work through it. The following asana types increase and decrease the different pranas.

Asanas and the Five Pranas

INCREASES		
Prana	Inward or forward moving postures	Pranayama
Udana	Upward moving postures	Standing poses
Vyana	Expanding and releasing postures	Extending poses
Samana	Contracting and centering postures	Sitting postures
Apana	Grounding and stabilizing postures	Sitting and prone postures

DECREASES		
Prana	Outward moving postures	Strong asanas that create exertion and promote fatigue
Udana	Downward and releasing postures	Inverted postures like shoulderstand
Vyana	Contracting and centering postures	Bound lotus pose, savasana
Samana	Expanding and releasing postures	Stretching the arms and legs
Apana	Upward moving postures	Standing postures, particularly with arms directed upward

The Five Pranas Work in Pairs

- Vertical forces (move up and down): What increases udana usually decreases apana and vice versa as opposite ascending and descending forces.
- Horizontal forces (move across): What increases vyana usually decreases samana and vice versa as opposite forces of expansion and contraction.

Forward Movement – Prana

Forward movement increases Prana, as in the case of postures that bring the chest forward like Virabhadrasana. These are important for stimulating the prana in order to do all other postures. Yet Prana is active in the movement of the other four pranas as well, particularly udana and vyana.

Expanding and Contracting Postures – Vyana and Samana

Vyana and samana represent the arterial and venous circulation, the blood moving away from the heart (vyana or expansion) and then returning to the heart (samana or contraction). They also represent extension (vyana) and contraction (samana) of the muscles. Samana represents the absorption of nutrients and vyana their circulation throughout the body.

- Contracting postures close or wrap the arms or legs.
- Expanding postures open or extend the arms and legs.
- Forward bends are contracting and calming.
- Backward bends are expanding and stimulating.
- Twists work on both vyana and samana and bring them into balance.

Generally, all asanas should maintain the center of energy in the navel because the purpose of asana practice is to develop stability (samana) and calm on a physical level. Samana keeps all the pranas in harmony and is responsible for their nourishment.

If an asana has no extension to it, we should try to extend the Prana (by increasing it) to maintain vyana, like doing pranayama in the bound lotus position.

Raising and Lowering Postures – Udana and Apana

Udana and apana represent the forces of rising up and sitting down and muscular actions like raising or lowering of the hands. If one raises the hands over the head to a vertical position that is a movement of udana. The lowered position is more normal and the raised position requires exertion (udana) because of the influence of gravity (apana).

- Upward movement, particularly of the head, neck and shoulders, increases udana.
- Raising of the hands or legs increases udana.
- Downward movement, particularly of the lower abdomen and legs, increases apana.

- Inverted poses can increase udana dramatically, particularly the headstand because these bring pressure into the upper part of the body. They also counter apana.
- Holding the spine and head erect stabilizes udana.
- Holding the lower legs still in a sitting posture, like the lotus pose, stabilizes apana (prevents it from sinking).

HOW TO PERFORM ASANAS RELATIVE TO THE FIVE PRANAS

One should consider the role of all five pranas in asana practice. An integral asana practice should work all the pranas. It requires energization (prana), expansion (vyana), contraction (samana), upward movement (udana) and downward movement (apana) in the right proportion and balance. But the degree of these pranic movements will vary by condition and by dosha.

If a person's energy is low or depressed (apana excess), asanas should aim at raising the energy (increasing udana), using upward moving and standing poses along with chanting and affirmations. If a person's energy is too elevated or spaced out (udana excess), asanas should aim at lowering and grounding the energy (increasing apana), using prone or inverted poses along with deep and slow breathing and refraining from talking.

If a person's energy is too contracted or introverted (samana excess), asanas should aim at expanding and releasing the energy (increasing vyana), employing various movement and extension oriented poses and vinyasas. If the person's energy is too expanded, diffused or fragmented (vyana excess), asanas should aim at centering, contracting and consolidating the energy (increasing samana), with seated meditation poses.

DOSHAS AND PRANAS

Each doshic type has its considerations relative to the five pranas.

Kapha

Kapha types have a lower level of activity that leads to dullness or depression (apana dominance), as well as contraction (samana dominance). They benefit by postures to increase ascension and expansion of energy (prana, udana and vyana).

As Kapha relates to the region of the chest and stomach, the pranas of that region help keep Kapha dosha under control. To throw up (vomit), cough, or throw out of the body through the mouth reduces Kapha (mucus), which is the function of udana. This is why Pancha Karma therapy uses therapeutic emesis (vomiting or vamana) to eliminate Kapha from the body. Postures that increase udana will reduce Kapha in the most radical way.

Vata

Apana or the descending prana is responsible for the absorption of food in the body and for grounding. Apana derangements occur along with most diseases of the physical body, which rests upon food, particularly Vata diseases, which are the most numerous. For treating Vata we should aim at calming, controlling and strengthening apana, the lower abdomen and the reproductive system that it rules. Vata is alleviated downward through apana but in a gentle way. This is why in Pancha Karma employs cleansing enemas (basti) to remove Vata from the body.

Vata also benefits from increasing samana, the contracting and consolidating energy, but along with vyana, which releases tension and opens circulation. Creating pressure on the muscles or actions that massage the body reduces Vata.

Pitta

Samana vayu is responsible for Agni, the digestive fire, and keeps Pitta in balance. Asanas for

Pitta aim at the region of the small intestine and samana vayu that rules it. Asanas that keep the energy in the navel balanced and flowing harmonize Pitta. Pitta is removed downward from the body by the action of apana and samana. This is why therapeutic purgation is used in Pancha Karma to remove Pitta dosha from the body. Promoting apana helps reduce Pitta by draining it from the region of the abdomen.

2. HEATING AND COOLING – AGNI

The heating and cooling aspect of asanas depends upon how they affect Agni or the digestive fire. Agni at a physical level dwells in the small intestine. Asanas that open up the central abdomen region, like Supta Virasana or Dhanurasana, increase Agni, while those that close it decrease Agni.

Aerobic exercise has a warming but diffusive effect, drawing Agni to the periphery. Seated postures with pranayama stabilize Agni in the center of the body. Pranayama in general increases Agni because it promotes heat in the body. Relative to the five pranas, heat is ascending or upward moving (udana), while cold is descending or downward moving (apana). Hot air rises and cold air sinks.

Heat is expanding (vyana) and cold is contracting (samana). Heat makes us sweat. Cold causes us to contract, shiver and stop sweating. Yet heat makes us sweat in order to cool us off, so expanding movements long-term can release heat. Cold makes us contract in order to preserve our heat, so contracting movements long-term preserve heat. This means that expansive postures will initially create heat but in the long term can have a cooling effect. Meanwhile, contracting postures will initially create cold but in the long run have a heating effect.

Similar qualifications must be borne in mind for any classification of asanas as heating or cooling. For example, prone postures are generally cooling but not if we put a blanket over ourselves. Active postures like running create heat; but through exhaustion coolness can be created if we push ourselves too far. Sitting postures, though cooling in themselves, can be used to generate heat through pranayama because they allow for consolidation.

POSTURAL CONSIDERATIONS

- Forward Bends are cooling; especially open-leg forward bends like Upavista Konasana.
- Backward Bends are heating.
- Standing postures are heating with the exception of standing forward bends.
- Sitting and Prone postures are cooling.
- Inverted postures are heating; except where there is a bending of the neck, as in shoulderstand, which is cooling.
- Twists are neutral or balancing.

However, all asanas have heating and cooling effects depending upon where they direct our energy. The regions where asana increases circulation or contracts tend to be heated. The regions where the asanas withdraw circulation or relax tend to be cooled.

PRANIC CONSIDERATIONS OF HEATING AND COOLING

Breathing creates heat in the body and propels the heart-lungs system and the process of circulation. However, there are cooling aspects to the breath.

Inhalation Versus Exhalation

- Inhalation tends to be cooling.
- Exhalation tends to be heating.

Retention

- Retention after inhalation is heating.
- Retention after exhalation is cooling.

During inhalation we take in air, which has

a cooling effect. During retention the air is digested which creates heat. That heat is directed and dispersed upon exhalation. Holding the breath is generally heating. However, holding the breath after exhalation becomes cooling.

Right Nostril Versus Left Nostril Breathing

- Right nostril breathing is heating and stimulating.
- Left nostril breathing is cooling and sedating.

The right/left, male/female, heating/cooling predominance of the body is reflected in the nostrils. Right nostril breathing increases the flow through the channels and organs on the right side of the body. Stimulating these increases heat in the body and promotes all thermogenic processes like digestion. Left nostril breathing increases the flow through the channels and organs on the left side. Stimulating these increases cold in the body and promotes all consolidating processes in the body like tissue formation and stabilization. This is the basis of alternate nostril breathing (Nadi Shodhana) that is perhaps the most important and cleansing of the pranayamas.

Nose Breathing Versus Mouth Breathing

- Breathing through the nose is heating.
- Breathing through the mouth tends to be cooling.

Mouth breathing can be used to release heat as in Shitali pranayama. However, mouth breathing generally increases mucus and should only be done for short periods of time, mainly on exhalation.

Fast or Slow Breathing

- Fast or rapid breathing, as in Bhastrika, is heating.
- Slow breathing is cooling.

Exercise that makes us breathe faster increases body heat. Exercise that slows our breath down has a cooling effect. General rapid breathing will promote the aging process and energy loss. Slow breathing retards the aging process and conserves energy.

The Breath and the Doshas

Heating forms of pranayama like right nostril breathing, Bhastrika and Kapalabhati increase Pitta and decrease Kapha. Cooling forms like left nostril breathing, Shitali and Sitkari increase Kapha and decrease Pitta. Vata is reduced by a combination of heating and cooling pranayamas but more on the heating side as Vata mainly tends to be cold.

3. TONIFYING AND REDUCING (BRIMHANA AND LANGHANA)

The two basic types of all therapies in Yoga and Ayurveda are 'tonifying and reducing' (Brimhana and Langhana), also called nourishing and detoxifying. Generally, we are either suffering from toxins and excesses in the body or from tissue deficiency and lack of energy. This twofold approach is the basis of various systems of traditional Yoga therapy like that taught by T.K.V. Desikachar, the son of the great Yogi Krishnamacharya.

An excess condition is defined either as too much tissue formation (particularly excess fat) or by the accumulation of toxins in the body. These toxins may consist of excess ama (poorly digested food), some pathogen indicated by fever, inflammation or infection, or a parasite lodged in the system.

A person who is significantly overweight needs reduction of the tissues. A person with internal heat, infection or fever needs removal of toxins. These are examples of reduction therapy. Kapha and Kapha-Pitta types tend toward excess and often require reduction therapies. High Kapha causes an excess build-up of the tissues or accumulation of mucus and water in the body. High

Pitta causes internal heat and toxic blood conditions.

On the other hand, a person who is underweight, low in energy and chronically cold needs to be nourished and strengthened. Such are usually Vata types but can occur among the other types as well. When Vata becomes high it usually results in tissue deficiency. Vata as cold, dry and light has a natural depleting effect upon the tissues.

There is also an age factor. Young people need more reduction therapy because they have adequate energy and tissue formation but tend toward excess or heat. Older people need more tonification therapy because their energy level is falling and their tissues are getting depleted.

Yet we all possess some degree of toxins and excesses to be reduced and some degree of weakness or tissue deficiency that requires strengthening. The general rule is that first we reduce and eliminate toxins and second we build and rejuvenate. If we try to tonify first we may only increase the toxins in the body.

The main Ayurvedic reduction therapy is Pancha Karma. It consists of the five detoxification measures of therapeutic vomiting, purgatives, enemas, nasal medications and blood purification. But all forms of fasting and herbs that promote elimination and cleansing of the blood promote various forms of reduction or detoxification. The main Ayurvedic tonification therapy is rejuvenation or Rasayana, which consists of special foods, herbs and exercise to rebuild the tissues and organs. But all forms of nourishing diets and tonic herbs are useful in this regard.

Asana and pranayama can be classified as either tonifying or reducing. Asana practice that is quick, strong or forceful will be reducing. That which is slow and consolidating in its effect is tonifying and can aid in rejuvenation. Pranayama that increases lightness in the body has a more reducing effect long-term. However, it is also a source of energy, so pranayama done along with a nutritive diet has a weight-increasing action.

Asana, like other therapies, should aim at reduction before tonification. Only if toxins are first removed can the tissues be rebuilt in a wholesome manner. A typical asana practice should have an initial phase aiming at reduction followed by a second step aiming at tonification. This is why asana practice begins with more active postures and ends with savasana or the corpse pose in which our energy can be renewed.

- Moving or expanding asanas (vinyasas) are generally reducing.
- Still, sitting or closing asanas are generally tonifying.
- Pranayama that emphasizes deep inhalation followed by prolonged retention is tonifying and increases earth, water and fire elements.
- Pranayama that emphasizes prolonged exhalation followed by retention is reducing and increases air and ether elements.

Asanas aimed at reduction should try to methodically reduce the doshas. Asanas to reduce Kapha promote elimination of mucus, mainly from the upper body. Asanas that reduce Pitta reduce heat, inflammation and infection mainly in the mid-abdomen. Asanas that reduce Vata counter dryness, agitation and debility mainly in the lower abdomen.

Asanas can aim at reduction through promoting the movement of the waste materials, particularly sweat. Sweating reduces water and fat from the body, mainly reducing Kapha, but it also cleanses the blood, reducing Pitta. Asanas can aim at raising Agni or the digestive fire in order to burn up toxins. Asanas that strengthen the navel and the digestive fire will help eliminate any toxins forming from poor digestion.

Asanas can have a reducing effect on different organs, like the liver or lungs, or on different parts of the body like the legs. Wherever we improve circulation will have as an initial effect to remove stagnation and eliminate toxins, but in the long term can promote healing and growth.

Asanas for tonification aim at building up the bodily tissues, primarily the muscle tissue that is the support of the entire body. But they can aim at different organs as well, like strengthening the heart or the liver. They reduce Vata, which tends to deficiency, by countering it with better circulation leading to stronger tissue development.

GLOSSARY OF SANSKRIT TERMS

Agni — fire as a cosmic principle

Ahamkara — ego or sense of separate self

Ahimsa — non-violence or non-harming

Ananda — bliss or divine love

Apana — downward-moving prana

Asanas — yogic postures

Ashtanga Yoga — eight-limbed Yoga system made famous by Patanjali

Atman — true Self, sense of pure I am

Ayu — life, longevity

Ayurveda — yogic science of healing

Bandha — yogic locks

Basti — ayurvedic enemas

Bhakti Yoga — yoga of devotion

Brahman — Absolute Reality

Buddhi — intelligence

Chakras — energy centers of subtle body

Charaka Samhita — Ayurvedic classical text of Charaka

Darshana — Vedic systems of philosophy

Dhanvantari — deity of Ayurveda, a form of Vishnu

Dharana — concentration

Dharma — the law of our nature, truth principle

Dhyana — meditation

Gunas — three prime qualities of Nature of sattva, rajas and tamas

Guru — spiritual guide

Hatha Yoga — Yoga of asana, pranayama and meditation, effort oriented Yoga

Homa — Vedic fire offerings

Ida — left nostril or lunar nadi

Jiva — individual soul

Jnana Yoga — Yoga of Self-knowledge

Kapha — biological water humor

Karma — effect of our past actions, including from previous births

Karma Yoga — Yoga of ritual, work and service

Kundalini — latent energy of spiritual development

Mahat — Divine Mind or Cosmic Intelligence

Manas — outer or sensory aspect of mind

Mantra — seed sounds used for healing or yogic purposes

Nadis — channel systems of subtle body

Nasya — ayurvedic nasal treatments

Neti Pot — small pot for pouring salt water through the nostrils

Niyamas — yogic disciplines and principles of personal behavior

Ojas — vital essence of Kapha

Pancha Karma — ayurvedic detoxification procedure

Patanjali — great Yoga teacher, author of Yoga Sutras

Pingala — right nostril or solar nadi

Pitta — biological fire humor

Prakriti — nature

Prana — vital force, breath

Pranayama — control or expansion of vital force

Pratyahara — control or introversion of the mind and senses

Purusha — inner spirit, Self

Raja Yoga — Integral Yoga system of Patanjali in *Yoga Sutras*

Rajas — quality of action and agitation

Rajasic — of the nature of rajas

Rishis — ancient Vedic seers

Samadhi — absorption

Samana — balancing vital force

Samkhya — philosophy of the 24 tattvas, closely connected to classical Yoga

Samskaras — deep-seated conditioning and motivation

Sattva — quality of harmony

Sattvic — of the nature of sattva

Shakti — power, energy, particular of the deepest level, the Goddess

Shiva — divine power of peace and transcendence

Soma — water as a cosmic and psychological principle

Sushumna — central channel or nadi of subtle body

Sushruta Samhita — Ayurvedic classical text of Sushruta

Svastha — health or well-being

Tamas — quality of darkness and inertia

Tamasic — of the nature of tamas

Tanmatras — sensory potentials or subtle elements (sound, touch, sight, taste, smell)

Tantra — energetic system of working with our higher potentials

Tattvas — cosmic truth principles

Tejas — fire on a vital level

Udana — upward-moving prana

Ujjayi — a form of pranayama

Upaveda — secondary Vedic text

Vata — biological air humor

Vayu — another name for prana or vital force

Vedas — ancient Hindu spiritual system of Self and cosmic knowledge

Vedanga — limb of the Vedas

Vedanta — Self-knowledge aspect of Vedic teaching

Vishnu — divine power of love and protection

Vyana — expansive vital force

Yajna — sacrifice or worship

Yamas — yogic values and principles of social conduct

Yoga — science of reintegration with the universal reality

Yoga Chikitsa — Yoga therapy

Yoga Darshana — Yoga philosophy or the Yoga tradition

Yoga Sutras — classical text on Yoga, compiled by Patanjali

GLOSSARY OF ASANA NAMES

Adho Mukha Svanasana — Downward Facing Dog Pose

Adho Mukha Vrksasana — Hand Stand (also Downward Facing Tree)

Akarna Dhanurasana — Near Ear Bow Pose

Anantasana — Lying Serpent Pose

Ardha Baddha Padma Paschimottanasana — Half lotus Forward Bend also called ABP

Ardha Chandrasana — Half Moon Pose

Ardha Matsyendrasana — Half Fish Twist

Ardha Navasana — Half Boat Pose

Baddha Konasana — Bound Angle Sitting Pose

Bakasana — Crane Pose

Bharadvajasana — Bharadvaja Pose, Legs Side Sitting Twist

Bhekasana — Frog Pose

Bhujangasana — Cobra Pose

Chaturanga Dandasana — Plank Pose

Dandasana — Staff Pose

Dhanurasana — Bow Pose

Dipada Pidam — Bridge Pose

Dwi Pada Viparita Dandasana — Inverted Arch
Eka Pada Rajakapotasana — Pigeon Pose
Eka Pada Sarvangasana — One Leg Extended Shoulderstand
Eka Pada Urdhva Dhanurasana — Upward Bow with One Leg Up
Eka Pada Viparita Dandasana — Inverted Arch with One Leg Up
Eka Pada Viparita Dandasana — Inverted Arch Leg Up Pose
Halasana — Plow Pose
Hanumanasana — Prayer Splits, also known as Hanuman's Pose
Hasta Padangusthasana — Extended Hand & Foot
Janu Sirsasana — Head To Knee Pose
Jathara Parivartanasana — Revolving Stomach Twist
Kandasana — Knot Pose
Karnapidasana — Knees to Ears Pose
Kurmasana — Tortoise Pose
Makarasana — Locust Variation
Malasana — Garland Pose
Marichyasana — Sage Twist
Natarajasana — Dancer's Pose
Navasana — Boat Pose
Niralamba Bhujangasana — Unsupported Cobra Pose
Niralamba Sarvangasana — Unsupported Shoulderstand
Padahastasana — Feet on Hands Pose
Padangusthasana — Foot-Big Toe Pose
Padma Mayurasana — Lotus Peacock
Padmasana — Lotus Pose
Padottanasana — Spread Feet Forward Bend Pose
Paripurna Ardha Matsyendrasana — Complete Twist
Parivrtta Ardha Chandrasana — Revolving Half Moon Pose
Parivrtta Janu Sirsasana — Revolved Head To Knee Pose
Parivrtta Parsvakonasana — Revolved Extended Side Angle
Parivrtta Paschimottanasana — Revolving Forward Bend
Parivrtta Trikonasana — Revolving Triangle Pose
Parivrttaikapada Sirsasana — Rotated Open Legs Headstand

Parsva Eka Pada Sirsasana — One leg side in Headstand Variation

Parsva Halasana — Sideways Plow Pose

Parsva Sarvangasana — Sideways Shoulderstand

Parsva Sirsasana — Rotated Legs Headstand

Parsva Upavistha Konasana — Over One Open Leg Forward Bend

Parsva Urdhva Padmasana — Upward Lotus in Headstand

Parsva Urdhva Padmasana Sarvangasana — Sideways Lifted Lotus in Shoulderstand

Parsvaikapada Sarvangasana — Foot Sideways Shoulderstand Variation

Parsvakonasana — Extended Side Angle Pose

Parsvottanasana — Intense Sideways Stretch Pose

Parvatasana — Lotus-arms stretched up Pose

Pasasana — Noose Twist

Paschimottanasana — Full Forward Bend, also called Intense Stretch of West

Pincha Mayurasana — Arm Stand

Pindasana Sarvangasana — Lotus Fetal Shoulderstand

Purvottanasana — Intense Front Extension Pose

Salabhasana — Locust

Sarvangasana — Shoulderstand

Savasana — Corpse Pose

Setu Bandha Sarvangasana — Bridge Pose from Shoulderstand

Siddhasana — Perfect Sitting Pose

Sirsasana — Headstand

Sukhasana — Easy Sitting Pose

Supta Konasana Sarvangasana — Open Angle Shoulderstand

Supta Kurmasana — Lying Tortoise Pose

Supta Padangusthasana — Lying One Leg Stretched Up

Supta Virasana — Reclining Hero Pose

Surya Namaskar — Sun Salutation

Tadasana — Mountain Pose

Tolasana — Scales Balance (in Lotus)

Triang Mukhaikapada Paschimottanasana — Three Limbs Facing Leg Pose, also called TMP

Trikonasana — Triangle Pose

Ubhya Padangusthasana — Balancing Foot Big Toe Pose

Upavistha Konasana — Open Legs Forward Bend

Urdhva Dhanurasana — Upward Bow

Urdhva Konasana in Sirsasana — Upward Angle in Headstand

Urdhva Mukha Paschimottanasana — Upward Facing Full Forward Bend

Urdhva Mukha Svanasana — Upward Facing Dog

Urdhva Prasarita Ekapadasana — Upward Leg Forward Bend Pose

Urdhva Prasarita Padasana — Upward Extended Feet Pose

Utkatasana — Power Chair Pose

Uttana Padasana — Stretched Back Legs Up

Uttanasana — Intense Extension Pose

Vasisthasana — Side Plank Pose

Viparita Karani — Special Inversion

Virabhadrasana — Warrior Pose

Virasana — Hero Pose

Visvamitrasana or Ardha Baddha Vasisthasana — Half Bound Sideways Plank Pose

Vrksasana — Tree Pose

Vrschikasana — Scorpion Pose

Yoga Mudrasana — Yoga Seal

Yoga Nidrasana — Yoga Sleep Pose

BIBLIOGRAPHY

Anderson, Sandra, and Sovik, Dr. Rolf, *Yoga, Mastering the Basics*, The Himalayan Institute, 2000.

Chidananda, Swami, *The Philosophy, Psychology and Practice of Yoga*, The Divine Life Society, 1991.

Desikachar, T.V.K., *The Heart of Yoga*, Inner Traditions, 1995.

Douillard, John. *Body, Mind and Sport*, Harmony, 1994.

Farmer, Angela and Van Kooten, Victor, *From Inside Out*, Ganesha Press, 1998.

Feuerstein, Georg. *The Yoga Tradition*, Hohm Press, 1998.

Feuerstein, Georg. *The Shambhala Encyclopedia of Yoga*, Shambhala Books, 1997.

Frawley, David. *Ayurvedic Healing*, Lotus Press, 2000.

Frawley, David. *Ayurveda and the Mind*, Lotus Press, 1997.

Frawley, David. *Tantric Yoga and The Wisdom Goddesses*, Lotus Press, 2000.

Frawley, David. *Yoga and Ayurveda*, Lotus Press, 1999.

Frawley, David and Vasant Lad. *Yoga of Herbs*, Lotus Press, 1986.

Hari Dass, Baba, *Ashtanga Yoga Primer*, Sri Rama Publishing, 1981.

Iyengar, B.K.S., *Light on Yoga*, Schocken Books, 1979.

Joshi, Dr. Sunil. *Ayurveda and Pancha Karma*, Lotus Press 1997.

Kraftsow, Gary. *Yoga for Wellness*, Penguin-Arkana, 1999.

Kuvalayananda, Swami, and Vinekar, Dr. S.L., *Yogic Therapy*, Ministry of Health and Welfare, 1994.

Lad, Vasant. *Complete Guide to Ayurvedic Home Remedies*, Harmony, 1998.

Lassater, Judith, *Relax and Renew*, Rodmell Press, 1995.

Mishra, Dr. Rammurthi, *Fundamentals of Yoga*, Harmony Books, 1987.

Scarvelli, Vanda, *Awakening the Spine*, Harper Collins, 1991.

Schiffman, Erich, *The Spirit and Practice of Moving into Stillness*, Pocket Books, 1996.

Smith, Atreya. *Practical Ayurveda.* Samuel Weiser, 1997.

Tobias, Maxine and Stewart, Mary. *Stretch and Relax*, The Body Press, 1985.

ꙮ INDEX ꙮ

OTHER NAB PUBLICATIONS ON YOGA

HEALING THE FUTURE (The Journey Within)—*Deepak Kashyap*

The greatest possibilities of body-cure, says the author, lie in forgetting the body. To the extent we lose body-consciousness and identify with the Spirit, physical disability and mental trauma disappearing on their own. *Healing the Future* is then, an attempted tip-off on the little secrets of holistic living that can be mastered in easy, small steps. This book urges you to treat consciousness as a canvas, and begin adding new colour, shine and texture to your tomorrow from this very instant.

ISBN: 81-7822-039-3

KUNDALINI YOGA (A Brief Study of Sir John Woodroff's "The Serpent Power")—*M.P. Pandit*

The search for inner awakening and unfolding of hidden powers has brought man to the threshold of the last frontier: himself. For it is deep within that we find the secret key and unlock the door long held secure from our sight. The ancient philosopher's call "Know Thyself" continues to beckon us on the path of knowledge as the final object of our ongoing investigation.

ISBN: 81-7822-076-8

PRANAYAMA (A Conscious Way of Breathing)—*Ranjit Sen Gupta*

Pranayama is for readers living in the modern world of high-tech environment and life style, and searching for a soothing opposite pole to the external hectic life in the world of constant and fast changing surroundings to live an inner life in balance and harmony. The book introduces us intelligently to the basic breathing practices and describes the fundamental aspects of their psycho-physiology.

ISBN: 81-7822-083-0

STRESS-FREE WORK WITH YOGA AND AYURVEDA—*Vinod Verma*

Dr. Verma's advice for a stress-free work environment begins with a daily yoga program. The aim of this book is to provide a guide for building a better work atmosphere based on an understanding of Ayurvedic personality types—according to your fundamental nature or *prakriti*. It is also important to learn how to acquire a state of satisfaction in your personal life, which is essential for both better work performance and your health. It helps you to build your own good atmosphere—even in the worst of circumstances.

ISBN: 81-7822-000-8

THE YOGA COOKBOOK (Vegetarian Food For Body and Mind)—*Sivananda Yoga Vedanta Centres*

The Yoga Cookbook is the classic guide to a healthy, healing diet. The teachings of Yoga advocate a vegetarian diet with special emphasis on foods that bring peace to body, mind and spirit. The book makes this health giving yogic diet available to everyone. The easy-to-follow recipes use pure, wholesome foods that increase vitality, energy, health and joy.

ISBN: 81-7822-048-2

THE YOGA OF KNOWLEDGE (Based on Sri Aurobindo's Synthesis of Yoga)—*M.P. Pandit*

The Yoga of Knowledge gives the necessary background to pursue one's quest in whatever direction chosen with the maximum benefit. The book embraces all that can be known, and helps one to realise—not necessarily in the mental way—all that is still unknown. Most of the presentations here are followed by questions and answers touching a wide range of topics not necessarily related to the theme of the talks but of considerable spiritual importance.

ISBN: 81-7822-078-4

THE YOGA OF LOVE (Based on Sri Aurobindo's Synthesis of Yoga) —*M.P. Pandit*

Love is the crown of knowledge. True knowledge ends in love, even as real, wide, spontaneous love which is either vouchsafed to one or springs from the fount of the heart leads one to the perception of the existence of God everywhere. Love opens many windows on the Reality that is God; one cannot escape perceiving God when one is filled with love for God. Even as knowledge culminates in love, love leads to an integral knowledge.

ISBN: 81-7822-057-1

THE YOGA OF WORKS (Based on Sri Aurobindo's Synthesis of Yoga) —*M.P. Pandit*

The Yoga of Works is perhaps the first and most important aspect of yoga for seekers to take up. It deals with the problems of—energy, action and direction which confronts us all whenever we try to integrate our spiritual aspirations with the daily life around us and the need to "work" in the society and play a role in the vast undertakings of the Western world.

ISBN: 81-7822-079-2

THE YOGA OF SELF-PERFECTION (Based on Sri Aurobindo's Synthesis of Yoga)—*M.P. Pandit*

The Yoga of Self-Perfection represents a unique contribution of Sri Aurobindo to the science of yoga. The book recognizes a Divine purpose in life and starts from the premise that the ultimate aim of life is not simply escape, but rather, to work out the divine perfection in manifestation.

ISBN: 81-7822-077-6